STUDIES IN LITERATURE, 1500-1800

General Editor

Robert W. Uphaus

Whilst Butler in Immortal Glory Sits
Enthron'd, as King of Poets and of Wits;
Ward Seeks not to usurp his Endless Fame,
But Courts his Genius to revive his Name

NED WARD

The

London Spy

Edited by Paul Hyland

From the Fourth Edition of 1709

East Lansing

Colleagues Press

1993

STUDIES IN LITERATURE, 1500-1800: NO. 5

ISBN 0-937191-47-7 (cloth)
ISBN 0-937191-50-7 (paper)
Library of Congress Catalog Card Number 92-74223
British Library Cataloguing-in-Publication data available
Copyright 1993 by Paul Hyland

Published by Colleagues Press Inc.
Post Office Box 4007
East Lansing, Michigan 48826

Distribution outside North America
Boydell and Brewer Ltd.
Post Office Box 9
Woodbridge, Suffolk IP12 DF3
England

Printed in the United States of America
Typeset by Bristol Academic Press, Bristol, England

Contents

Acknowledgements

I am very grateful to many friends and colleagues who have helped over the years to bring this project to fruition. In particular, many thanks are due to Les Arnold, Janet Clare, Mara Kalnins, Mpalive Msiska and Neil Sammells. I am also grateful to the staff of the British Library, and especially Nick Drew, Librarian at Bath College of Higher Education. My greatest debt, however, is to Jon Press whose encouragement, good humour, patience and scholarship have proved invaluable. Its faults apart, this book is as much his as it is mine.

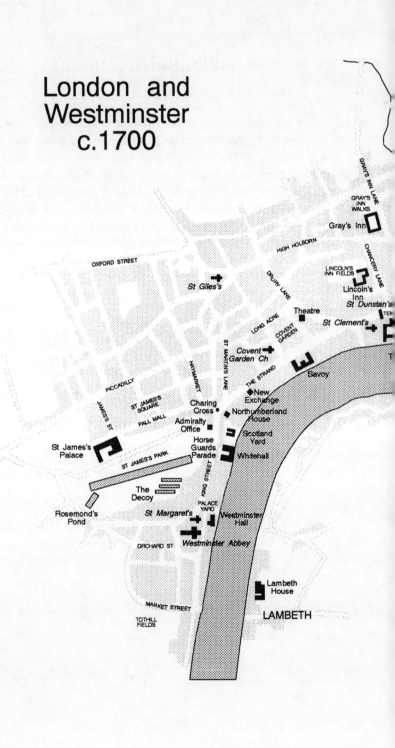

London and Westminster c.1700

OXFORD STREET

HIGH HOLBORN

GRAY'S INN LANE

GRAY'S INN WALKS

Gray's Inn

CHANCERY LANE

LINCOLN'S INN FIELDS

DRURY LANE

St Giles's

Lincoln's Inn

St Dunstan's

Theatre

St Clement's

LONG ACRE

COVENT GARDEN

ST MARTIN'S LANE

Covent Garden Ch

THE STRAND

Savoy

HAYMARKET

PICCADILLY

New Exchange

ST JAMES'S SQUARE

Charing Cross

Northumberland House

PALL MALL

JAMES'S ST

Admiralty Office

Scotland Yard

Horse Guards Parade

Whitehall

St James's Palace

ST JAMES'S PARK

KING STREET

The Decoy

PALACE YARD

Rosemond's Pond

St Margaret's

Westminster Hall

ORCHARD ST

Westminster Abbey

Lambeth House

MARKET STREET

TOTHILL FIELDS

LAMBETH

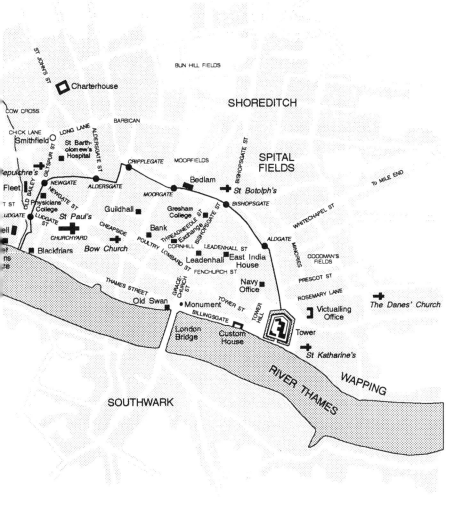

ST JOHN'S ST

Charterhouse

BUN HILL FIELDS

SHOREDITCH

COW CROSS

CHICK LANE

BARBICAN

Smithfield

LONG LANE

St Barth-
olomew's
Hospital

GILTSPUR ST

ALDERSGATE ST

CRIPPLEGATE

MOORFIELDS

BISHOPSGATE ST

SPITAL
FIELDS

epulchre's

Fleet

NEWGATE

ALDERSGATE

Bedlam

St Botolph's

T ST

OLD BAILEY

Physicians'
College

NEWGATE ST

MOORGATE

BISHOPSGATE

TO MILE END

LUDGATE

LUDGATE
ST

St Paul's

Guildhall

Gresham
College

WHITECHAPEL ST

ell

CHURCHYARD

CHEAPSIDE

Bank

THREADNEEDLE ST

BISHOPSGATE ST

ALDGATE

ef
ns
te

Blackfriars

Bow Church

POULTRY

CORNHILL

Exchange

LOMBARD ST

LEADENHALL ST

Leadenhall

East India
House

MINORIES

GOODMAN'S
FIELDS

GRACE
CHURCH
ST

FENCHURCH ST

PRESCOT ST

THAMES STREET

Old Swan

Monument

TOWER ST

Navy
Office

ROSEMARY LANE

The Danes' Church

BILLINGSGATE

London
Bridge

Custom
House

TOWER HILL

Victualling
Office

Tower

St Katharine's

SOUTHWARK

RIVER THAMES

WAPPING

| 0 | 0.25 | 0.5 | 0.75 | 1.0 |

MILES

Introduction

SINCE ITS APPEARANCE three hundred years ago the *London Spy* has remained one of the greatest portrayals of popular culture in English literature. It is by no means coincidental that it has also remained one of the most inherently subversive. To the guardians of Augustan culture, such as the poet Alexander Pope, Ward's writings were simply spawned in the gutters of Grub Street and fit only for transportation to 'ape and monkey lands' (the American colonies) where, presumably, they could do no harm. Nor have Ned Ward's cheerfully iconoclastic works seemed less threatening in more recent times. Twice in the twentieth century the *London Spy* has been released in modernised editions but on both occasions, due to 'the grossness of the language' and 'passages largely of a scatalogical nature' which would 'disgust the modern reader', it has been deemed suitable for the general public only in corrupt and expurgated forms. Undaunted by such literary hostility and emasculation, generations of historians have plundered the text to decorate their descriptions of social life in eighteenth-century England. But while this has helped to ensure that at least parts of Ward's extraordinarily creative and vivacious voice can still be heard, it has not altered the fact that whether scorned, sanitised, or cited, he continues to be dismissed as just another 'unbalanced Grub Street hack'.

A key to the suspicion with which the *London Spy* has always been regarded lies in the lowly nature of Ward's background and career. Among his contemporary critics, the most persistently expressed belief was that he was 'of low extraction and irregular education', though there is little evidence, aside from Ward's own writings, to support this or most other claims about his life. According to his own accounts, he was born in the Midlands in 1667, was raised and educated there, and left for London about the time of the Glorious Revolution in 1689, when the brief reign of the Catholic King James II was terminated by the general antipathy of his subjects and the invasion of his Protestant son-in-law, Prince William of Orange. Whether or not Ward had friends or relations to introduce him to the capital at this time of crisis is uncertain, but it appears that in 1691 he went back to Leicestershire in the hope of collecting an inheritance from the death of his grandmother, only to find

that the old lady 'had not left poor Ned a louse'. Soon afterwards, the
trip was comically depicted in what appears to have been the first of
Ward's published writings, *The Poet's Ramble after Riches* (1691): a
mock-heroic poem that evidently made no impression on the public.

It seems that for the next six years Ward scratched a living at least
partially with his pen until, in January 1697, wearied by debts and
disappointments, he took a passage for Jamaica. By the end of the year
he had returned to London determined to exorcise the island, and his own
experience, in a pamphlet that would repulse even the most desperate of
prospective emigrants. Although *A Trip to Jamaica* (1698) borrowed
freely from former travelogues, there were no precedents for the flood of
images, comic sketches and indecencies with which Ward depicted the
corruption of the English colony. Indeed, his judgement soared to biblical
proportions:

> The Dunghill of the Universe, the Refuse of the whole Creation, the
> Clippings of the Elements, a shapeless Pile of Rubbish confus'dly
> jumbl'd into an Emblem of the Chaos, neglected by Omnipotence
> when he form'd the World into its admirable Order. The Nursery of
> Heaven's Judgements, where the Malignant Seeds of all Pestilence
> were first gather'd and scatter'd thro' the Regions of the Earth, to
> Punish Mankind for their Offences. The Place where Pandora fill'd
> her Box, where Vulcan Forg'd Joves Thunder-bolts, and that Phaeton,
> by his rash misguidance of the Sun, scorched into a Cinder. The
> Receptacle of Vagabonds, the Sanctuary of Bankrupts, and a Close-
> stool for the Purges of our Prisons. As Sickly as an Hospital, as
> Dangerous as the Plague, as Hot as Hell, and as Wicked as the Devil.

The colonists were not amused, but sales ensured that the pamphlet was
reprinted seven times in eighteen months — a popular success by any
standards. Not surprisingly, Ward immediately composed a sequel which
he published as *A Trip to New-England* in the Spring of 1699. Though
written in the same provocative style as his former essay, it is unlikely
that the *Trip* was drawn from a similar experience as there is no
evidence, outside the text, to suggest that Ward ever went to Boston.
Rather, it appears that the materials for the pamphlet were gathered
entirely from the writings and recollections of other travellers. Even if
some readers were aware of this, it hardly mattered, for Ward had
already embarked upon a far more ambitious and authentic project.

Although there can be no doubt that it was Ward's intention to found a monthly journal when, in November 1698, he launched the first issue of the *London Spy*, it seems unlikely that he would have anticipated the speed and scale of its success. He commented in the second number: 'The first part of this undertaking I popped into the cautious world as a skilful angler does a new bait among wary fish who have oft been pricked in their nibbling.' But, novelty apart, no other hint was given for 'the public snapping at it'. Certainly, the first number's proposition that it was 'intended to expose the vanities and vices of the Town' in order to protect the innocent, was mere convention; though this was swiftly undercut by the suggestion that it would be done 'by accident'. Moreover, the idea of a narrator who had left the country due to 'an itching inclination in myself to visit London' after years of useless reading, was neither original nor reassuring. Since the Spy was to be 'an utter stranger in the Town', it was no small 'good fortune' that just as he entered the metropolis he ran into an old acquaintance. The former schoolfellow would act as the narrator's foil, a voice of knowledge and experience to set against the Spy's supposed innocence. But even this transparent artifice would soon break down, not least grammatically, once it had served its initial dialogic purposes.

Such scant concern for the maintenance of literary pretexts and pretences by which characters could be developed, plots unfurled and moral ends accomplished, was typical of Ward's casual method in the *Spy*. Thus, while the first six numbers, issued through the winter of 1698-9, covered the first three days and nights of the Spy's activities in London, by the seventh number he was suddenly reporting on May Fair. Thereafter, seasonal and contemporary events, such as Bartholomew Fair, the roasting of an ox at the King's Head Tavern and the trial of two astrologers at the Guildhall, were stitched into the story-lines to produce loose conjunctions of historical and fictive time, without my sense of difficulty or inconsistency. Similarly, a trip to Mob's Hole in Essex was admitted into number six, even though it was reckoned 'something of a digression, or rather a deviation from the title'. And, in order 'to vary a little from our former method', the fifteenth number began 'to treat more upon men and manners' by devoting almost a whole issue to the depiction of three character-types; victuallers, astrologers and constables. These were an addition to those types, such as the foot-soldier and the modern critic, that had appeared previously, and a preparation for the series of studies, including descriptions of an Irishman, a banker and a beau, that would dominate the final numbers. Yet, as Ward admitted, the inclusion of more character studies, or 'microcosmographies' as he called them, was primarily intended to revive readers' interest in the journal:

> As a fair Town Miss, of twelvemonth's standing, when she has surfeited the appetites of those debauchees who are always ranging after novelty, and rendered herself contemptible by being too common, puts on a dark foretop, blacks her eyebrows, changes the mode of her dressing, her lodging, and her name, and sets up for a new creature.

The ploy was unsuccessful. In the sixteenth number, the Spy was 'left to range the Town by myself' as even his old companion had become 'tired of his office' as guide and mentor. A few pages later the Spy and his friend were reunited at a supper party, but despite offering fascinating reports on Dryden's funeral and the legal action between astrologers John Partridge and George Parker, without further warning the *Spy* was discontinued after eighteen issues.

The ease with which Ward slipped in and out of prose in order to publish some fifty, often unashamedly 'doggerel' poems in the *Spy* well illustrates his open and informal style, and life-long interest in the relationship between prose and verse. But, month by month, perhaps the most striking evidence of the openness of Ward's design sprang from the apparent aimlessness with which the Spy and his unnamed companion were allowed to 'ramble', 'stumble', 'stroll' and 'blunder' around the capital. Prompted by no more than gossip, curiosity, hunger and a host of other conspicuously circumstantial factors, the Spy and his companion 'sailed about, we cared not whither' and often wandered through the city 'like a couple of runaway apprentices, having confined ourselves to no particular port, uncertainty being our course and mere accident our pilot.' Clearly, this allowed Ward freedom to explore whatever he considered would continue to 'divert the reader', but it also enabled him to draw those everyday experiences and activities which lay outside or on the periphery of formal definitions of the city to the centre of attention.

It was no accident, then, that the first number of the *Spy* was dominated by the coffee-shop and tavern, the ordinary junctions of popular society where each sixpenny issue of the *Spy* would have been sold, perused, and read aloud along with other newspapers and journals. Not until the third issue, after a night in a bawdy-house, did the Spy and his friend run up against any of the official sights or landmarks of the city, and then, just as the 'stately fabric' of the Custom House came into view, in front of it the Spy observed 'a parcel of robust mortals [who] were as busy as so many flies upon a cow-turd.' Similarly, on the occasion of the Lord Mayor's Pageant, the Spy chose Cheapside as his station: 'where I thought the triumphs would be most visible, and the rabble most rude, looking upon the mad frolics and whimsies of the latter to be altogether as diverting (provided a man takes care of the danger) as the solemn grandeur and gravity of the former.' Nor was he disappointed: the counter-culture of the 'plebeian gentry', tossing dead cats and excrement in merriment, proved every bit as entertaining as the pomposities of the civic ceremony.

By 'staring at the spectators much more than the show', Ward brought the supposedly marginal or insignificant work and recreations of common people to the fore, habitually sketching characters and setting scenes to dramatise the words and actions of his subjects. Moreover, though never stinting on hyperbole or comic simile, the dramatic scenes and episodes that he depicted were nearly always founded not only upon a thorough knowledge of the physical and social topography of each locality, but also an acute, and sometimes over-powering, awareness of the Spy's sensory experiences. Thus, on writing of his first night's sojourn in the city the Spy recalls his amazement at the 'dazzling lights whose bright reflections so glittered in my eyes', and the sounds of 'sundry passing-bells, the rattling of coaches, and the melancholy ditties of "Hot Baked Wardens and Pippins!"', before his revere is interrupted by the thundering panic of a 'rumbling engine in the dark, which I took for a dead-monger's wagon laden with a stinking corpse (by reason of long keeping).' A little later, the Spy and his companion are looking for a boozing-ken in Billingsgate:

> in a narrow lane, as dark as a burying-vault, which stunk of stale sprats, piss and sir-reverence, we groped about like a couple of thieves in a coal-hole, to find the entrance of that nocturnal theatre in whose delightful scenes we proposed to terminate the night's felicity. At last we stumbled upon the threshold of a gloomy cavern where, at a distance, we saw lights burning like candles in a haunted cave where ghosts and goblins keep their midnight revels.

This was typical of Ward's method, setting scenes and moods by allowing the Spy some freedom to express his feelings. On the surface the Spy's tone is often supercilious, creating space for his bombastic flourishes, but this serves to mask a far more complex range of attitudes and emotions. Having been compelled to spend a night among the rude and unruly prisoners of the Poultry Compter, the Spy sees the inmates as so many pigs and dogs. Yet, despite the seemingly unflattering imagery, capped by a comparison of the living with the dead, the Spy writes about his experiences in a way that leaves little doubt about the true nature of his sympathies:

> Now the whole family were grown as silent as so many hogs when their bellies are full, nothing being heard but snoring, except now and then a crack from the stretching of a louse's skin, or an ingrateful sound from the untuneable drone of a filthy bagpipe, which is never heard but by the assistance of a stinking breath. With this sort of music were our ears entertained all night, and that my eyes might be obliged with answerable satisfaction, I thought it now the only time to look about me. I observed men lay piled in cabins one upon another, like coffins in a burying-vault, possessing only the same allowance above ground as the dead have under, their breadth and length, that's all. Other poor curs, that wanted the convenience of kennels (being supernumerary to the sleeping-huts), were lain upon benches, as if they had been bred up courtiers' footmen. Others coiled underneath like dogs, and slept as sound as Low Country soldiers. Some lay round the fire, almost covered with ashes, like potatoes roasting, with their noses in conjunction with one another's arses, like hogs upon a dunghill. These, I suppose, were tender mortals bred up at the forge, and as great enemies to cold weather as the mad fellow that walks about the town naked. Another was crept into a corner and had whelmed over his head the ash-tub, and so made a nightcap of an ale-firkin, to defend his head from the coldnness of the weather.

In such graphic passages, elements of descriptive realism are often subverted by the Spy's inclusion of some comic interjections. These undermine the reader's confidence in a single, literal reading of the text, and expose the complex interplays of the ridiculous and the serious which pervade the journal's rhetoric. Thus, almost indiscriminately, characters from contemporary dramas, Ancient gods, philosophers and artists, Christian saints and famous personages are all alluded to for comic purposes, often in disparaging analogies. And, on touring the Tower of London, the most enduring symbol of the legendary power and strength of John of Gaunt lies in the volume of his codpiece. Similarly, 'a good emblem for the world' can be found in a moment's reflection upon the tennis court at Whitehall, where 'the gamesters are the great men, the rackets are the laws, which they hold fast in their hands, and the balls are we little mortals which they bandy backwards and forwards from one to t'other, as their own will and pleasure directs 'em.' Even at his most censorious, as when the Spy offers his 'real sentiments' on the 'shameful indecencies' suffered by women as part of their punishments in Bridewell, his companion warns us that we could read this as an attempt 'to curry favour'.

For all his ambivalences, Ward has much to say about the vices and follies of the capital. Not only does he show how the self-seeking and dishonest behaviour of the governing orders has corrupted so many of its charitable, judicial and commercial institutions, from the hospitals, prisons and lawcourts to the Admiralty Office and East India Company. He also shows how all ranks and sexes prey upon one another's needs and weaknesses. There are some notable victims, such as the 'poor orphans' whose monies have been taken by 'corrupted magistrates' in order to fund the Monument to the Fire of London, and the women who, rather than prostitute themselves to the tallyman, have been imprisoned for their debts. Indeed, in a society in which a love of money, 'that filthy dross which defiles the virgin, corrupts the priest, [and] contaminates the fingers of the judge', can be seen to have put a price on everything, women themselves, as well as their services, are just commodities for sale and purchase, as the Spy learns at the end of his first day.

Such injustices and inequalities are well illustrated by the stories and activities of the hordes of whores, beggars, thieves and cheats that are repeatedly encountered in the text. Yet, for all the wickedness of this 'well-governed Christian city', the Spy is seldom given to despair. Even among 'the very scum of the kingdom', the 'despicable paupers' of Rag Fair, the Spy discerns a 'vigour and vivacity' that he much admires, and 'more content and cheerfulness than you shall find in an assembly of great and rich men'. Here, the discourse is both sympathetic and apologetic, but there is no hint of social deference as the Spy reports that the magistrates have 'used the utmost of their endeavours' to suppress the people, but 'their numbers bid defiance to all molestation, and their impudence and poverty are such that they fear neither jail nor punishment'. On the other side of the city, where art and nature have been combined to produce St James's Park, after just 'an hour's enjoyment' of the royal order the Spy has 'rendered the beauty of the Park but dull and flat.'

If it is part of Ward's achievement to have pioneered the exploration, representation and study of the life and character of the city as a literary science, it is equally part of his legacy that we have come so readily to regard his writings as essentially a faithful record. How his vision of the common people as proud, mostly cheerful and energetic, both loyal and unruly, fiercely individual and perversely sociable, often downtrodden but never beaten, has come to be seen as historically authentic is not easily determined. Nor is it possible to measure how many, if any, of the half a million people who inhabited the city (perhaps one tenth of England's otherwise predominantly rural population), would have heard or read his text as part history, part story, and part mythology in the making. Few contemporary responses have survived. A few years after the closure of the *Spy*, however, John Dunton emphasised Ward's ingenuity as a writer; a brief comment that should not be forgotten:

> Ingenious *Ward (the Famous Author of the* London Spies) ... *was truly born a Poet, not made, not form'd by Industry, and (which is a great Service to a Man that follows the CALLING of an Author) his Muse is never subject to the Curse of bringing forth with Pain; for ... he writes with the greatest Ease. He is a Man of a peculiar Stile, and his Works are in great Esteem.*

Although the *London Spy* was brought to an end in May 1700, its closure did not mark a fall in Ward's enthusiasm for writing. On the contrary, the popularity of the work, which now appeared in several book editions, encouraged Ward to write with the knowledge that he had created an audience capable of supporting his literary enthusiasms. This was of great importance, for the nature of his success, rooted in the use of vulgar literary forms and native idioms, could not have been expected to endear him to the great patrons of Augustan literature. Nor, judging by Ward's later comment that he had 'the happiness of knowing the world a little too early, ever to be much deluded with fair promises, or to waste much time in precarious dependencies upon such persons', did this disturb him. Thus, by choice and necessity, his writings continued to explore the nature of contemporary life in ways that were accessible and interesting to his audiences. In jest and honesty, he frequently saw writing as akin to prostitution:

> The condition of an author is much like that of a strumpet ... and if the reason be required why we betake ourselves to so scandalous a profession as whoring or pamphleteering, the same excusive answer will serve us both, viz. That the unhappy circumstances of a narrow fortune hath forced us to do that for our subsistence which we are much ashamed of.

In the eyes of belletrists like Pope, and some modern critics, such mocking disregard for the proprieties and principles of 'Art' was tantamount to heresy. For, by analogy, Augustan authors were more likely to see themselves as priests. Yet if, by his own admission, Ward's conception of his work was lowly, his naive rejection of Augustan ideology and decorum did not rob him of moral purpose and responsibility. Nor did his relatively humble origins.

Even while the *London Spy* was being written, Ward had produced over twenty other pieces. These were a mixture of traditional and experimental items in prose and verse, on topics such as the baiting of a tiger, the Lord Mayor's show, dancing schools, alehouses, astrology, Ludgate prison, poverty, seduction and prostitution. Under titles such as *The Insinuating Bawd: And the Repenting Harlot. Written by a Whore at Tunbridge, and Dedicated to a Bawd at Bath* (1699), and *Laugh and be Fat, or an Antidote against Melancholy, containing a variety of Comical Intreagues in Town and Country; with pleasant Humours, Frolicks, Fancies, Epigrams, Satyrs and Divertisements. To which is added, Nine Delightful Tales* (1700), Ward clearly showed no signs of suffering from exhaustion. Nor did the production of travel tales and character sketches falter. By 1700 he had taken trips to Bath, Tunbridge Wells, Sturbridge Fair near Cambridge, and Horn Fair at Charlton, and added profiles of the 'vicious courtier', 'the City lecher', 'the country squire' and many others to his portfolio of character studies. In all these pieces, as in the *London Spy*, Ward explored the representation of the common world to common people, drawing upon his and their observations, experiences and activities to express a view of life that both shaped and undermined the most elevated of Augustan visions. Though often slight as individual pieces, the eagerness with which Ward began to compile various collections of his writings suggests that by 1700 he was already eager that his works should not be viewed in isolation but, rather, as an epic panorama of popular society and culture.

In the decade following the completion of the *London Spy*, Ward's productivity and popularity flourished. Indeed, in many respects they were unsurpassed. By the end of Queen Anne's reign (1702-14), he had produced over seventy original titles including a two-volume adaptation of *Don Quixote* (1711-12), a three-volume versification of Clarendon's *History of the Grand Rebellion* (1713-15), a 400-page characterisation of London clubs, a collection of fifty-five marital dialogues, two plays, and no less than nine periodicals. Some of these works, such as the monthly *London Terraefilius* (1707-8), were unashamed attempts to develop ideas and devices that had been tried or tested in the *London Spy*. Others, such as the pantomime-play *Honesty in Distress* (1705), were more genuinely innovative. Judging by the numbers of reprinted titles, there were failures in both categories, but also enough successes to encourage How and other publishers to promote their author by selling several editions of a five-volume collection of his writings. Although our knowledge of Ward's life in these his most prolific years is sketchy, it seems that by 1713 he was rich enough to open an alehouse in Clerkenwell, thereby turning one of his most cherished subjects, the relationship of ale and art, into a motif of his subsistence, as in *The Hudibrastick Brewer: Or, A Preposterous Union Between Malt and Meter* (1714). We also know that in this period, due to his outspoken manner, he attracted less desirable attention.

Considering Ward's talents, it is not surprising that he soon ran into trouble. Although the Revolution of 1689 had settled William and Mary on the throne, in the following twenty-five years the country was beset by political controversy and uncertainty. As private doubts and public disputes over the legitimacy of William's rule persisted, so, inevitably, they undermined the foundations of national harmony and stability. Most people had been opposed to James II's policies, but in many quarters there was a lingering allegiance to the exiled king, and hope, among Jacobites at least, that his son would be restored to the throne at some future opportunity. Moreover, the events of 1689 were traumatic for the Church of England. Not only did a small proportion of the clergy refuse to recognise the 1689 revolution constitution, but the majority continued to hold serious misgivings about the security of the Anglican Church's privileges and authority under William. In particular, they feared that the religious toleration granted to half a million protestant nonconformists in 1689 placed the Established Church in danger of competition from that growing body of Dissenters and, ultimately, of dissolution. William hoped that war with France (where James was exiled) would help to heal these differences; but the unprecedented military, financial and political strains of engagement in the European wars which dominated his and Queen Anne's reign merely deepened the divisions. Since the public demanded news and commentary on each of the recurrent crises, once pre-publication censorship had lapsed, in 1695, the press responded with enthusiasm. But as Ward and others drew their unlicensed views to the attention of the public, so the libel laws were increasingly invoked to curb their opinions by arrest and prosecution.

Ward's first encounter with the law was in 1699 when the eighth issue of his *Weekly Comedy* denounced the politics of sheriffs elected in the capital. Although, by his own account, this swiftly led to the suppression of the journal, it did not deter him from recasting it as a play, "The Humours of a Coffee-House, a Comedy", for publication in the second volume of his *Writings* (1703). A few years later he was under fresh examination. This time his attempted epic *Hudribras Redivivus, or a Burlesque Poem upon the Times* (1705-7) had cast aspersions upon the Queen's administration 'in a little too lively Colours', most obviously in a line asserting that her 'Fine Words don't countervail a F[ar]t'. Such insolence invited prosecution, and in 1706 the *London Gazette* reported:

Edward Ward, being convicted of Writing, Printing, and Publishing, several Scandalous and Seditious Libels ... highly Reflecting upon Her Majesty and the Government; was likewise on Thursday last fined for the same by the Court of Queen's-Bench 40 Marks, and ordered to stand in the Pillory on Wednesday next at Charing-Cross for the space of One Hour, between Twelve and Two in the Afternoon, with a Paper on his Head denoting his Offence; and also to stand in the Pillory on Thursday next near the Royal Exchange in Cornhill in like Manner: And, before he be discharged out of Prison, he is to give Security for his good Behavior for One Year.

Considering Ward's earlier transgressions, and the punishments meted out to similar offenders, this was not a stringent sentence. Perhaps it had been lightened by his plea of guilty to the charges. As with his response

to the suppression of the *Weekly Comedy*, however, there was no sign
that his spirit had been broken. Nor his wit. When the second edition of
Hudibras Redivivus appeared in 1708 with 'An Apology', the vulgar line
had been revised to read 'Fine Words are full of Fraud and Art'.

Whether libellous or not, the delight that Ward took in challenging the
assumed authority of 'literary' language, and those who wielded it above
the vulgar, is evident throughout his work. It appears at every turn of his
observation and imaginative construction of contemporary life, for while
the direct or reported speech of common people frequently informs his
subject, the rhetoric of literary English is substantially suppressed. Far
from being inspired by 'the powerful eloquence which drops from the
silver tongues of the ingenious company' of literati at Wits' Coffee-
house, the Spy hears only fawning poets and carping critics whose
'admirable flights' and 'unaccountable thoughts' he fails to recollect.
Even on the most solemn of occasions, the funeral of Dryden, the Spy's
triumphal report of the procession is punctured by a lowly interjection:
'(After these [trumpeters], the undertaker with his hat off, dancing
through the dirt like a bear after a bagpipe. I beg the reader's pardon for
foisting in a jest in so improper a place; but as he walked by himself
within a parenthesis, so I have here placed him, and hope none will be
offended.)'

While the 'wondrous flights' at Wits' are deemed unworthy of
inclusion (except a lowly poem that has been stolen), every opportunity
is seized to relay the banter, tales and declarations by which the views
and feelings of the unlettered are expressed. Usually, these voices are
recorded by the Spy without intrusion, as when he relates the country
bumpkin's efforts to engage a waxwork figure in conversation, or when
he overhears some sailors vying with one another over their adventures:

'I never was in so hot a climate as that, but I have been so many
degrees to the nor'ward, where it has been so cold it has frozen our
words in our mouths, so that we could not hear one another speak till
we came into a warmer latitude to thaw 'em; and then all our
discourses broke out together like a clap of thunder, that there was
never such a confusion of tongues ever heard at Babel.'

At times, however, the Spy is keen to enter a discussion; as when he
challenges an old gentleman he suspects of voyeurism, engages women
in a parley over 'watches', or mistakes the cries of 'Oars' and 'Scullers'

as a call for whores and scholars. On most of these occasions the Spy is easily outflanked by the verbal agility of those whom he encounters, but this does not deter him from continuing to venture his opinions. Nor does his friend's warning that, at least in speaking of affairs of state, 'You must be careful ... how you ask questions'.

That words are to be used with caution is most forcefully and ironically attested by the evidence of Bedlam. A madman protests:

'Truth is persecuted everywhere abroad, and flies hither for sanctuary, where she sits as safe as a knave in a church, or a whore in a nunnery. I can use her as I please and that's more than you dare do. I can tell great men such bold truths as they don't love to hear, without the danger of a whipping-post; and that you can't do. For if ever you see a madman hanged for speaking the truth, or a lawyer whipped for lying, I'll be bound to prove my wig a wheelbarrow.'

The Spy has little patience with such ranting but, soon after, having aggravated an officious constable, one Mr Stablecunt, with a display of wit, he does not hesitate to extricate himself from prison by lying through his teeth. A little later, when a bull-necked prisoner of Bridewell tells us 'I was committed here by Justice Codplate, for saying I had rather hear a blackbird whistle "Walsingham" or a peacock scream against foul weather, than a parson talk nonsense in a church, or a fool talk Latin in a coffee-house', the Spy insists that he was rendered speechless by this impudence, but we may well not be convinced.

The language that Ward chooses to explore the culture of the capital might well have been described by his contemporaries as 'cant'. The term is best explained by reference to *A New Dictionary of the Terms Ancient and Modern of the Canting Crew* (1698) which, as well as listing many of the obscure words and phrases that Ward uses, defines the term as representing 'the Cypher or Mysterious Language' of the lower orders, 'Rogues, Gypsies, Beggers, Thieves' and others of that ilk. This language (which could only have arisen from a long and oppressed oral-tradition among the poor) was therefore deemed so different from the English of the much-smaller literate and elite literary groups, it was reckoned to require an explicit process of decoding before such groups would be able to construe its meaning. Moreover, the social and linguistic challenge which this posed to the literary English of the privileged did not go unnoticed. Indeed, it was explicitly endorsed by the extended title of the dictionary as it stated its intention to be 'Useful to all sorts of People, (especially Foreigners) to secure their *Money* and preserve their *Lives*'. Ward clearly did not need a dictionary, a rare and expensive commodity, to decypher the 'disguised modes of speaking' that others found so alien. Nor, more particularly, did he need telling that his fascination with 'beargarden discourse' was just a wanton interest in 'common, filthy, nasty Talk', according to the dictionary of cant. Charged with vulgarity and obscenity, there could be little doubt that Ward was guilty on both counts.

Far from being a superficial streak of impudence or indecency to be expurgated or tolerated as historic bawdy, Ward's refusal to observe the conventions of polite expression therefore forms an inescapable part of our responses to his work; for we, no less than the Augustans, have preconceptions about what constitutes 'fine' writing. While these may have allowed us to excuse, or more often to ignore, say, the racism and sexism that abound within the literary tradition, Ward's vulgarity may still confront us as a problem. Should we search for evidence of literary techniques and qualities that would enable us to exonerate or historicise his vulgarity and bigotries? This is the well-trodden path of critical apology, and Ward's persistent 'deviation' from high Augustan manners of expression might well be cited in mitigation. Yet, to see Ward's work as merely deviant or low, is largely to accept the literariness of the men-of-letters as a universal standard, discounting the very differences that, through their writings, they strove so vigorously to establish.

Although it had been Ward's use of English rather than his politics that had led to his prosecution in 1706, throughout Anne's reign he had produced several highly successful works attacking the Whigs and the Dissenters. These included his contribution to the *Secret History of the Calves-Head Club* (1703), a sensational exposé of an alleged republican club that celebrated Charles I's execution by dining on a calf's head; two notoriously anti-militarist pamphlets, *The Wooden World Dissected, In The Character Of A Ship of War* (1706) and *Mars Stript of his Armour: Or, The Army Display'd in all its True Colours* (1708); and *Vulgus Britannicus* (1710), a long poem offering an eyewitness account of the High Church riots which, on 1 March, had destroyed the meeting-house of the famous preacher Daniel Burgess, one of Ward's bugbears in the *Spy*. It is not surprising, therefore, that after the collapse of the Tories at the death of Anne in 1714, he was in even greater danger of incarceration. Faced with riot and rebellion at the accession of King George, the

Whig regime did not hesitate to stamp its authority upon the country by seizing every opportunity to silence opposition; not least among those who showed any hint of disaffection in their writings. In these circumstances, the record of Ward's earlier assaults upon the Whigs certainly aroused suspicions. Yet it seems that he escaped the harrassment and imprisonment that was the fate of scores of fellow dissidents. This was partly due to the fact that it was particularly difficult to investigate and prosecute the political tracts that he wrote in the early years of George's reign as most were issued not only anonymously but illegally, without even the imprint of a publisher. But it was also due to the skill with which he denounced the Whigs, in pamphlets such as *The Republican Procession* (1714) and *The Lord Whig-Love's Elegy* (1715), without openly endorsing opposition to the Hanoverians.

Within three years of the trauma caused by Queen Anne's death and the onslaught of Whig government, Ward had left his alehouse in Clerkenwell to become keeper of the more prestigious Bacchus Tavern in Moorfields. Judging by 'a merry poem', *The Delights of the Bottle, or the Compleat Vintner* (1720), which he later wrote in order to promote the business, much of his time was now taken up with the 'Table Whitlers' (vandals), 'Bubble Upstarts' (speculators), 'Spoon Pinchers' (thieves) and other 'tavern Tormentors' among his genteel customers. Thus the thirteen years he spent as 'Jolly Master', trying 'everything to please / All Pallats, Humours, and Degrees', were not his most productive as an author. Yet, by 'fits and starts', he still added over a dozen works to his collected writings. Some of these new pieces, such as *The Merry Travellers* (1721), a poetic 'Trip upon Ten-Toes, From Moorfields to Bromley', and *The Amorous Bugbears* (1725), a breezy description of a masquerade 'Intended as a Supplement to the London-Spy', were largely penned to well-worn formulas. Others, such as *The Parish Guttlers* (1722), a powerful indictment of the poverty and cruelty inflicted upon a parish by the corruption of its local government, and *The Dancing Devils* (1724), a long essay on a pantomime-spectacular at Lincoln's Inn Theatre, marked significant developments in Ward's treatment of social and artistic problems.

Unfortunately, however, it is for two pamphlet attacks on Pope that Ward's final years are now remembered. Having been cast among the Grub Street hacks and dunces who were destroying literature and culture, according to Pope's *Dunciad* (1728), Ward responded: first with *Durgen [a dwarf]. Or, A Plain Satyr Upon A Pompous Satyrist* (1728), and then

(after *The Dunciad Variorum* had appeared, confirming and extending
Pope's original allegations) with *Appolo's Maggot in his Cups* (1729). In
these pamphlets, the latter being 'too disgusting to quote' according to
one modern critic, Ward berated both Pope's physical deformity and the
stylistic and moral pretensions of his epic poetry. He also corrected what
he regarded as the wilful slurs that Pope had cast upon him without 'the
minutest Provocation'; in particular, that he was just an alehouse-keeper
whose chief appeal was in America. 'As for Ward's Works, which he
never was proud of, they have had as great a sale in England', so Ward
retorted, 'as ever they had Abroad, without much expensive Advertising
or the recommendation of Flatterers'. Apart from a poem celebrating the
election of a Lord Mayor of London in 1730, this bitter exchange with
Pope marked the end of Ward's career. Appropriately, their quarrel had
been over the relationship between literature and ideology, for behind the
personal abuse lay deep divisions about what an author's role and
responsibilities should be within society. While belletrists like Pope had
much to say upon the subject, Ward's general reticence should not be
regarded as indifference. The *London Spy* and over ninety other works
offer ample evidence of his purpose and achievement.

As his biographer, H.W. Troyer, remarked in 1946, 'much of the last
chapter, as much of the first' of Ward's life still 'remains unknown'.
Sometime between 1729 and 1730, when in his early sixties, he moved
with his wife and family from Moorfields to the British Coffee-house in
Fullwood's Rents, near his earlier home in Gray's Inn. Why he moved
and how long he had been married are uncertain, though we know that
while living at the Bacchus Tavern he had made a poetic will, leaving his
blessings and whatever he possessed to his wife and children. We also
know that he wanted to be buried with a simple funeral in the churchyard
of St Pancras, and that following his death in June 1731 this wish was
granted. There is little to be added. The newspapers reported that Mr
Edward Ward was 'famous for his poetical Performances' and 'celebrated
for his Writings'. The story that Ward told a few years earlier, in a rare
moment of self-reflection, was both more modest and engaging:

The Fifth and last of our Company [of masqueraders], was I, quoth
the Dog, a poor harmless honest Fellow, almost crazed with playing
the Fool, because I would not play the Knave, half starved in a Calm,
yet always a loser when I fish in troubled Waters; one that hates

Scribling as he does Poverty, yet, like a Dutchman in the Rasp-House, is forced to Pump or Drown.

Note on the Text

THE *LONDON SPY* originally appeared in eighteen monthly parts between November 1698 and May 1700; each part consisting of sixteen pages in folio half-sheet, published during or soon after the month on the title-page of each number. The publisher of the first six issues was John Nutt, but when Part VII appeared in May 1699 responsibility for the rest of the journal was transferred to his printer John How. The reason for this change cannot be documented, but it was probably due to the immediate success of the series, prompting both Nutt and How to publish some second, third, and collected folio editions between 1699 and 1702.

The first octavo edition of the *Spy* was published by How in July 1703 as the first of two volumes of Ward's writings. Numerous changes in substantives and accidentals were made in this edition. A brief list of the contents of each part of the journal was entered before each of the eighteen numbers. The first three paragraphs of the original preface, which had appeared in Part II of the folio editions, were moved to the beginning of the journal. Two other paragraphs from the original preface were omitted (restored here), as were 'The Contents to the Twelve Parts of the first Volume of the London Spy' which had appeared as an index in Part XII of the folio editions. In 1704, 1706 and 1709, How published three more octavo editions, and in 1718 a fifth octavo edition was published by Arthur Bettersworth as the first volume of a new collection of Ward's *Miscellaneous Writings in Verse and Prose.*

The aim of the present edition is to provide a substantially authentic version of the *London Spy*, freed from awkward and erratic conventions of eighteenth-century spelling, punctuation and typography, which were usually the printer's responsibility. The text is based upon How's last octavo edition of the *Spy*, issued in 1709, almost certainly with Ward's approval. How made innumerable small alterations, and occasionally some substantive changes, in each of his editions. So, for example, the phrase 'made a vigorous assault upon his Enemies *Dunghil*' in Part III of the first folio edition, became 'made a vigorous Assault upon his Enemy on his own *Dunghill*' in the 1703 edition, 'made a Vigorous assault upon his Enemy on his own *Dunghil*' in 1704, and 'made a vigorous Assault upon his Enemy on his own Dunghill' in 1709. In a few cases where How's alterations have created new errors or ambiguities, I have usually preferred the first folio reading. A small number of substantive changes have also been made where the original grammar or paragraphing is thoroughly confusing.

THE

London-Spy

COMPLEAT,

In Eighteen Parts.

The First Volume of the Author's Writings.

The Fourth Edition.

LONDON,

Printed and Sold by J. How, *at the*
Seven Stars *in* Talbot-Court, *in*
Grace-Church-Street, MDCCIX.

Contents

PART IV

A description of a Quakers' tavern in Finch Lane. The Quakers' method of drinking. A song. A character of the vintner. The Spy and his friend go to the Angel in Fenchurch Street, from whence they are committed to the Poultry Compter, which the Spy describes. Their examination before a Justice. A poetic curse upon the constable. Remarks on Bow Church steeple. The giants in Guildhall. The Sheriff's Court. The Court of Conscience. The pictures of the judges. Of an old man with a great nose. A man that goes half naked. Upon one in St Paul's Churchyard.

PART V

Remarks upon a picture-shop. On a blind ballad-singer. On St Paul's Church. On the working of the labourers there. On the fire at St Paul's and what use the Dissenters made of it. On the choir. A countryman's observation upon the church. Remarks upon the people that walk there. On the woollen-drapers' apprentices. On the Prerogative Office, with observations on Heraldry, &c. Upon a popular weasel. The Ecclesiastical Court and Doctors' Commons. Ludgate. The Sessions House in the Old Bailey and Newgate. Remarks upon Smithfield Market. On the Crown Tavern at Duck Lane end. A description of the salesmen in Long Lane and a curse upon them in verse. Remarks on the Bear and Ragged Staff. On a parcel of hog-drivers. On the Lame Hospital and the Blue-Coat boys.

PART VI

The College of Physicians described, with observations thereupon. Remarks upon Fleet Bridge and the humours of the people, with the character of a horse-mountebank. The character of a quack in verse. Remarks upon Fleet Ditch. Bridewell described. The miserable condition of one of the criminals. The manner of trying 'em. The correction given there to young women no proper way to reform 'em. A poem on the ancient and modern state of Bridewell. A ramble to Mob's Hole, in Essex. A description of the hunters' feast, with the humours of the guests.

PART VII

The Spy's return from Mob's Hole in a coach, with reflections thereupon. The diversion he met with on the Thames. Remarks on the playhouse in Dorset Gardens and the inhabitants of Salisbury Court. A description of a famous tobacco-shop in Fleet Street. Remarks on Whitefriars, with a poem on the same. A description of the Temple, with reflections upon the sharpers, &c. Remarks on the motto of a sundial, and a song thereupon. A description of May Fair.

PART VIII

The Spy and his friend go to St James's. The opinion of an Irish Dear Joy upon the whale's rib there. A description of the Park and the ladies of the Court, with a copy of verses upon Woman. A description of Westminster Abbey. A company of trainbands. Westminster Hall and the Courts of Justice, with the character of a pettifogger. A story of the great bell at Westminster. Remarks upon the tennis court at Whitehall, and the ruins there, with the character of a foot-soldier.

PART IX

A story on the Admiralty Office. A description of Man's Coffee-house, with the humours of the beaus, and a copy of verses thereon. Remarks upon the Horse Guards. On the famous cobbler at Charing Cross. On the statue of King Charles the First. A copy of verses on that unhappy prince. Remarks upon the New Exchange. Upon the devotion of the Covent Garden ladies, &c. And upon Covent Garden Market. The Hummums, or sweating-house, described. Several diverting stories told by the rubber.

PART X

A description of the Wits' Coffee-house, with a character of the modern poets. The character of a critic. A poetical letter from a lawyer in Town to an officer in the country. Remarks upon the playhouse in Drury Lane. A description of Bartholomew Fair. Remarks on the cooks at Pie Corner and Bartholomew Fair.

PART XI

A further description of Bartholomew Fair. Remarks upon the eclipse of the sun. The observations of a vintner and an upholsterer thereupon. The judgement of a famous astrologer upon the same.

PART XII

A description of a famous coffee-house in Aldersgate Street and how the Spy engaged an auctioneer there. A wonderful relation of a pleasant gentleman. A description of the splitting, roasting and eating of a whole side of an ox at the King's Head Tavern at Chancery Lane End, with a copy of verses to the vintner. A description of the City triumphs on the Lord Mayor's Day.

PART XIII

The countrymen's reports of the Tower. Remarks upon Tower Hill. A blind beggar and a mumping parson. A description of the Tower and the rarities that are to be seen there. Remarks on the Tower Wharf and the guns upon it. Reflections upon a tavern and an astrologer in Prescot Street in Goodman's Fileds. On the Salamanca Doctor's meeting-house.

PART XIV

Reflections on St Catherine's alehouses and the tars that frequent them. A seaman that had spent his money, reprehended by an hostess. The wheedles of the Wapping hostess to gull the sea-calves. A description of a famous music-house in Wapping. Reflections upon the Danes' Church. Rag Fair described. Remarks upon a coffee-house in Goodman's Fields, with a poem in praise of punch. Remarks upon lotteries in general, and on that at the Mercers' Chapel in particular, with some verses upon lotteries.

PART XV

The character of victuallers in general. The character of a common victualler in verse. Of astrologers and wise-women. Of a cunning-man in verse. Of a modern reformer of vice, or a reforming constable, in prose and verse. Comical accidents and occurrences.

PART XVI

A description of a company of sea-commanders drinking in a tavern. The character of a master of a vessel in verse. An account of the pleasant conversation, in a private house, of two country parsons and a sharp Town Quaker. A description in verse of a merry Levite in his cups. Reflections upon Gray's Inn Walks and the persons that frequent them. The character of an Irishman. Of a beau. Of a modish lady in verse. Reflections upon the stockjobbers at Jonathan's Coffee-house. The character of a stockjobber.

PART XVII

Reflections upon money and the bankers in Lombard Street. A story of their extortion. The character of a banker in verse. A comical description of a christening, with the humours of the gossips. A grace before and after meat, in verse. The character of a gossip in verse.

PART XVIII

The description of Mr Dryden's funeral, together with the manner of his death. His elegy. Some passages of Hackney coachmen in quarrelling. Of the mob conducting home a prize-fighting gladiator. A character of a prize-fighter in verse. Of two astrologers going to law. Of the vanity of astrologers and astrology, in verse. The end of their suit.

To the Reader

PREFACES ARE NOW become so common to every little treatise that I wonder there is not one to the horn-book; and indeed oftentimes, like women's faces, they are found the most promising and inviting part of the whole piece. But when a thing is usual (though never so ridiculous in the eye of reason), yet a man, like him that spoils his stomach with a mess of porridge before dinner, may plead custom to excuse his error. I therefore hope it will be no offence to conform with others, and show myself a fool in fashion.

Some authors are mere beaus in writing, and dress up each maggoty flirt that creeps from their mouldy fancy with a fine *Dedication*, though to John-a-nokes, and provide a long *Preface* to a little matter, like an alderman's grace to a scholars' commons; thinking their pigmy product looks as naked without these ornaments as a Puritan without his band, or a whore without her patches.

For my part, I only use this preamble as a sow-gelder does his horn. By hearing the latter you may give a shrewd guess at his business. So, by reading the former, you may rightly understand my design, which I assure you in the first place, is not to affront or expose anybody, for all that I propose is to scourge vice and villainy without levelling characters at any person in particular. But if any unhappy sinner, through the guilt of his own conscience, shall prove himself such an ass as to take that burden upon his own shoulders which hundreds in the Town have as much right to bear as himself, he has no reason to be angry with me, but may thank himself, or his destiny, for making his tender back so fit for the pack-saddle!

The first part of this undertaking I popped into the cautious world as a skilful angler does a new bait among wary fish who have oft been pricked in their nibbling. And finding the public snapping at it with as much greediness as a newsmonger at a *Gazette*, or a City politician at a new *Proclamation*, makes me purpose to continue it monthly, as long as we shall find encouragement.

When I have taken a complete survey of the most remarkable places, as well as the common vanities and follies of mankind (both day and night), I question not but the world will find it a useful as well as diverting history. Herein, Town gentlemen may see the view of the Town (without their experience), and learn the better to avoid those snares and practised subtleties which trepan many to their ruin. In order to expose these the dark mysteries of iniquity in so corrupt an age, we have projected this monthly journal as the best method we could take. I hope all will read it with pleasure, and some will make it profitable to themselves.

I

AFTER A TEDIOUS confinement to a country hut, where I dwelt like
Diogenes in his tub, or an owl in a hollow tree, taking as much delight
in my books as an alchemist does in his bellows, I tired with seven
years' search after knowledge, and began to reckon with myself for my
time and examine what a Solomon my diligent enquiry into the uncertain
guesses of our forefathers had made me. But I soon fell upon the opinion
of Socrates, and found myself as much the wiser as if, like the looby
Hercules, I had spent my hours at a distaff. This was no little vexation
to a man of my genius, to find my brains loaded to no purpose with as
many antiquated tringam-trangams as are lodged in the whimsical noddle
of an old astrologer, and yet could make twice ten no more than a junior
soph or a chalk-accountant. These reflections put me into as great a
passion with myself as a beau when he daubs his clothes or makes a
false step in the salutation of his mistress. So I resolved to be no longer
Aristotle's sumpter-horse, or like a tinker's ass to carry a budget for my
ancestors stuffed full of their frenzied notions and the musty conceits of
a parcel of dreaming prophets, fabulous poets and old doting philosophers, but shifted them off one by one (with a fig for St Augustine and
his doctrines, a fart for Virgil and his elegance, and a turd for Descartes
and his philosophy), till by this means I had eased my brains of those
troublesome crotchets which had raised me to the excellence of being
half fool and half madman in studying the weighty difference betwixt
upside-down and topsy-turvy, or to be more knowing in some such
nicety than the rest of my neighbours.

Having thus broke loose from the scholar's gaol, my study, and
utterly abandoned the conversation of all my old calf-skin companions,
I found an itching inclination in myself to visit London. But to shun the
censure of my sober country friends I projected, for their satisfaction and
my own diversion, the following journal intended to expose the vanities
and vices of the town as they should, by any accident, occur to my
knowledge, that the innocent might see by reflection what I should gain
by observation and intelligence, and not by practice or experience.

With this design I pursued my journey, and the second day entered
our metropolis, with as much wonder and amazement as the Hatfield

fiddler did Old Nick's palace in the time of the Christmas holidays. I had not long passed through Aldgate, like a ball through a port of a billiard-table, but by good fortune met an old schoolfellow who, I found, had laid down the gown and taken up the sword, being tricked-up in as much gaiety as a dancing-master upon a ball day, or a young sheriff at a county assize. After we had mutually dispatched our compliments to each other, and I had awkwardly returned in country scrapes his *à la mode* bows and cringes, he would needs prevail with me to dine with him at a tavern hard by, with some gentlemen of his acquaintance, which happy opportunity I, being an utter stranger in the town, very readily embraced. He entered the tavern first, like a young squire attended with his father's chaplain, for a black coat and band are as great signs of a parson or a pedagogue as a blue frock is of a butcher or a tallow-chandler. Besides, my hat, by often handling, being tugged into a canonical flap, I looked like a young deacon who had laid by his crape in order to rebaptise his soul in claret, without the danger of being seen staggering in his faith, to the scandal of his function.

As soon as we came near the bar, a thing started up, all ribbons, lace and feathers, and made such a noise with her bell and her tongue together that had half a dozen paper-mills been at work within three yards of her, they'd have signified no more to her clamorous voice than so many lutes to a drum, or ladies' farts to a peal of ordnance. This alarmed two or three nimble-heeled fellows aloft, who shot themselves downstairs with as much celerity as a mountebank's mercury upon a rope from the top of a church steeple, each one charged with a mouthful of 'Coming! Coming!' This sudden clutter at our appearance so surprised me that I looked as silly as a bumpkin translated from the plough-tail to the playhouse when it rains fire in the *Tempest*, or when Don John's at dinner with the subterranean assembly of terrible hobgoblins. He that got the start and first approached us of these greyhound-footed emissaries desired us to walk up, telling my companion his friends were above; then, with a hop, stride and jump, ascended the stairhead before us, and from thence conducted us to a spacious room where about a dozen of my schoolfellow's acquaintances were ready to receive us. Upon our entrance they all started up, and on a sudden screwed themselves into so many antic postures that had I not seen them first erect, I should have queried with myself whether I was fallen into the company of men or monkeys.

This academical fit of wriggling agility was almost over before I rightly understood the meaning on't, and found at last they were only

showing one another how many sorts of apes' gestures and fops' cringes
had been invented since the French dancing-masters undertook to teach
our English gentry to make scaramouches of themselves, and how to
entertain their poor friends and pacify their needy creditors with
compliments and congees. When every person, with abundance of pains,
had shown the ultimate of his breeding, contending about a quarter of an
hour who should sit down first (as if we awaited the coming of some
herald to fix us in our proper places, which with much difficulty we at
last agreed on), we proceeded to a whet of old hock, to sharpen our
appetites to our approaching dinner. I confess, as to my own part, my
stomach was as keen already as a greyhound's to his supper after a day's
coursing, or a miserly liveryman's, who has fasted three days to prepare
himself for a Lord Mayor's feast. The honest cook gave us no leisure to
tire our appetites by a tedious expectancy, for in a little time the cloth
was laid, and our first course was ushered up by the *dominus factotum*
in great order to the table, consisting of two calves' heads and a couple
of geese. I could not but laugh in my conceit to think with what
judgement the caterer had provided so lucky an entertainment for so
suitable a company.

After the victuals were pretty well cooled by the complimenting of
who should begin first, we all fell to; and, i'faith, I found by their eating
they were no way affronted at their fare, for in less time than an old
woman could crack a nut we had not left enough to dine the bar-boy.
The conclusion of our dinner was a stately Cheshire cheese, of a
groaning size, of which we devoured more in three minutes than a
million of maggots could have done in three weeks. After cheese comes
nothing; then all we desired was a clear stage and no favour. Accordingly, everything was whipped away in a trice, by so cleanly a conveyance
that no juggler by virtue of hocus-pocus could have conjured away his
balls with more dexterity. All our empty plates and dishes were, in an
instant, changed into full quarts of purple nectar and unsullied glasses.
Then a bumper to the Queen led the van of our good wishes, another to
the Church Established, a third left to the whimsy of the toaster, till at
last their slippery engines of verbosity coined nonsense with such a facile
fluency that a parcel of alley-gossips at a christening, after the sack had
gone twice round, could not with their tattling tormentors be a greater
plague to a fumbling godfather than these lame jests and impertinent
conundrums were to a man of my temper. Oaths were as plenty as weeds
in an almshouse garden, and in triumph flew about from one to t'other

like squibs and crackers in Cheapside, when the cuckolds-all-in-a-row march in splendour through the City. But, thanks to good fortune, my friend in a little time redeemed me out of this purgatory and, perceiving my uneasiness, made an apology for our going, and so we took our leaves.

I offered to pay my proportion, but the whole body of the society stood up *nemine contradicente* and bid me heartily welcome to so small a collation, with a thousand thanks to me for my good company, though I had sat all the time as silent as a Quaker unmoved by the Spirit at a humdrum meeting. As we walked out, we were attended by the whole family to the door, with as many welcomes at our arses as a man has 'Thank-ye's' and 'Lord bless-ye's' from a gang of mumpers for a pennyworth of charity.

As soon as we were got clear of our noisy flatterers I began to ask of my friend what sort of generous gentlemen those were who had so kindly treated us. He smiled at my enquiry, and told me I could scarce guess by what measures they buoyed up such a seeming grandeur. 'Did you take notice,' says he, 'of the gentleman in a blue coat, red stockings, silver-hilted sword, and edged hat, who sat at the upper end of the table? He was a sword-hilt maker by his trade, but proved so very ingenious at his tools that he hath acquired the art of cutting medals or stamps, and is mighty great with most of the bankers and topping goldsmiths about Town. You may guess from thence how he employs his talent. He keeps his brace of geldings, and a great many brace of worse cattle, living at the rate of a thousand pounds a year, and passes, to those that know him not, for a gentleman of good account in the North of England; and his bills will pass as current in Lombard Street as the best merchant's in the City.

'There was a handsome, lusty young fellow who sat next him, with a wheelbarrowful of periwig on, and a whole piece of muslin about his neck, and stunk as strong of orange-flower water as a Spaniard does of garlic. He was the other day but a wine-cooper's apprentice, but a brisk young dame in the City, who was forced by her father to marry an old merchant for the sake of his riches, maintains him in that equipage you see, for supplying the defects of her feeble husband. And now he is grown so prodigal that he won't wash his hands in anything but juice of oranges and Hungary-water; dines every day at the tavern; goes to the playhouse every night; stirs nowhere without a coach; has his fencing-master, dancing-master, singing-master, French-master; and is as complete a City beau (notwithstanding he was bred to the adze and driver) as you shall see in Lombard Street Church on a Sunday, or in Drapers' Gardens an hour before dinner-time.

'If you observed, there was a little demure spark in a diminutive cravat and fox-coloured wig, with a hat as broad as an umbrella, whose level brims discovered it was carefully preserved in that order by a hat-case and smoothing-iron. He seems greatly to affect antiquity, as you might see by his garb, though the coat he has on has not been made above this two months; yet he would have it in the ancient mode, with little buttons, round cuffs, narrow skirts, and pockets within two inches of the bottom, as the most proper fashion for his business. And for all 'tis so scanty, he makes it serve him for a cloak, with which it covers abundance of shame and a great deal of knavery. He's an incomparable herald, and will give you an exact genealogy of most good families in England, and has the art of making himself akin when he sees it convenient. To be short with you, he is one of those genteel mumpers we call cadators; he goes a circuit round England once a year, and under pretence of a decayed gentleman gets both money and entertainment at every good house he comes at. And if he has opportunity to handsomely convey away a silver beaker, or a spoon or two, he holds no long dispute with his conscience about the honesty of the matter. Then he comes up to Town and enjoys the benefit of his rural labours.

'Another you needs must take particular notice of, that plucked out a pair of pocket pistols and laid them in the window. He had a great scar across his forehead, a twisted wig and laced hat on, and the company called him Captain. He's a man of considerable reputation amongst birds of the same feather, who I have heard say this much in his praise, that he is as resolute a fellow as ever cocked pistol upon the road. And, indeed, I do believe he fears no man in the world but the hangman, and dreads no death but choking. He's as generous as a prince; treats anybody that will keep him company; loves his friend as dearly as the ivy does the oak, and will never leave him till he has hugged him to his ruin. He has drawn in twenty of his associates to be hanged, but had always wit and money enough to save his own neck from the halter. He has good friends at Newgate, who give him now and then a squeeze when he is full of juice, but promise him, as long as he's industrious in his profession and will but now and then show them a few sparks of his generosity, they will always stand between him and danger. This he takes as a verbal policy of insurance from the gallows till he grows poor

through idleness, and then (he has cunning enough to know) he may be
hanged through poverty. He's well acquainted with the ostlers about
Bishopsgate Street and Smithfield, and gains from them intelligence of
what booties go out that are worth attempting. He accounts them very
honest tykes and can with all safety trust his life in their hands, for now
and then gilding their palms for the good services they do him. He
pretends to be a disbanded officer, and reflects very feelingly upon "the
hard usage we poor gentlemen meet with, who have hazarded our lives
and fortunes for the honour of our prince, the defence of our country,
and safety of religion; and after all to be broke, without our pay, turned
out without any consideration for the dangers and difficulties we have
run through. At this rate, Wounds, who the devil would be a soldier?" At
such sort of cant he is excellent, and utters himself with as little
hesitation and as great grace as a Town stallion when he dissembles with
his generous benefactress, who believes all he says to be as true as the
Gospel.

'He that sat over against him, in the plate-buttoned suit and white
beaver hat, is a kind of an amphibious rascal, a compound of two sorts
of villainy. He is one half town-trap and the other half sweetener. He
always keeps at his beck three or four handsome young wenches, well
equipped and in good lodgings, who are all modesty without and nothing
but lewdness within; who can seem as innocent as doves and be as
wicked as devils; whose education, from their cradles, under some skilful
matron in iniquity, has made them pleasant companions, taking bedfellows, expert jilts, incorrigible sinners, and good managers of a bad
design. They had whores to their mothers, rogues to their fathers, bawds
to their tutors, and under a deceitful countenance are so case-hardened in
impudence that they never were sorry for anything, but that they were
too young to be whores when they were old enough to endeavour it.
These are his working tools, who, by their beauty, youth and airiness,
insinuate into the affections of young merchants, shopkeepers' apprentices &c., whose juvenile fury carries them too often into the ruinous
embraces of these treacherous strumpets. When, with their wanton
gestures, they seem most obliging to their admirers, their mercenary
thoughts are projecting something to their injury, like a Water Lane
Protestant who when at church seems most devout, yet is picking the
pocket of some over-penitent Christian who is so zealous at his prayers
that he neglects to watch, and whilst he has God in his heart has the
devil fumbling about his breeches.

'He accounts them rare cattle if they calve once in a year, for there's never a child they have but is worth two or three hundred pounds to him, besides by-advantages he makes by their inspecting into the affairs and secrets of those whom they can manage. And when the filthiness of their practice hath rendered them, like a pathway by common treading, nasty and infertile, he ransacks their wardrobe, strips them of their plumes, and discards 'em. So they are forced to fly to some common bawdy-house for refuge, and walk the streets for subsistence, and thus sin on, in public shame and misery, till the gallows or an hospital at last brings them to repentance.

'The other part of his life is tricking people out of their money by false dice and cards, which he handles with more gainful dexterity than the German artist, and preaches the parson with such a fraudulent deception of the sight, that he will drain the pockets of a large company in six minutes as clean as the Royal Oak lottery shall in six hours. He is often to be seen with a country cloth-coat on, all over dirt, or according to the weather, as if he had come a fifty-mile journey, though he's only travelled from Salisbury Court to Smithfield, where he keeps the market as constantly as a young whore does Bartholomew Fair, or an old one the Sacrament, looking in his rusty garb as much like an honest grazier as a City hypocrite in his black coat and band does like a good Christian. He is constant to no sort of dress, but changes his clothes as often as a whimsical woman does her mind, and, statesman-like, always suits his apparel to his project. Being a rare tongue-pad, and excellent at these following qualifications, he can out-flatter a poet, out-huff a bully, out-wrangle a lawyer, out-cant a Puritan, out-cringe a beau, out-face truth, and out-lie the Devil. The rest that you saw were a kind of supernumerary men, assistants who have not cunning enough to project a piece of roguery themselves, but, like a well-meaning brother, will lend a shoulder to the villainy. The former are your rare sycamore rogues, who flourish and spread finely for a season, and the other are the caterpillars that hang upon 'em.'

'But pray, old aquaintance,' said I, 'what is your employment in the world, that you are so well acquainted with this scandalous society?' 'Why, I'll tell you,' says he. 'I studied a little physic at the University, and some small knowledge I have gained in surgery since I came to Town. This the narrowness of my fortune hath obliged me to the use of, so that I have had most of these dark engineers you saw as my patients, for they are seldom free from clap, pox, thumps, cuts or bruises, and pay as generously for their cure as an old maid would do for a night's recreation with the man she likes, parting with pounds to their surgeon as freely as fools did with their pence to the Wheel of Fortune lottery.

'Come,' says my friend, 'let us step into this coffee-house here. As you are a stranger to the Town it will afford you some diversion.' Accordingly, in we went, where a parcel of muddling muckworms were as busy as so many rats in an old cheese-loft; some going, some coming, some scribbling, some talking, some drinking, others jangling, and the whole room stinking of tobacco like a Dutch scoot, or a boatswain's cabin. The walls were hung with gilt frames, as a farrier's shop with horseshoes, which contained abundance of rarities, viz., Nectar and Ambrosia, May Dew, Golden Elixirs, Popular Pills, Liquid Snuff, Beautifying Waters, Dentifrices, Drops, Lozenges, all as infallible as the Pope. 'Where everyone' (as the famous Saffold has it) 'above the rest, Deservedly has gained the name of best.' Good in all cases, curing all distempers; and every medicine, being so catholic, pretends to nothing less than universality. Indeed, had not my friend told me 'twas a coffee-house I should have took it for Quacks' Hall, or the parlour of some eminent mountebank.

When we had each of us stuck in our mouths a pipe of sotweed, we began to look about us. 'Do you mind,' says my friend, 'yonder old sophister with an Indian pipe between his meagre jaws, who sits staring at the candle with as much steadfastness as a country passenger at Bow Steeple, or a child at a raree-show? That's a strange, whimsy-headed humorist. Observe his posture; he looks like the picture of Aesculapius behind an apothecary's counter! And he has as many maggots in his noddle as there are mice in an old barn, or nits in a mumper's doublet. He has a wonderful projecting head, and has lately contrived one of the prettiest pocket-engines for the speedy blanching of hazel-nuts and filbert kernels that ever was invented; he'll crack and skin two for a squirrel's one, and in a few years, by a little alteration, will improve it to the use of walnuts. I'll assure you he's a member of the Royal Society and had as great a hand, for many years together, in bringing the weather-glass to perfection, as any of them. He puts great faith in the philosophers' stone and believes he shall one time or other be as rich as Croesus, though he has almost beggared himself in the search on't, and has as large a pair of bellows in his laboratory as ever an alchemist in Town.

'He tried a notable experiment the other day, in setting fire to a large haystack he had in the country, and ordered the ashes to be brought to

Town, from whence he proposed to prepare a medicine, called *Sal-Graminis*, which should infallibly cure all distempers in horses, and be the rarest medicine for cows, sheep, or oxen, and all sorts of creatures that feed upon grass, that any grazier or farrier can use in any distemper. But sending it up in an ill season, the ashes got wet in their carriage and quite lost their virtue, so that he was forced to sell them to a West Country bargeman in order to dung land. But, it's thought by the wise, he might have sold it in the hay to ten times the advantage.

'He has abundance of whims in him, very remarkable. He lives over against the church, so that when he dies he might not have far to travel upon four men's shoulders. As soon as the clock begins nine, if he gets not his shoes off before it has done striking, in order for bed, he is immediately seized with such a violent fit of the gout that he roars like a Tower lion at a woman pregnant with a male child. If he is not up just as the clock strikes five in the morning, he thinks himself bedridden. If his victuals be not brought to the table whilst the clock goes twelve, he eats nothing all that day; his stomach is always at the meridian height the same time as the sun is, and if he finds by his observation it's declined, he is as much out of humour for letting slip the critical minute as a married lady (without children to employ her thoughts) is for losing of her lap-dog.

'He's a wonderful antiquary, and has a closet of curiosities that out-does Gresham College. He tells ye that he has a toothpick of Epicurus, which he always uses after eating. It is made of the claws of an American humming-bird, and is to be used like a rake, and will pick four teeth at once. He has Diogenes' lantern, which he carried about Athens at noonday to seek for an honest man. He says he has some of Heraclitus's tears, which dropped from him in a hard winter and are frozen into crystal. They are set in a locket, and everytime anybody looks upon it they cannot forbear weeping. Also a tenpenny nail drawn out of the Ark, and though it's iron, toss it into a tub of water and 'twill swim like a feather. He pretends to have one of Judas's thirty pence, and everytime he looks upon't he is ready to hang himself. A mighty collection of these sort of trinkets he tells the world he's master of, and some give credit to his ridiculous romances.

'Mind that spark who has just come in. Four years since, his reputation was but slender, and in so little a time he has had three wives, all good fortunes to him, and now is looked upon to be worth ten thousand pounds.' ''Tis observed,' said I, 'that money is thrown into the very mouths of Fortune's minions, and some men must grow rich if all the lucky accidents that Chance can give will make them so.' My friend, in pursuance of this particular, expressed himself to this purpose: that he believed there was some foul play practised, because, says he, it is a thing so common in this city for a man to grow rich by plurality of wives, and send them one after another so methodically to the grave, as if he had a flight of translating them into another world a little before their time. 'For, I must confess,' says he, 'I know an apothecary who, if a man will trust him with the care of his family, once in a twelvemonth's time will certainly take an opportunity to do him such a piece of service if he gives him but the least item of his slender affections towards his helpmate. And I have often heard him say that women are always the best patients, especially if they die under his hands, for then, says he, let me make never so unreasonable a bill, it's never disputed but generously satisfied, with as good a will as a married man pays the tax for the birth of the first child, or an extravagant heir the charges of his father's funeral.

'Mind the little blade in the cloak that's talking with a parson. He's a bookseller in this city, and has got an estate by starving authors. I'll warrant you, the priest has been conjuring his brains together and has raised some wonderful work to the Church's glory and his own fame. He has been providing "A Scourge for the Pope's Jacket; or a Cudgel for Antichrist", or else a mess of good Protestant porridge to scald the mouth of an unbeliever, or some such business. But as to the wit-monger, I'll tell you, he's as honest a man as ever betrayed his trust, or built his own welfare upon another's ruin. He was appointed trustee for a young gentlewoman, and had the charge of an estate of between two or three hundred pounds per annum, which he very carefully secured to himself by marrying her to his apprentice and obliging him, upon that consideration, to buy his stock, whereby he became well paid for a great deal of waste paper. So he is crept into the estate, and they are got into his books for it. There is abundance of such sort of plain dealing practised amongst our worthy citizens, for you must know they do not always tell the truth in their shops, or get their estates by their honesty.'

Being half-choked with the steam that arose from their soot-coloured ninny-broth, their stinking breaths and the suffocating fumes of their nasty puffing-engines, my friend and I paid for our Muhammadan gruel and away we came. And passing along Leadenhall Street I saw some ships painted upon the outside of a great wall, which occasioned me to enquire of my schoolfellow what place that was. He told me 'twas the house belonging to the East India Company, which are a corporation of men with long heads and deep purses, who had purchased that with their money which nobody ought to sell, and dealt in those commodities, to get money, which it's a pity anybody should buy. They are very rich in England and very poor in the Indies. Were a schedule of their effects scored on one side and their Indian debts scored on the other, it is believed more bad debts would arise upon the reverse than are due to tradesmen from all the persons of quality in Town, or, perhaps, than were ever found owing to either Army or Navy; which they have neither will to pay nor power to satisfy, to the great honour of Christianity in that heathenish country. There are two companies now, and it's greatly hoped by many honest traders and merchants in the City that they may luckily prove the breaking of each other. Both have sent ships to the Indies, and 'tis thought they will give one another a warm salutation by the way, and maintain the truth of the old proverb that two of a trade can never agree.

'Pray take notice,' says my friend, 'of that gentleman that is stepping into his coach. I will tell you a pretty story of him. There was a poor woman, not far from this place, who sold earthenware, and had lately the good fortune to have a rich relation die and leave her worth forty thousand pounds. On hearing this, he, though a man of considerable quality, thought it a bait worth snapping at. In order to do this he became one of her earliest suitors and was very importunate with her to have the cracking of her pipkin, but she soon gave him a repulse and told him Man was an earthen vessel too brittle for her to deal in, and she had heard he had a great many flaws in his fortune which she would not be at the expense of mending. And since she had never received any testimonials of his affections before the happy change of her condition, she had reasons to believe his desires tended to her money and not her person, and therefore she would not be made a lady at so great an expense. She added that his pretensions would be ineffectual, and she hoped he would give himself no further trouble, assuring him that as her mind was steadfast so would his pains be fruitless. Upon this he feigned a melancholy humour and, sighing like a man at his wife's funeral, told her his passion was so great for her that unless she gave him a more satisfactory answer he would drown himself in the Tower Ditch. To this she replied, smiling, "Perhaps, sir, you propose that to yourself which is not in your power to do. You know not but Heaven has decreed for you a drier destiny." Upon this he rose in a great passion, crying, "Zounds, madam! Do you think I'll hang myself?" and so departed.

'Now,' says my schoolfellow, 'we'll spend the evening over a cheerful glass. Here's a tavern, hard by, which a parcel of pleasant companions of my acquaintance use. We'll see what diversion we can find in their society.' Accordingly we stepped in, and in the kitchen found half a dozen of my friend's associates, in the height of their jollity, as merry as so many Cantabrigians at Stourbridge Fair, or cobblers at a Crispin's feast. After a friendly salutation, free from all foppish ceremony, down we sat, and when a glass or two round had given fresh motion to our drowsy spirits, we abandoned all those careful thoughts which make man's life uneasy. Wit begot wit, and wine a thirsty appetite to each succeeding glass. Then open were our hearts, and unconfined our fancies. My friend and I contributed our mites to the treasure of our felicity. Songs and catches crowned the night, and each man in his turn elevated his voice to fill our harmony with the more variety. Amongst the rest, we had one song against music which, because of its being the first essay of this nature, I have thought it worth inserting:

A Song against Music

Music's a crotchet the sober think vain;
    The fiddle's a wooden projection;
Tunes are but flirts of a whimsical brain,
    Which the bottle brings best to perfection.
Musicians are half-witted, merry and mad;
    The same are all those that admire 'em;
They're fools if they play, unless they're well paid;
    And the others are blockheads to hire 'em.

Chorus

The organ's but humming,
Theorbo but thrumming,
The viol and voice
Is but jingle and noise.
The bagpipe and fiddle
Goes tweedle and diddle,
The hautboy and flute

Is but toot-a-toot-toot.
Your scales and your clefs, keys, moods and dull rules,
Are fit to please none but madmen and fools.

The novelty of this whimsy gave great diversion to the whole
company except one, who was by nature a poet. But, having Fortune to
his nurse, the blind malkin, careless of her charge, dropped him from her
lap, bruised the noddle of the tender babe and made his fancy rickety,
numbed his faculties, and so eclipsed his genius that he dwindled into a
musician.

Being as angry as a Tom turd-man to hear his profession so dispar-
aged, he resolved immediate revenge upon the author, called for pen and
ink, and went to work with as much eagerness and inveteracy as a parson
when he writes an order to his attorney to sue a parishioner for neglected
tithes. After some intervals of deliberation, wherein he sat like a virtuoso
at a philosophical lecture, this following crotchet started from his brain,
like Aesop's mouse from the mountain, to the great laughter of the whole
company:

A Song by a Musician against Poetry

Poetry's fabulous, loose and profane,
    For truth you must never depend on't.
'Tis the juvenile froth of a frenzical brain,
    Hung with jingling tags at the end on't.
Poets are poor, full of whimsy and flight
    For amorous fops to delight in.
They're fools if they write, lest they get money by't,
    And they're blockheads that pay 'em for writing!

Chorus

Their soft panegyric
Is praise beyond merit.
Their lampoon and satire
Is spite and ill-nature.
Their plays and romances
Are fables and fancies.
Their drolls and their farces

Are bald as our arses.
Their figures and similies only are fit
To please the dull fool that gives money for wit.

This raised amongst the whole society such an evil spirit of poetry, that it began to have as much power over us as the Devil has over a gang of Lapland witches. We now (Ovid-like) were so highly inspired we could scarce speak without rhyme and measure, and everyone, like a country fellow at a football meeting, was for showing what he could do, or telling what he had done. Among others, the following verses were lugged out of a pocket-library, written (as the author insinuated to the company) on this occasion.

Being blest with the conversation of some young ladies, one, whose wit and beauty were aspiring above the rest, knowing that he had some little fancy in poetry, told him she took it very unkindly of him that he never thought her worthy of his muse's notice. To this he replied that he was at all times provided to oblige so fair a lady, adding, if she would be pleased to lend him a pen and ink, he would take a copy of her perfections while she was there ready to sit for her picture. These she instantly fetched and very nimbly placed upon the table, with a pleasing expectancy of being flattered to her great glory as well as satisfaction. Upon this he obliged her with these following lines:

Madam, how great and good your virtues are,
I can't well tell, or truly do I care.
Nor can that wit which you from plays have stole
Admired be by any but a fool
Who may, perhaps, through his weak judgement, own
That you have sense, 'cause he himself has none.
Believe, I no such wrong opinion hold.
I can discern false metal from true gold!
Your ill-timed jests, so sharp in your conceit,
Are spoiled for want of judgement to repeat,
Like an unskilful play'r who lames each line
Which by the poet read, or spoke, is fine.
    If you have wit which you can boast your own,
Let it in some return to this be shown,
Or I, proud lady fair, shall justly think you've none!

This he presented to the lady, who, upon the first glance, blushed at her disappointment, and ran into her closet, fired with indignation and revenge, soon showing the pregnancy of her wit by the speediness of her answer, which I have also given you:

> Two lively figures in one piece you've shown,
>   A true-bred poet, and an ill-bred clown;
> Virtues not understood by you, I boast,
> Such that in our weak sex are valued most,
> As truth, good nature, manners, though not wit,
> Graces that never crowned a poet yet.
>   To rail at a weak woman is a strain
> Does little merit in its wit contain;.
> It may be like a scribbler, but unlike a man.
> A self-opinion from your lines I'll raise,
> And fancy you discovered in my face
> Virtues beyond your reach, and so above your praise!
> As envious beggars spitefully disdain,
> And rail at blessings which they can't obtain.
>   Tho' I'm abused, yet I'll good-humoured be,
> And beg for once you'd take advice of me.
> Much rather let your wit in silence rest,
> Than lose a friend, or mistress, for a jest.
> Mix manners and good nature with your parts,
> And you'll deserve more thanks, and win more hearts.

This, being the product of a female genius, was very much admired by our whole assembly of poetasters, who are always so favourable to the fair sex as to seem as much opinionated of what they write as a fond father is of the witty sayings of his own progeny; it being as natural for a young poet to dote upon Woman as 'tis for a hound to love horseflesh. And I must confess, whenever we rail at 'em, it is more for their virtues than their vices; for the latter we are as busy to seduce them to as the rest of our neighbours, and are never very angry with them but for denying us what they impart to others, or when by their prudence they secure that treasure to themselves at which we want to be nibbling. A pretty woman is but a a piece of Heaven's poetry, wherein as many changes are to be seen as in Ovid's *Metamorphoses*, and whenever she is attempted to be read by our earthly sons of Apollo, she is found to be a crabbed piece, and the measure of her verse too long for human scanning.

Another in the company being willing to contribute something to our mirth and pastime, communicated to the board this poem in manuscript, written by a fellow in Bedlam who ran mad, through ambition, and fancied himself a king; but not being contented with the government of his sublunary dominions, he was ambitious (as you will find by his lunatic raptures) of conquering larger territories above the moon, or somewhere whither his frenzy led him. Therefore, as the poetical pill-maker says of his learned works, 'Read, try, judge, and speak as you find.'

The Madman's Flight

Could I the sceptre of the Heavens sway,
And make Dame Nature my commands obey,
The ocean I'd unbound, and quench the fiery day.
Fearing no thunder could from Jove be hurled,
I'd then in darkness ravage through the world
Till met by devils in amazing throngs,
Armed with huge scorpions and infernal prongs!
Shrieking like souls oppressed, I'd bid 'em come,
And stare so fierce I'd brazen out my doom.
Knowing my soul is too divine an air
For fiends or devils to torment or tear,
I'd forwards press and to repulse their aim
Would drive those hellish tribes from whence they came,
    Then mount to Heaven and kindle up the sun
To see what mischiefs I on earth had done.
Behold, like cruel tyrants, with delight
The crimson ills that stained the sable night.
My power, like theirs, I'd build on others' fate,
And glory in black deeds that made me great.
When I through all these purple crimes had run,
That could be, by unbounded greatness, done,
Then the bright chariot of the sun I'd seize,
And drive it where my godlike soul should please.
The moon would I compel to be my guide.
Thus splendidly through Heaven would I ride,

There huff and strut, and kick the gods aside.
In my career, my fury to expose,
I'd cast down stars upon the heads of those
That either Fate or choice had made my foes,
    Then the proud demons of the air to scare,
The clouds in sundry pieces would I tear,
And puff 'em up like bubbles in the air.
I'd jostle clouds, Heaven's harmony confound,
And fix those orbs that now dance nimbly round.
If any bold Olympian sent'nel dare
Question my office, or my business there,
Or if against me offer to rebel,
I'd grasp his air and strike him down to Hell.
    Thus by degrees would I the gods unthrone,
Till Heaven should at last become my own.
Then to demolish earth's infernal crew,
I'd damn this old world and create a new.

This frantic piece of bombast pleased wonderfully. No profane jest to an atheist, or bawdy story to an old bachelor, could have been more acceptable. One commended the loftiness of the fancy; another the aptness of the language; a third, the smoothness of the verse; so that the madman had like to have run away with the bays from us all had not one in the company been an author in print to the great applause of the whole nation, who, if he would have worn as much bay as the common vogue of the people had given him a title to, his head would have appeared as fine as a country casement in the midst of the Christmas holidays.

By this time the nimble spirits of the reviving juice had rather overpowered than enlivened the noblest of our faculties, and had seized our brains as their proper thrones in order to hold a sovereign sway over the dominions of the flesh, driving out weak reason by a power invincible, and making her become a weak subject till the next morning.

My friend and I thought it high time to take our leaves; which, after the payment of our clubs, we did accordingly, agreeing to give ourselves the pleasure of two or three hours' ramble in the streets. Having spent the time at the tavern till about ten o'clock with mirth and satisfaction, we were now desirous of prying into the dark intrigues of the Town, to experience what pastime the night accidents, the whims and frolics of

staggering bravadoes and strolling strumpets, might afford us. An account
of which we shall give you in our next.

II

ACCORDING TO THE wisdom of our forefathers, we had carefully taken the Old Gentleman by the forelock; for though we thought it ten o'clock when we left the blessings of dear Hymen's palace, yet, by the night, it proved but the miser's bedtime, the modest hour of nine being just proclaimed by Time's oracle from every steeple. The joyful alarm of Bow Bell called the weary apprentices from their work to their paring-shovels, to unhitch their folded shutters and button up their lying sanctuaries, their shops, till the next morning. In these there are more untruths asserted in one day than false oaths taken in Westminster Hall in a whole term. The masters have more canting reservations to indemnify their consciences from the danger of deceitful protestations than an old strumpet, or a plot-evidence, being more afraid of breaking than they are of damnation. Indeed, a trader thinks he has made but an ill market if he has not saved himself.

The streets were all adorned with dazzling lights whose bright reflections so glittered in my eyes that I could see nothing but themselves. Thus I walked amazed, like a wandering soul in its pilgrimage to Heaven when it passes through the spangled regions.

My ears were so serenaded on every side with the grave music of sundry passing-bells, the rattling of coaches, and the melancholy ditties of 'Hot Baked Wardens and Pippins!' that had I had as many eyes as Argos and as many ears as Fame, they would have been all confounded, for nothing could I see but light, and nothing hear but noise.

We had not walked the usual distance between a church and an alehouse, when some odoriferous civet-box perfumed the air and saluted our nostrils with so refreshing a nosegay that I thought the whole city (Edinburgh-like) had been overflowed with an inundation of sir-reverence. By and by, came thundering by us a rumbling engine in the dark, which I took for a deadmonger's wagon laden with a stinking corpse (by reason of long keeping), driving post-haste to the next churchyard in order to inter it. But I was soon undeceived by my friend, who told me 'twas a gold-finders' caravan carrying treasure to their land-bank by the saltpetre-houses. The projectors of this notable design, says my friend, have, at no small expense, discovered the fallacy of an old proverb and can (by your leave, sir) by sound reason and true experience deny shitten luck to be good luck. For, after two or three thousand pounds' disbursement to turn a turd into gunpowder, they found their project would not signify a fart; which, if their designing noddles could have brought it to perfection, our foes then, like themselves now, would have doubtless been in a stinking condition.

As we stumbled along, my friend bid me take notice of a shop wherein sat three or four very provoking damsels, with as much velvet on their backs as would have made a burying-pall for a country parish, or a holiday coat for a physician, being glorified at bottom with gold fringes, so that I thought at first they might be parsons' daughters who had borrowed their fathers' pulpit cloths to use as scarves to go a-visiting in. Each had as many patches in her market-place as there are spots in a leopard's skin, or freckles in the face of a Scotsman.

I asked my friend what he took them for. He answered, they were a kind of first-rate punks by their rigging, of about a guinea purchase. I further queried what reason he had to believe them to be lechery-layers. He replied, because they were sitting in a head-dresser's shop, 'which,' says he, 'is as seldom to be found without a whore as a bookseller's shop in Paul's Churchyard without a parson.

'Come,' says my friend, 'we'll call here hard by, at the Widow's Coffee-house and drink a dish or two. I have some female patients that use the house who are a little in my debt, and if the lewdness of the town has lately thrown a cully in their way, they may chance to be able to make me satisfaction.'

Accordingly we blundered through the long dark entry of an ancient fabric, groping our way like subterranean labourers in the caverns of a coal-pit, till we found the stairs, which were raised as perpendicular as a tiler's ladder, so that had I not had the use of a rope which was nailed along the wall, as a clue to guide me, I could have climbed a country maypole, or have crawled up the buttock-shrouds of one of Her Majesty's first-rate men-of-war, with less danger and difficulty. At last an old weather-beaten Cerberus came to the stairhead with a candle, which to me was as welcome as a light in a dark night to a stumbling drunkard, or moonshine (when near land) to a doubtful mariner. She saluted us with 'Lord, gentlemen, why did you not call to be lighted up? I protest, I thought there had been a candle upon the stairs, but my careless baggage is so lazy, she minds nothing that she should do. She's but lately come out of the country, and stands staring about like a bumpkin in Paul's Church, or a libertine in a conventicle.'

With this sort of talk she ushered us into the coffee-room, where, at the corner of a long table next to her elbow-chair, lay a large old Bible open, with her spectacles upon one of St Paul's epistles; next to it was a quartern pot, two or three stone bottles, a roll of plaster, and a pipe of tobacco, with a handful of fire in a rusty grate, a pint coffee-pot before it, and a green earthen chamber-pot in the chimney-corner. Over the mantel-tree were two bastard-china dishes, a patch-box and a syringe. On a little shelf, among phials and gallipots, were half a dozen long bottles of *Rosa Solis*, with an advertisement of a rare whitewash for the face nailed on one side, and a brief account of the excellence of Doctor John Case's pills for the speedy cure of a violent gonorrhea without loss of time, or hindrance of business, on the other. A grenadier's bayonet, musket and cartouche-box were behind the door. A head-dresser's block and a quart pot (as terrible as a death's-head and an hourglass) stood frightfully in the window, also an old-fashioned clock in a crazy case, but as silent as a corpse in a coffin, stood bolt upright, like a stiff-necked constable, more for ornament than use. Next to this hung the reverend print of the Seven Golden Candlesticks, and against that a commode adorned with a scarlet topknot. Under it was an abstract of the Acts of Parliament against drinking, swearing, and all manner of profaneness. The broken floor was like an old stable, the windows were mended with brown paper, and the bare walls were full of dust and cobwebs.

After I had walked about and taken a complete view of this antiquated Sodom, I set myself down; but of a sudden I felt such a trembling in the fabric, that the windows jarred, the fire-irons jingled, in short all things in the room seemed to be in motion and kept time with a tinkling noise like the bells in a morris dance; so that had I not been furnished with some reasons to suspect the contrary, I should have been under the frightful apprehensions of an earthquake. But in a little time the violent pulsation that had given an ague to the whole house was over, and all things were again reconciled to their former rest. Presently after came downstairs from a loftier apartment reserved for private uses, a couple of airy youths who by their cropped hair, stone buckles in their shoes, broad gold hatbands, and no swords, I took to be merchants' sons, or the apprentices of topping traders. They stayed not above a minute in the coffee-room, but, magpie-like, asked what's o'clock, then made their honours after the newest fashion, and so departed.

My friend by this time (knowing the entertainment of the house) had called for a bottle of cock-ale, of which I tasted a glass but could not conceive it to be anything but a mixture of small beer and treacle. 'If this be cock-ale,' said I, 'e'en let coxcombs drink it. Prithee, give me a glass of brandy, or something that will dart lightning into my spirits, and not fill my guts with thunder.' With that the reverend doctress of debauchery (after she had approved my choice with a cheerful smile) signified her sympathizing appetite in these words: 'Sir, you are of my mind. I think there's nothing like a dram of true Nantes or some such comfortable cordial. Of the former, indeed, I have none, by reason of its scarcity, but I have an excellent distillation of my own preparing, which some call *Aqua Veneris*. It will restore an old man of threescore to the juvenility of thirty, or make a girl at fourteen, with drinking but one glass, as ripe as an old maid of twenty-four. 'Twill make a parson dance sellenger's round, a Puritan lust after the flesh, and a married man oblige his wife oftener in one night than without it he shall be able to do in seven. I sell it to most citizens' wives in Town, who are seldom without it in their closets, to oblige their husbands or gallants. For, though I say it that should not, it's the best cordial to strengthen a weak appetite, drank a little before bedtime, in the world. Here, Priscilla, bring the gentleman a quartern.'

Just as a cup of corroboration was moving round, who should bolt downstairs from fools' paradise above but a couple of mortal angels as nimble as squirrels, with looks as sharp and eyes as piercing as a tiger's, who, I suppose, after rumpling their feathers in a hot engagement, had stayed to rectify their disordered plumes and make ready for a fresh encounter. They presently saluted my friend (as the Devil did Doctor Edwards) with, 'Your servant, Doctor.' He returned their compliment and desired their company, which they as readily granted as a fortuneless jilt her consent to matrimony, or a poor scholar his company to a treat.

By the help of paint, powder and patches, they were of a waxwork complexion, and thus dressed: their under-petticoats were white dimity, flourished like a turkey-work chair, or a fool's doublet, with red, green, blue and yellow. Their pin-up coats of Scotch plaids were adorned with bugle lace, and their gowns were of printed calico, but their heads were dressed up to the best advantage, like a vintner's bar-keeper, or a churchwarden's daughter upon an Easter Sunday. These, I suppose, devil-like, would play at small game rather than stand out, and sooner condescend to the acceptance of a shilling than want employment.

By the time we had sipped off our nipperkin of my grannam's *Aqua Mirabilis*, our airy ladies grew so very mercurial, they could no longer contain their feigned modesty, but launched out into their accustomary wantonness, and showed us as many whimsical vagaries and diverting pranks as a young monkey with a mouse at his tail, or an owl upon a duck's back in the water.

This familiarity encouraged my friend to a further freedom. He took the boldness upon him to ask one if trading had been so good of late that she could pay the arrears due upon her last misfortune. To this she replied, 'The Lord confound your devices for a twat-scouring pimp! I owe you none till the breaking out of the next fire. Did not I agree with you, when first we dealt together, to pay you one cure under another? And therefore the last is not due till I next want your assistance. Pray, Mr Emplastrum, don't you come with that upon me, neither, for I am sure I have paid you hitherto as generously as any patient of my quality that ever you gave pill or bolus to, and have done you and your profession as much service as any girl of my function that trades between Aldgate and Temple Bar. You know when I was in keeping I let you have money to redeem your plaster-box, when I owed you not a groat, and I have had nothing in return of my kindness, as I know on, but a little Roman vitriol for a shanker, or a piece of orris-root for my issue, therefore you need not be so sharp with me, neither!'

This impudence so silenced my friend that he looked as tame as a City cuckold chided by his wife, and as dumb as a statue, being glad to appease her fury by calling for t'other quartern, which before we had drunk, who should grovel upstairs but, seemingly, a sober citizen in cloak and band, about the age of sixty. Upon this the old Mother of the Maids called hastily to Priss and, whispering, asked her if there were any rods in the house. I, sitting just by, overheard the question. The wench answered, 'Yes, yes. You know I fetched six pennyworth but yesterday.' Upon the entrance of this grave fornicator, our ladies withdrew themselves from our company and retired like modest virgins to their secret work-room of iniquity, and left the old sinner, in the winter of his lechery, to warm his grey hairs with a dram of invigorating cordial whilst we paid our reckoning, and were lighted downstairs. We left the lustful satyr (to the shame of his age) a prey to the two strumpets; for he, I believe, found himself in a much worse condition than a breech between two stools, or Lot in Sodom between the merry cracks his buxom daughters.

Time now, like a skilful gamester, had just nicked seven, and each parochial jack-o'-lantern was croaking about streets the hour of eleven. The brawny topers of the city began now to forsake the tavern and stagger hawking after a poop-lantern to their own houses. Augusta appeared in her mourning-weeds, and the glittering lamps which a few hours before had sparkled like diamonds fixed as ornaments to her sable dress, were now dwindled to a glimmering snuff, and burnt as dim as torches at a prince's funeral. Strumpets in the streets were grown a scarce commodity, for the danger of the compter had driven them home to their own poor sinful habitations where nothing dwells but shame, poverty and misery, the devil and themselves.

We now were at a stand which way to move. At last my companion proposed the dark house at Billingsgate, where, he told me, we need not question, amongst the various humours of the maritime mobility, but to find abundance of diversion. Besides, when our faculties should grow tired with our pastime, and Nature (for the refreshment of our drowsy microcosms) should require rest, we could there have the convenience of a bed to repose our weary members.

Accordingly we thither steered our course, and by the way I asked him what was the meaning, when the old lecher came into the coffee-room, that Mother Beelzebub asked the wench whether they had any rods in the house. He smiled at my question and told me he believed he should discover a new vice to me which I scarce had heard of.

'That sober-seeming saint,' says he, 'is one of that class in the black school of sodomy, who are called by learned students in the science of debauchery, flogging-cullies. This unnatural beast gives money to those strumpets which you saw, and they down with his breeches and scourge his privities till they have laid his lechery. He, all the time, begs their mercy, like an offender at a whipping-post, and beseeches their forbearance. But the more importunate he seems for their favourable usage the severer vapulation they are to exercise upon him, till they find by his beastly ecstasy when to withhold their weapons.'

We had not proceeded far towards our intended harbour, when, at the door of an eminent shopkeeper in Gracechurch Street, we heard, as we thought, the amorous squallings of some nocturnal revellers called cats, summoning, with their untuneable voices, the neighbouring mouse-hunters to their merry meeting. But by the help of a watchman's lantern, who met us in the passage, we discovered a hand-basket from whence we conceived proceeded this ingrateful discord. 'Hey-day,' says the watchman, 'what, in the name of the stars, have we got here? The unhappy fruits of somebody's labours, I'll warrant you, who had rather get ten bastards than provide for one.' He opens the wicker hammock, and finds a little lump of mortality crying out to the whole parish to lend him their assistance, with this inscription, written in a fair hand, pinned upon his breast:

> I was got by an honest poor man
>   Who sails in Her Majesty's service,
> My mother is called Whore Nan,
>   The name of my father is Jervice.
>
> My father's first letter is J,
>   My mother's with N does begin.
> They put them together to try
>   What it spelt, and 'twas luckily IN.
>
> Thus was I conceived in sin -
>   There's nobody got without!
> And though I went sinfully in
>   The iniquity's now come out.
>
> Have mercy upon me, I pray,
>   And carry me out of the weather.
> For all that my mother can say
>   The parish must be my father.

The unusualness of such a posy upon so unwelcome a present made us as merry as a young comedian over a lame jest, or a constable at a bellman's verse. The watchman coughed up a phthisical hem, as a signal to his associates of some mischance, which was conveyed from one to t'other till it alarmed the leader of the Hour-grunters, who soon came up, attended with his twinkling guard of superannuated sauceboxes, presently saddling his nose with a pair of glazed horns to read the superscription, and see to whom the squalling packet was directed. But when he found the poor infant lay drivelling upon a whole slabbering-bib of verses, 'Alack, alack,' says Father Midnight, 'I'll warrant 'tis some poor poet's bastard. Prithee, take it up, and let's carry it to the watch-house fire. Who knows but, by the grace of Providence, the babe may come to be a second Ben Jonson! Prithee, Jeffery, put the lappet of thy coat over it, I'll warrant 'tis so cold it can scarce feel whether it be a boy or a girl.' Away trooped his Midnight Majesty with his feeble band of crippled parish pensioners, to their nocturnal rendezvous, all tickled with the jest, and as merry over their hopeful foundling as the Egyptian Queen over her young prophet in the rushes.

We blundered on in pursuit of our night's felicity, but scarce had walked the length of a horse's tether, ere we heard a noise so dreadful and surprising that we thought the Devil was riding on hunting through the City, with a pack of deep-mouthed hell-hounds, to catch a brace of tallymen for breakfast. At last bolted out from the corner of a street, with an ignis fatuus dancing before them, a parcel of strange hobgoblins covered with long frieze rugs and blankets, hooped round with leather girdles from their cruppers to their shoulders, and their noddles buttoned up into caps of martial figure, like a knight errant at tilt and tournament with his wooden head locked in an iron helmet. One was armed, as I thought, with a lusty faggot-bat, and the rest with strange wooden weapons in their hands in the shape of clyster-pipes, but as long, almost, as speaking-trumpets. Of a sudden they clapped them to their mouths and made such a frightful yelling that I thought the world had been dissolving and the terrible sound of the last trumpet to be within an inch of my ears.

Under these amazing apprehensions I asked my friend what was the meaning of this infernal outcry. 'Prithee,' says he, 'what's the matter with thee? Thou look'st as if thou wert galleyed. Why these are the city waits, who play every winter's night through the streets to rouse each lazy drone to family duty.' 'Lord bless me!' said I. 'I am very glad it's no worse. I was never so scared since I popped out of the parsley-bed. Prithee, let us make haste out of the hearing of them, or I shall be forced to make a close-stool pan of my breeches.' At which my friend laughed at me. 'Why, what,' says he, 'don't you love music? These are the topping tooters of the town, and have gowns, silver chains, and salaries, for playing "Lilliburlero" to my Lord Mayor's horse through the city.' 'Marry,' said I, 'if his horse liked their music no better than I do, he would soon fling his rider for hiring such bugbears to affront His Ambleship. For my part, when you told me they were waits, I thought they had been the Polanders and was never so afraid but that their bears had been dancing behind them.'

The next scene the night presented to our imperfect view was a very young crew of diminutive vagabonds, who marched along in rank and file like a little army of Prester John's countrymen, as if advancing in order to attack a bird's nest. This little gang of tatterdemalions my friend was almost as great a stranger to as myself, and for our satisfaction, to be better informed, we saluted them after this manner: 'Pray what are you for a congregation of ragged sprites, and whither are you marching?' 'We, masters,' replied one of the pert frontiers, 'we are the City Black-Guard marching to our winter quarters, the glasshouse in the Minories. Lord bless you, masters, give us a penny or a halfpenny amongst us, and you shall hear any of us, if you please, say the Lord's Prayer backwards; swear the compass round; give a new curse to every step in the Monument; or call a whore as many proper names as a peer has titles.' 'I find,' said I, 'you are a parcel of hopeful sprouts.' However, we gave the poor wretches a penny, and away they trooped with a thousand 'God Bless-ye's,' as ragged as old stocking mops, and, I'll warrant you, as hungry as so many catamountains; yet they seemed as merry as they were poor, and as contented as they were miserable.

'What a shame it is,' said I, 'that such an infamous brood of vagabonds should be trained up in villainy, ignorance, laziness, profaneness, and infidelity, from their cradles, in such a well-governed Christian city as this, where are so many grave magistrates and parish officers whose care it ought to be to prevent such growing evils. And yet to suffer such a nest of heathens to be nursed up in blasphemy and contempt of religion, under the very walls of the churches, is certainly a scandal to our laws, and a shame to those in authority; to me 'tis very strange.'

'They are poor wretches,' says my friend, 'that are dropped here by gipsies and country beggars when they are so little they can give no account of parents or place of nativity, and the parishes, caring not to bring a charge upon themselves, suffer them to beg about in the daytime, and at night sleep at doors, and in holes and corners about the streets till they are so hardened in this sort of misery that they seek no other life till their riper years (for want of being bred to labour) puts them upon all sorts of villainy. Thus, through the neglect of churchwardens and constables, from beggary they proceed to theft, and from theft to the gallows.'

As we were thus reflecting upon the miserable condition of these unhappy wretches, another midnight King of Clubs was going his progress round his scanty dominions attended with his whole court of ravenous mobility. And, popping on us unawares, his well-fed majesty bid his garde du corps halt, and with a 'Hem,' clapping his painted sceptre to the ground as hard as a paver does his rammer, he bid us stand and come before the constable. We, like prudent ramblers, obeyed the voice of authority and, with uncovered heads, paid reverence to his awful presence.

He demanded of us, after an austere manner, who and what we were, and had as many impertinent questions at his tongue's end as an apothecary has hard words, or a midwife has bawdy stories. My friend, in order to satisfy His Worship's curiosity and make him something the wiser, answered his foolish examination with as much submission and respect as a proud peevish dunce in authority could expect, or a prudent man, when at the mercy of such as coxcomb, give.

He asked my friend what was his profession. He answered him, 'A surgeon.' 'A surgeon!' says our learned potentate in great derision, 'and why not a chirurgeon, I pray, sir? I could find in my heart to send you to the Compter for presuming to corrupt the King's English before me, his representative.'

''Twas a mistake, Mr Constable,' said I, 'pray excuse it, and be not so severe with us. We are very sober, civil persons, who have been about our business and are going quietly to our own habitations.'

'Civil and sober persons,' said he, 'how do I know that, Mr Prattle-box? You may be drunk for aught I know, and only feign yourselves sober before my presence to escape the penalty of the Act.'

My friend put his hand in his pocket and plucked out a shilling. 'Indeed, Mr Constable,' says he, 'we tell you nothing but the naked truth. Here is something for your watch to drink. We know it is a late hour, but we hope you will detain us no longer.'

With that, Mr Surlicuff directs himself to his right-hand janizary, 'Hem, hah, Amminadib. I believe they are civil gentlemen.' 'Aye, aye,' said he, 'Master, you need not question it; they don't look as if they had fire-balls about 'em.' 'Well, gentlemen, you may pass; but pray go civilly home. Here, Colly, light the gentlemen down the hill, they may chance to stumble in the dark, and break their shins against the Monument.'

'Thank you, sir, kindly,' said we, 'for your civility, but we know the way very well, and shall need no watchman. Your servant, sir, good night to you.'

'I am very glad,' says my friend, 'we got out of the clutches of this inquisitive coniwable. This grey-headed lump of grave ignorance takes as much pride in being the most officious fool in his parish as a victualler does to be one of the jury, or a vintner to be made an ensign of the trainbands. This is the most ill-natured, pragmatical blockhead that ever was centred in a circle of lanterns, and if he had said our heads had been made of Hackney turnips, one word of contradiction would have cost us a night's lodging in the Compter, for he makes no more of committing a man than a tavern-drawer does of kissing the cook. And his thirsty retinue that attend him are rare hard-mouthed fellows at an oath, and can swear as heartily as a Lancashire evidence you were drunk, though you drank nothing but coffee for three days before; and that you abused the constable, though you gave him not an ill word; and swore abundance of oaths, though your communication (Quaker-like) was nothing but Yea, yea, and Nay, nay.

'The great good these fellows do in the streets is to disturb people every hour with their bawling, under pretence of taking care they may sleep quietly in their beds, and call every old fool by his name seven times a night, for fear he should rise and forget it next morning. And often, instead of preventing mischief, they make it, by carrying honest persons to the Compter who would fain walk peaceably home to their own habitations. And they provoke gentlemen, by their sauciness, to commit those follies 'tis properly their business to prevent. In short, it is reasonable enough to believe they play more rogues' tricks than ever they detect, and occasion more disturbances in the streets than ever they hinder.'

By this time we were come to Billingsgate, and in a narrow lane, as dark as a burying-vault, which stunk of stale sprats, piss and sir-reverence, we groped about like a couple of thieves in a coal-hole, to find the entrance of that nocturnal theatre in whose delightful scenes we proposed to terminate the night's felicity. At last we stumbled upon the threshold of a gloomy cavern where, at a distance, we saw lights burning like candles in a haunted cave where ghosts and goblins keep their midnight revels.

We no sooner entered, but we heard such a number of female tongues so promiscuously engaged in a mess of tittle-tattle, that had a waterman knocked down his wife with a stretcher, and was being tried for the fact by a parliament of fish-women, they could not have exercised their nimble instruments with more impatience.

We turned ourselves into the smoky boozing-ken amongst them, where, round the fire, sat a tattered assembly of fat motherly flat-caps, with their fish-baskets hanging upon their heads instead of riding-hoods, with every one her nipperkin of warm ale and brandy, and as many rings upon their thumbs as belongs to a suit of bed curtains; every one as slender in the waist as a Dutch skipper in the buttocks, and looked together like a litter of squab elephants. Their noses were as sharp as the gnomon of a dial, and looked as blue as if they had been frost-nipped. Their cheeks were as plump as an infant's buttocks, but adorned with as many crimson carnosities as the face of a nobleman's butler who has lived forty years in the family, and plainly proved by the depth of their colour that brandy is a nobler dye than claret. Their tongues were as loud as the Temple horn, that calls the cuckold-makers to their commons, and every word they spoke was at least in the pitch of double-gamut. Their chief clamour was against high-heads and patches, and they said it would have been a very good law if Queen Mary had effected her design, and brought the proud minxes of the Town to have worn high-crowned hats instead of topknots.

Then one, looking over her shoulder and spying me behind her, accosts me after this manner: 'God save you, honest master, will you pledge me?' 'Aye, dame,' said I, 'with all my heart.' 'Why then,' says she, 'here's a health to mine arse, and a fart for those that owe no money.'

'Lord help my poor masters!' says another. 'They look as if they had disobliged their wives or their landladies, and they would not rise and let them in tonight.'

'Come, come away,' says my friend, 'let's seek another apartment. These saucy-tongued old whores will tease us to death.' These unhappy words one of them overheard and, starting up like a fury, thus gave her lungs a breathing:

'You white-livered son of a Fleet Street bumsitter, begot upon a chair at noonday between Ludgate and Temple Bar! You puppily offspring of a mangy night-walker who was forced to play the whore an hour before she cried out to pay the bawd, her midwife, for bringing you, you bastard, into the world. Who is it that you call whore?'

Away slunk my friend and I into another room and left them to spend their malignant spirits by themselves, and were as thankful to Providence we escaped so imminent a danger, as if delivered from the rage of so many wild cats. And, indeed, if their talons were as sharp as their tongues, they need not fear a combat with all the beasts of America.

We were now tumbled into a company composed of as many sorts of rakes as you may see whores at a buttock-ball. One, in a long wig and muff, looked as fretful as a broken gamester, biting his nails as if he were ready to curse aloud, 'Confound the dice.' Another was as dull as if his grey mare was the better horse, and had denied him entrance for keeping late hours. The next, as brisk and lively as if just come of age and had got his means in his own hands, bought his time of his master and feared no colours, but, thinking the day too short for his fortune, had resolved the night should make amends in lengthening out his pleasures.

Up in a corner sat a couple of brawny watermen, one eating broiled red herring, and the other bread and cheese and onions, so that had a Welshman spewed up his cous bobby and leek porridge into a Dutchman's close-stool pan, it could not have produced a finer nosegay to have poisoned the Devil.

Then in blunders a drunken tar, as great in his thoughts as an Admiral, and calls to the boy in the bar after this manner: 'You horse-turdly spawn of a freshwater lubber, why don't you hand me a candle, and induct me to my cabin, that I may belay myself?' As the boy lights him upstairs, he stumbles and curses. 'The devil damn the rattlings of these wooden shrouds, for I have broke my shins against 'em. I had rather run up to the cross-trees of the main topmast in a storm than six rounds of these confounded land ladders after the drinking a can of flip or a bowl of punch.'

Next came in a spruce blade with a pretended wife, and asked what time the boats went off to Gravesend. They told him about four in the morning. 'Alas,' says he, 'that will be too long to sit up. Can't my wife and I have a bed here?' 'Yes, yes, sir, if you please,' replied the pious beldam, 'God forbid else! We have several couple above in bed, that wait for the tide as well as you, sir.' So up they were lighted post-haste to the old trade of basket-making.

After these, in bolted two seamen with a little crooked fiddler before them, short pipes in their mouths, oaken truncheons in their hands, thrum-caps upon their heads, and canvas trunks upon their arses. We had the good luck for these to stagger upon our company. Their unpolished behaviour, apish gestures, and maritime nonsense, added no small pleasure to the night, but gave us hopes of as much mirth as a London apprentice finds at a Bartholomew Fair puppet-show, or a country squire among a gang of strolling comedians.

These two lousy subjects of the pickled god Neptune, having washed off their brine with a plentiful dose of freshwater ale, began to be as brisk as a Town rake that had shaked off his poverty, or a Court libertine an old mistress. In their frolics they happened to espy a hook driven into the mantel-tree, which they immediately converted to a very comical use, by laying violent hands on my little Lord Crowdero, and by the hind slit of his breeches hanging him upon the tenter. Being sorely affrighted at this unexpected elevation, he shot that into his trousers which made the crooked vermin out-stink a polecat. In this condition, pendant like a playhouse machine or a brazen cherub over a church branch, he hung sprawling, begging with humble submission to be set safe upon terra firma, all the time dripping his guts upon the hearth like a roasting woodcock. At last, by wriggling, he broke the string of his breeches, and down came our broiled scraper into his own sauce, upon his feeble instrument, and was a sweet-bit ready to be served up to a weak appetite.

This put the whole company into such an extravagant fit of laughter that had we seen a bailiff bogged, or a fellow break his neck at football, it could not have been a greater jest to the spectators. But as soon as the angry homunculus had gathered himself up from his own dunghill, he gave the two Tritons such an untuneable lesson upon his ill-tuned organ, that the whining of a dog-drawn bitch, or the winding of a cat-call could not have disobliged our ears with less grateful harmony. When he had thus given vent to his ungovernable indignation he cocked the arm of his humped shoulder upon his hip, and away rolled the runlet of gall, turning his unsavoury bung-hole upon the company.

The tarpaulins now began to talk to each other of their travels and of the sundry remarkable accidents which had happened in their voyages. One swore they once found it so excessive hot going to Guinea that they used no fire to boil their kettle, but dressed all their beef above deck in the sunshine and could bake, boil, fry or stew as well as in an admiral's cook-room.

Says the other: 'I never was in so hot a climate as that, but I have been so many degrees to the nor'ward, where it has been so cold it has frozen our words in our mouths, so that we could not hear one another speak till we came into a warmer latitude to thaw 'em; and then all our discourses broke out together like a clap of thunder, that there was never such a confusion of tongues ever heard at Babel.'

Says his companion: 'That's very strange, but I have known stranger things to be true. I once was sitting upon my chest, between-decks, lousing an old canvas jacket. We had found by our observations that day we were within a few minutes of being under the tropic of Cancer. And on a sudden it began to lower, and the larboard watch handed in our sails, for fear of a tornado or squall. At last a beam of lightning darted through an open port, melted one of the guns, went through a pair of buckskin breeches I had on, and burned the lappets of a blue shirt to tinder. It hissed as it came, like a rattlesnake, but did my body no manner of damage.'

As our salt-water wits were thus romancing, who should stagger into our company but an old acquaintance of my friend's, who (as I understood by his talk) was an exchange commodity broker; a kind of mongrel matchmaker between cock-bawd and pimp, or rather a composition of both. He made more a-roaring than half a dozen drunken porters, and was as full of freaks as a madman at the full of the moon. He guzzled and rattled, smoked and stared like a fury. And everytime he spoke 'twas with so much earnestness that I thought his eyes would have flown out of his head in pursuit of his words. All he talked was loud nonsense, and the heat of his brain setting fire to his tongue, made everything he said so wonderfully hot that the ears of all people glowed that heard 'em. At last he plucked out a catalogue of what fortunes he had at his disposal, viz.:

'A mercer's daughter in Cornhill, about seventeen, who was unluckily kissed by her father's appprentice; which being spread among the neighbourhood, he is willing to give her two hundred pounds advance above an equality, to salve up the flaw, to any honest young shopkeeper that will wink at a fault to better his condition.

'An old maid that has lived thirty years in an alderman's family who, with her wages, lady's old clothes, and money got for private service, is worth about three hundred pounds, and thinks herself qualified for keeping a victualler's bar. She is willing to bestow herself upon any honest freeman, if clear in the world, though not worth a groat.

'A young buxom widow, on the back-side of the 'Change, who was married five years but never had a child, is still in her mourning, wonderfully pretty and tolerably honest. She is willing to dispose of herself to a brisk, likely man, within or without the year; is in a good shop, well customed and needs no money.

'About half a hundred Exchange girls, some tall, some short, some black, some fair, some handsome, some housewifely, some homely, some virtuous, but all with Whitechapel portions, and will make very good wives for those who have more money than wit, and more faith than jealousy.

'A vintner's daughter, bred at the dancing-school, becomes a bar well, steps a minuet finely, plays "John, Come Kiss Me, Now, Now, Now" sweetly upon the virginals, makes a very graceful figure, and is as proud as she's handsome. Will have a great many quart pots, old pewter, linen and other household stuff to her portion, but whoever marries her must ride her with a curb or she may prove unlucky, to the bane of her rider.'

When he had thus diverted us with his catalogue of Job's comforters, which he pretended were upon sale and at his disposal, my friend began to put me in mind of the considerable business we had upon 'Change, at Gresham College, Bedlam, and other places on the morrow. This occasioned us to think of bed, though with as much indifference as a worn-out stallion does of a pretty punk, or a new-married woman of her prayers. For the pleasures of the night were so engaging, and every various humour such a wakeful piece of drollery, that a mountebank and his Jack-pudding, or a set of morris dancers, could not give more content to a crowd of country spectators than the lively action of what is here only repeated did afford us. But to qualify ourselves the better for our task, we thought it necessary to take some rest. So, accordingly, we were conducted to a room which stunk as bad of pitch, sweat and tallow as a ship between-decks when the tars are in their hammocks. But the unseasonableness of the hour forced us to be content. And so good night to ye.

III

WHEN WE HAD cooled the fever of our brains with a plentiful dose of that reviving cordial, sleep, and our wakeful faculties had shaken off Morpheus's leaden plummets from our drowsy eyelids (after a few slug-abed yawns and lazy stretches), we found by the advancement of the day it was high time to make our resurrection. Accordingly, with mutual resolutions, we started from sluggard's paradise, the bed, and collected our scattered garments in order for equipping.

When with abundance of rubbing, scrubbing, washing and combing we had made ourselves tolerable figures to appear by daylight, we descended from our snoring-kennel, so finely perfumed by the fusty jackets of the tarpaulin guests that it smelt as odoriferously grateful as a Suffolk cheese toasted over a flaming pitch-barrel. Its walls were adorned with as many unsavoury finger-dabs as an Inns of Court bog-house. The ceiling was beautified like a soldier's garret, or a Compter chamber, with smutty names and bawdy shadows sketched by unskilful hands with candle-flame and charcoal. The bed, 'tis true, was feathers, but most of them large enough to make pens or tooth-pickers. And an earthen chamber-pot, as big as a three-gallon stein, glazed o'er with green, looked as fine as any Temple mug, or country pudding-pan.

Having turned our backsides upon these cubicular conveniences, we crept, being cold, to a new-kindled smoky fire, where we fortified our appetites against the contagious breaths of funking carmen with a pennyworth of burnt bread softened in a mug of porters' guzzle, improved with a slice of Cheshire. This we gobbled up (being hasty to be gone) with as much expedition as a citizen's wife does an Islington cheesecake when treated by her husband, and then satisfied our tun-bellied hostess and left the infernal mansion to the sinful sons of darkness, there to practise their iniquities.

We now turned down to the Thames Side, where the frightful roaring of the Bridge waterfalls so astonished my eyes and terrified my ears that, like Roger in his mill, or the inhabitants near the cataracts of the Nile, I could hear no voice softer than a speaking-trumpet, or the audible organ of a scolding fish-woman. After I had feasted my intellects with this surprising novelty, we turned towards Billingsgate, where a parcel of fellows came running upon us in a great fury, crying out, as I thought, 'Scholars, scholars, will you have any whores?' 'Lord bless me,' said I to my friend, 'what wicked place is this, that a man in a black coat cannot pass about his business without being asked in public such an abominable question? Hauling and pulling him about by the arms, they would force him to commit fornication in spite of his teeth!' Notwithstanding I told 'em we wanted no whores, nor would we have any, yet they would scarce be satisfied. My friend laughed heartily at my innocent mistake and undeceived my ignorance, telling me they were watermen who distinguished themselves by the titles of 'Oars' and 'Scullers,' which made me blush at my error, like a bashful lady that has dropped her garter, or a modest man who cripples his jest by a forgetful hesitation.

After we had loosed ourselves, with much difficulty, from the unparalleled insolence of Charon's progeny, we turned into a crowd of thumb-ringed flat-caps, from the age of seven to seventy, who sat snarling and grunting at one another over their sprats and whitings, like a pack of domestic dogs over the cook-maid's kindness, or a parcel of hungry sows at a trough of hog-wash. Every one looking as sharp as a strolling fortune-teller, I feared they would have picked my pocket with their eyes or have brought me under an ill tongue before I could have shot this dangerous gulf, where the angry surges of a tempestuous tittle-tattle ran mountain-high, dashing into my ears on every side. I was as glad when I had weathered this storm of verbosity as an insolvent creditor that had slipped the villainous grips of a gang of protection cursors.

Having thus happily quitted the stink of sprats and the untuneable clamours of the wrangling society, we passed round the dock, where some salt-water slaves, according to their well-bred custom, were pelting 'sons of whores' at one another about the berths of their oyster-boats. One, unhappily being acquainted how to touch the other in his tenderest part, galled his impatient adversary with the provoking name of cuckold. This intolerable indignity so fermented the choler of the little snail-catcher, that he resolved to show himself a champion in defence of his wife's virtues, and leaping into the other's boat, there, like a true-bred cock, made a vigorous assault upon his enemy on his own dunghill. But a disaster attended the poor combatants, for in their scuffle they fell overboard. The tide being half spent, the water was not high enough to cool their courage. Notwithstanding, they maintained an amphibious fight and battled like ducks and drakes, in two elements at once, till the

cuckold had bravely subdued his antagonist, and made his poor victim
(half drowned and half knocked o' the head) publicly acknowledge the
unspotted reputation of the victor's duchess. She, at the end of the fray,
having received intelligence of her lord and master's engagement, came
down to the dock-side crowned with an oyster-basket, and there, with an
audible voice, set up a passionate justification of her own honesty, to the
great diversion of the whole auditory. Her leviathan shape was a good
testimony of her virtues, for had our first she-parent been but half so
homely, the Devil would have been damned nine times deeper into the
infernal abyss before he would have robbed her of her innocence, or
anticipated Adam in the enjoyment of his helpmate.

From thence we moved on to a stately fabric before which a parcel
of robust mortals were as busy as so many flies upon a cow-turd, some
running about in circular gimcracks, like so many turnspits labouring in
their jack-wheels; others as deeply engaged in the hooping of casks as if
they were taking all imaginable care that every tub should stand upon its
own bottom. Many scales were at work, and such abundance of eagle-
eyed vermin hovering about 'em that I thought at first Justice might have
resided there. But my friend told me no, these were her agents balancing
the miseries against the sins of the nation. 'Prithee, friend,' said I, 'what
is that grizzly Bacchanalian, with a pen twisted in his hair, whose face
looks as if it cost as much in dyeing as would set up a topping vintner?'
Says my friend, 'He's one of those cormorants called a land-waiter. His
business is to take care nobody cheats the Queen but himself. His post
is honestly worth a hundred a year; but with the help of an open hand
and a close mouth he can (without burden to his conscience) make it
worth thrice the money.' 'What is he in the long wig with his fox-skin
muff upon his button, and his pocket-book in his hand?' 'Why he,'
replies my schoolfellow, 'is a beau, apprentice to some topping merchant,
and is taking the weight of his master's goods so that he is not wronged
in the Customs. He is very careful nobody cheats him abroad, and his
master is forced to be as watchful Mr Finikin does not injure him at
home. For a flattering companion, or a jilting mistress, will at anytime
make him dip his fingers in the cash, to treat them with a new play, or
solace them with a bottle.

'Pray,' says my friend, 'take notice of that gentleman in the camlet
cloak. He will tell you from his own experience that any man may grow
rich from humility and industry, and that 'tis nothing but pride and
laziness that begets poverty and misfortune. When he came first to town,

he had but threepence in the world, which he prudently laid out in a new broom that might sweep clean. This he very dexterously applied, with his utmost labour, to the dirty wharf, without anybody's bidding; but he had sense enough to consider it belonged to somebody, who would at least give him thanks, if not recompense his trouble. The master of the wharf happening to espy him at his task, gave him some small encouragement to continue his cleanliness. This he practised daily, with as much diligence as is used by a younger brother in the courtship of a fortune, till he had gained his end and curried favour with the merchant, who lent him his assistance by degrees which, the other improving, he is now become a man of a great estate and considerable authority. But if any poor man asks him for alms, he tells him there are riches buried in the dirt, and good fortune in a broom, and if he will sweep, as he was forced to do, he may come in time to be Lord Mayor of London. To this a cross old mumper replied, "If you had not got more by knavery and usury than ever you did by your honesty and industry, you might have been apprenticed to your broom till this time, and never have been made a freeman." '

I now enquired of my friend what they called this busy spot. He told me 'twas the Custom House, and in that stately edifice the Commissioners sat, about whom I asked some questions, but found my friend too shy to give me satisfaction, saying, 'If I tell you the truth, I'm a fool to myself; if false, unjust to my friend, and make you become a liar to the world. I shall therefore, instead of what you expect, give you a proverbial caution, viz., they are a parcel of edged tools, with whom there is no jesting, and he that attempts to eat fire to please a crowd, if he find cause to complain he has burnt his mouth, maketh himself but a laughing-stock.'

By the advice of my companion, we turned back till we came to a place called Pig Hill, which resembling the steep descent down which the Devil drove his hogs to a bad market, I suppose it is therefore honoured with the aforesaid title. In regard to this, they are always in a condition of turning the stomach of a Jew, or poisoning a Scotsman; and can satisfy an epicure's appetite, or save a lady's longing, with pig or pork in any hour of the day, or any day in the year. The cooks, according to report, keep many spaniel bitches as wet-nurses for the due suckling of their sow babies, which adds, they say, such a sweetness to their flesh, that they eat as fine as any puppy-dog. And all such persons who are admirers of this luxurious food may the whole winter have it there ready dressed, without the danger of fly-sauce, which is more than in summer I'm able to promise you. All the elements contribute to their cooking of every squeaker they dress. He is first scalded in water, then dried in the air, and half baked in the sun. Then he is roasted by the fire, afterwards dissected by a choleric executioner, and his quarters disposed of to several gates of hungry citizens, where teeth are the portcullises, as if the poor pig had been convicted of a plot and died as a traitor.

As we walked up the Hill, as lazily as an Artillery captain before his company upon a Lord Mayor's day, or a Paul's labourer up a ladder with a hod of mortar, we peeped in at a gateway where we saw three or four blades well dressed, with hawks' countenances, attended with half a dozen ragamuffinly fellows, showing poverty in their rags and despair in their faces, mixed with a parcel of young wild striplings like runaway apprentices. I could not forbear enquiring of my friend about this ill-favoured multitude patched up of such awkward figures that it would have puzzled a Moorfields artist well read in physiognomy to have discovered their dispositions by their looks.

'That house,' says my friend, 'which they are entering, is an office where servants for the Plantations bind themselves to be miserable as long as they live, unless a special Providence prevents it. Those fine fellows, who look like footmen upon a holiday crept into the cast suits of their masters, that want gentility in their deportments answerable to their apparel, are kidnappers, who walk the 'Change and other parts of the town in order to seduce people who want service, and young fools crossed in love and under an uneasiness of mind, to go beyond sea. They get so much a head from masters of ships and merchants who go over, for every wretch they trepan into this misery. Those young rakes and tatterdemalions you see so lovingly herded, are drawn, by their fair promises, to sell themselves into slavery, and the kidnappers are the rogues that run away with the money.

'Now,' says my friend, 'I'll show you a towering edifice, erected through the wisdom and honesty of the City as a very high memorandum of its being laid low, either by a judgement from Heaven for the sins of the people or by the treachery of the Papists, according to the inscription of the Monument, which, I suppose, is as ignorant of the matter as myself, for it was neither built then nor I born. So I believe we are equally as able to tell the truth of the story as a quack astrologer is, by the assistance of the signs and planets, to tell what was the name of Moses's great-grandfather, or how many quarts of water went to the world's drowning. You'll be mightily pleased with the loftiness of this slender column, for its very height was the first thing that ever occasioned wry necks in England, by the people staring at the top on't. To the glory of the City, and the everlasting reputation of the worthy projectors of this high and mighty Babel, it was more ostentatiously than honestly built, by the poor orphans' money. Many of them since have begged their bread, and the City has here given them a stone. Look ye, now you may see it; pray view and give me your opinion.'

'What! Is it of no use but only to gaze at?' 'Yes, yes,' says my friend. 'Astrologers go often to the top on't when they have a mind to play the pimp and see Mars and Venus in conjunction, though the chief use of it is for the improvement of vintners' boys and drawers, who come every week to exercise their supporters and learn the tavern trip by running up to the balcony and down again, which fixes them in a nimble step, and makes them rare light-heeled emissaries in a month's practice. Do you observe the carving which contains the King's and his brother's pictures? They were cut by an eminent artist, and are looked upon by a great many impartial judges to be a couple of extraordinary good figures. Pray what think you? I know you have some judgement in proportion.'

'Why truly,' said I, 'they are the only grace and ornament of the whole building. But 'tis a thousand pities the stones formed into so noble order, should be so basely purchased, to the ruin of so many thousand fatherless and widows. But I suppose it was politically done, to fix the King's effigy as a testimonial of loyalty upon a structure so unjustly raised, that the one might, in some measure, wash away the stain of the other. And to prevent the high-flown loyalists reflecting upon their treachery to the poor orphans, they may pretend (though they cheated them of their money) 'twas with a pious design of setting up the King's picture, in reverence of his person (who all the world knows they had a wonderful respect for), and in honour of the City which, to be sure, was as dear to them as their lives and fortunes. But I have heard their chief drift in this memorable undertaking was to get estates for themselves without mistrust, so that they might enjoy them without molestation.'

'As you say, this edifice, as well as some others, was projected as a memorandum of the Fire, or an ornament to the City, but it gave those corrupted magistrates that had the power in their hands, the opportunity of putting two thousand pounds into their own pockets whilst they paid one towards the building. I must confess all I think that can be spoke in praise of it is that 'tis a monument to the City's shame, the orphans' grief, the Protestants' pride and the Papists' scandal; and only serves as a high-crowned hat, to cover the head of the old fellow that shows it.'

When my friend had thus obliged me with a full prospect of our metropolitan maypole, we turned up Gracechurch Street, in order for Gresham College, where we met a fellow in a gown, with a piece of prodigality called a mace upon his shoulder. Another, like one of Justice's sumpter-horses, was laden with scales, weights and measures, and a third was armed, like a round-headed cuckold marching to Horn Fair, with a pickaxe. These advanced in the front attended with a troop of loiterers in gowns, who hobbled after with as much formality as a parcel of gossips at a christening in the parish church, behind Mother Grope and her fine mantle. They had matched themselves together with abundance of discretion, mixed fat and lean like so many Scotch runts in Smithfield Market amongst the like number of Lincolnshire oxen. I thought it a lively representation of Pharaoh's dream, appearing to me as a true emblem of plenty and famine, for one part of them looked as if they would eat up the other. By and by they pitched down a triangular device with as many legs as Tyburn and began of a sudden to be all as busy as so many sheriff's men at an execution.

I enquired of my friend how these mortals were dignified or distinguished, and what was the weighty affair they were so pryingly engaged in. He told me these were a part of the worthy members of the Quest, whose business was to inspect weights and measures, taking care that every shopkeeper's yard be of the standard length, whilst the wife (sitting behind the counter) laughs in her sleeve all the time they're measuring. Also they give warning for the mending of pavements, and removing all nuisances, under the penalty of a fine. Their meeting is generally at a hall, except they have a Quest House, from whence they go to church to prayers, and return back to be drunk. They detect very few people in their faults, for they honestly take care not to injure their neighbours, but inform them when they shall walk their rounds, so that they may remove their false weights and measures out of the way, and have larger ready to produce to conceal their roguery. The inhabitants of every precinct are obliged to give 'em their company at dinner; where he that does not behave himself generously, and purchase his security at the expense of half a piece shall be surely returned upon the jury at the next empanelling. They have an old custom of brewing spiced ale, and he that does not take care to send his wife a jugful, runs the hazard, by his negligence, of raising an evil spirit in his family that no conjurer can lay in a fortnight. They have as many several offices amongst 'em as are in a nobleman's family, viz., Foreman, Controller, Treasurer, Steward, Butler, &c. They have a groat a house from each inhabitant, besides their fines, with which they feast their ingurgitating stomachs with luxurious excesses. The questman's generosity and the alderman's humility are commonly equal. The Quest contribute in every ward, through benevolence, their crowns apiece to give His Worship a collation answerable to his dignity.

From thence we passed, without anything remarkable, till we came to Wiseacres' Hall, more commonly called Gresham College, which we entered as gravely as a couple of eleemosynary smokers into Man's shop, or a couple of sanctified harlots into Burgess's meeting-house. We stepped through a little brick court, and then came into a spacious quadrangle, where, in a melancholy cloister, we saw a peripatetic walking, ruminating, as I suppose, upon his entities, essences and occult qualities, or else upon the philosophers' stone, looking as if he very much wanted it. His steps he measured out with such exactness and deliberation that, I believe, had just such a number failed by bringing him to the end of the cloister, he would have been in a great passion with his legs. During his perambulation, his eyes were fixed upon the pavement, from whence I conjecture he could see as far into a millstone as another. All the time we observed him he took great care to follow his nose, fearing, I suppose, if he turned his guide towards either shoulder he should have lost his way and have wandered upon some other stones, out of that direct line to which he had confined his walk. His countenance was mathematical, having as many lines and angles in his face as you shall find in Euclid's *Elements*, and he looked as if he had fed upon nothing but Cursus Mathematicus for a fortnight. He seemed to scorn gloves as much as Diogenes did his dish, crossing his arms over his breast and warming his hands under his armpits. His lips quaked as if he'd had an ague in his mouth, which tremulous motion, I conceived, was occasioned by his soliloquies, to which we left him.

My friend conducted me up a pair of stairs to the laboratory-keeper's apartment, and desired him to oblige us with a sight of the rarities. He very courteously granted us the liberty, opening his warehouse of Egyptian mummies, old musty skeletons, and other antiquated trumpery. The first thing he thought most worthy of our notice was the magnet, with which he showed some notable experiments. It made a paper of steel filings prick up themselves one upon the back of another, so that

they stood pointing like the bristles of a hedgehog, and gave such life
and merriment to a parcel of needles that they danced the hay, by the
motion of the stone, as if the devil were in them. The next thing he
presented to our view was a parcel of shellflies almost as big as lobsters,
armed with beaks as big as those of jackdaws. Then he commended to
our observation that wonderful curiosity the unicorn's horn; made, as I
suppose, by an ingenious turner, of the tusks of an elephant; it is of an
excellent virtue and, by report of those that know nothing of the matter,
will expel poison beyond the mountebank's Orvietan.

Then he carried us to another part of the room, where there was an
aviary of dead birds, collected from the extreme parts of Europe, Asia,
Africa, and America, amongst which were an East India owl, a West
India bat, and a bird of paradise, the last being beautified with variety of
colours, having no discernible body but all feathers; feeding, when alive,
upon nothing but air, and though 'tis as big as a parrot 'tis as light as a
cobweb. It is reported by the sage philosophers of this society that a
feather of this fowl, carried about you, is an infallible security against all
evil temptation; for which reason they have pretty well plucked it, to
carry home presents of it to their wives and daughters.

Then he ushered us among sundry sorts of serpents, as the Noy,
Pelonga, Rattlesnake, Alligator, Crocodile, &c., so that, looking round
me, I thought myself hemmed in amongst a legion of devils. When we
had taken a survey of these pincushion monsters, we turned towards the
skeletons of men, women and monkeys, birds, beasts and fishes;
abortives put up in pickle, and abundance of other memorandums of
mortality. They looked as ghostly as the picture of Michaelangelo's
'Resurrection'; as if they had collected their scattered bones into their
original order, and were about to march in search after the rest of their
appurtenances.

When we had taken this short view of the wonders of the world, and
had crossed the hand of our raree-show interpreter with a piece of silver,
he, like the crooked orator to the Abbey tombs, made a notable harangue
upon every bauble in this storehouse. Glutted with the sight of those
rusty relics and philosophical toys, we determined to steer our course
towards Bedlam. So we removed from Maggotmongers' Hall, to survey
Madman's College.

In the midway, between both, my friend bid me take notice of a man
who was scuffling along in as much haste as a scrivener to make a will,
or a poor quack to a rich patient. 'That man,' says he, 'that walks like a

Mercury, as if he had wings to his heels, is a topping virtuoso, and a Member of the Royal Society. He is, by his profession, a labourer to a physician, but has made himself, by a curious inspection into the mysteries of universality, a jack of all trades, and is thought by the learned to be as knowing a philomath as he that has peeped seven years into a pitch-barrel. He's a wonderful artist at the cleansing of a foul stomach or the sweeping of a gut. He was one of the chief promoters of men's ease and brought that savoury receptacle called a close-stool to its true perfection. He publishes a weekly paper for the improvement of trade and husbandry, wherein, for the benefit of the public, he has inserted the most choice recipes for the making of pancakes, fritters, puddings, dumplings, also to make porridge or thick-milk, that ever were extant. He likewise, through his wisdom and generosity, has taught the world, at the expense of half a crown, how to sweeten a dozen of glass bottles, which you may buy new for two shillings, also how, at thirty shillings charge, we may improve an acre of land not valuable at one shilling to be worth twenty. Amongst the rest, he is a joiner of sexes and will learnedly prove, upon such occasions, that generation was the main end of our creation. Whatever match he makes, he seldom fails of his double reward, that is, to get money on one side, and curses on t'other, for he is a man of such conscience and consideration that he generally takes care to couple those who are worth money to such as want it.'

Thus we prattled away our time till we came in sight of a noble pile of building, which diverted us from our former discourse, and gave my friend the occasion of asking me my thoughts on this magnificent edifice. I told him, I conceived it to be my Lord Mayor's Palace, for I could not imagine so stately a structure could be designed for any quality inferior. He smiled at my innocent conjecture, and informed me this was Bedlam, an hospital for mad folks. 'In truth,' said I, 'I think they were mad that built so costly a college for such a crack-brained society,' adding, it was pity so fine a building should not be possessed by such as had a sense of their happiness. 'Sure,' said I, 'it was a mad age when this was raised, and the chief of the City were in great danger of losing their senses, so contrived it the more noble for their own reception, or they would never have flung away so much money to so foolish a purpose.' 'You must consider,' says my friend, 'this stands upon the same foundation as the Monument, and the fortunes of a great many poor wretches lie buried in this ostentatious piece of vanity; and this, like the other, is but a monument of the City's shame and dishonour, instead of its glory. Come let us take a walk in, and view its inside.'

Accordingly we were admitted in through an iron gate, within which sat a brawny Cerberus of an indigo colour, leaning upon a money-box. We turned in through another iron barricade, where we heard such a rattling of chains, drumming of doors, ranting, hollering, singing and rattling, that I could think of nothing but Don Quevedo's *Visions*, where the damned broke loose and put Hell in an uproar. The first whimsy-headed wretch of this lunatic family that we observed, was a merry fellow in a straw cap, who was talking to himself that he had an army of eagles at his command. Then clapping his hand upon his head, he swore by his crown of moonshine that he would battle all the stars in the skies but he would have some claret. In this interim came a gentleman, to stare at him, with a red face. 'No wonder,' said His Aerial Majesty, 'that claret is so scarce, look there's a rogue carries more in his nose than I, that am Prince of the Air, have had in my belly this twelvemonth.' 'If you are Prince of the Air,' said I, 'why don't you command the man in the moon to give you some?' To which he replied, 'The man in the moon's a sorry rascal. I sent to him for a dozen bottles but t'other day, and he swore by his bush, his cellar had been dry this six months. But I'll be even with the rogue. I expect a cloud laden with claret to be sent me by the Sun every day, and if a spoonful of lees would save him from choking, the old drunken whore's bird should not have a drop.'

We then moved on till we found another remarkable figure worth our observing, who was peeping through his wicket, eating bread and cheese, and talking all the while like a carrier at his supper, chewing his words with his victuals. All that he spoke was in praise of bread and cheese. Bread was good with cheese, and cheese was good with bread, and bread and cheese was good together, and abundance of such stuff; to which my friend and I, with others, stood listening. At last he counterfeits a sneeze, and shot such a mouthful of bread and cheese amongst us that every spectator had some share of his kindness, which made us retreat. He called after us, 'Masters, masters.' Some went back to hear what he had to say, and he had provided them a plentiful bowl of piss which he cast very successfully amongst them, crying, in a laugh, 'I never give victuals but I give drink, and you're welcome, gentlemen.'

The next unhappy object amongst this shatter-brained fraternity was a scholar of St John's College in Cambridge, who was possessed with melancholy, but was very inoffensive, and had the liberty of the gallery.

This was a very musical man, which is thought to be one great occasion of his distemper. My friend walked up to him, and introduced some talk, to divert himself with a few of his frenzical extravagancies. Another lunatic, in this interval, who had the liberty of ranging the house, caught hold of my schoolfellow's arm, and expressed himself after this manner: 'Dost thou know, friend, what thou art doing? Why, thou art talking to a madman, a fiddling fellow, who had so many crotchets in his head that he cracked his brains about his thoroughbasses.' 'Prithee,' says my companion, 'what was the occasion of thy distemper?' To which he answered, 'I am under this confinement for the noble sins of drinking and whoring, and if thou hast not a care it will bring thee into the same condition.'

We peeped into another room, which smelt as strong of chamber-lye, as a bottle of sal-ammoniac, where a fellow was got as hard at work as if he'd been treading mortar. 'What is it, friend,' said I, 'thou art taking all these pains about?' He answered me thus, still continuing in action: 'I am trampling down conscience under my feet, lest he should rise up and fly in my face. Have a care he does not fright thee, for he looks like the Devil and is as fierce as a lion, but that I keep him muzzled. Therefore get thee gone, or I will set him upon thee.' Then he fell a-clapping his hands, and cried, 'Halloo, halloo, halloo, halloo, halloo,' and thus we left him raving.

Another was holding forth with as much vehemence against Kingly government as a brother of Commonwealth doctrine rails against plurality of livings. I told him he deserved to be hanged for talking of treason. 'Now,' says he, 'you're a fool, for we madmen have as much privilege of speaking our minds, within these walls, as an ignorant dictator when he spews out his nonsense to a whole parish. Prithee come and live here, and you may talk what you will, and nobody will call you in question for it. Truth is persecuted everywhere abroad, and flies hither for sanctuary, where she sits as safe as a knave in a church, or a whore in a nunnery. I can use her as I please and that's more than you dare do. I can tell great men such bold truths as they don't love to hear, without the danger of a whipping-post; and that you can't do. For if ever you see a madman hanged for speaking the truth, or a lawyer whipped for lying, I'll be bound to prove my wig a wheelbarrow.'

We then took a walk into the women's apartment to see what whimsical vagaries their wandering fancies would move them to entertain us withal.

The first that we looked upon stood straddling with her back against the wall, crying: 'Come, John, come, your master's gone to 'Change. I believe the poor fool's afraid of forfeiting his indentures. Did you ever see the like? Why, sure, you won't serve your mistress so, John, will you? Hark, hark, run, you rogue, your master's come back to shop. Yes, you shall have a wife, you old rogue, with seven hundred pounds, and be married six years and not get a child! Fie, for shame, out upon't! A husband for a woman, a husband for the Devil! Hang you, rot you, sink you, confound you!' And thus at last she ran raving on into the highest degree of madness.

Another was talking very merrily at her peeping-hole to a crowd of auditors, most of them young wenches. A foolish girl amongst the rest asked the madwoman how old she was. She replied, 'I am old enough to have hair where you have none.' This made the young creature betake herself to her heels, to avoid the mockery of her companions. In this interim came by a beauish blade with his wig very much powdered. 'Look, look!' cries Bess of Bedlam. 'Yonder goes a prodigal puppy, an extravagant rascal that has got more flour in his wig than my poor mother has in her meal tub to make a pudding withal!'

The next poor object that happened under our observation was a meagre, old grey-headed wretch, who looked as wild as an angry cat, and all her tone was, 'The wind is _____ blow, devil, blow. The wind is _____blow, devil, blow.' A seaman who was staring at her, and listening to what she said, must needs be inquisitive how the wind sat, and asked her, 'Where is the wind, mother?' She hastily replied, 'The wind is in my arse! Blow fool, blow.' Being so pleased she had sold him a bargain, she fell into an extravagant fit of laughter, in which we left her.

Having pretty well tired ourselves with the frantic humours and rambling ejaculations of the mad folks, we took a turn to make some few remarks upon the looseness of the spectators, amongst whom we observed abundance of intriguing. Mistresses, we found, were to be had of all ranks, qualities, colours, prices and sizes, from the velvet scarf to the Scotch plaid petticoat. Commodities of all sorts went off, for there wanted not a suitable Jack to every Jill. Every fresh comer was soon engaged in an amour; though they came in single, they went out in pairs. 'Tis a new Whetstone's Park, now the old one's ploughed up, where a sportsman, at any hour in the day, may meet with game for his purpose. 'Tis as great a convenience to London as the Long Cellar to Amsterdam, where any stranger may purchase a purge for his reins at a small expense, and may have a pox by chance flung into the bargain. All that I can say of it is this: 'Tis an almshouse for madmen, a showing-room for whores, a sure market for lechers, and a dry walk for loiterers.

We needed now no clock to give the hour of the day. Our stomachs, as true as that of the 'Change, went One, and after redeeming our liberties from this piss-burned prison, at the expense of twopence, we were led by our appetites into a cook's shop. And when we had refreshed Nature with a necessary supply of what she most coveted, we marched towards the Royal Exchange, to which traders were trotting in as much haste as lawyers to Westminster, or butchers to Smithfield.

The pillars at the entrance of the front portico were adorned with sundry memorandums of old age and infirmity, under which stood here and there a Jack-in-the-box, like a parson in a pulpit, selling cures for your corns, glass eyes for the blind, ivory teeth for broken mouths, and spectacles for the weak-sighted. The passage to the gate was lined with hawkers, gardeners, mandrake-sellers and porters. After we had crowded a little way amongst this miscellaneous multitude, we came to a pippin-monger's stall, surmounted with a chemist's shop where drops, elixirs, cordials and balsams had justly the pre-eminence of apples, chestnuts, pears and oranges. The former were ranked in as much order upon shelves as the works of the Holy Fathers in a bishop's library, and the latter were marshalled with as much exactness as an army ready to engage. Here were drawn up several regiments of Kentish pippins, next some squadrons of pearmains, joined to a brigade of small nuts, with a few troops of booncritons, all formed into battalions. The wings were composed of oranges, lemons, pomegranates, dried plums and medlars. The decayed of these lower gross bodies, drawn over the helm, are fitted by the help of ginger, nutmeg and liquorice to stand upon the upper shelf under a saleable title, to cozen madmen and fools out of their health and their money. And to let you know it's truly prepared, it is made by him who may write himself physician, chemist, apothecary, confectioner, and costermonger.

We then proceeded and went on to the 'Change, turned to the right, and jostled in amongst a parcel of swarthy buggerantoes (preternatural fornicators, as my friend called them) who would ogle a handsome young man with as much lust as a true-bred English whore-master would gaze upon a beautiful virgin. Advertisements hung as thick round the pillars of each walk as bells about the legs of a morris dancer, and an incessant buzz, like the murmurs of the distant ocean, stood as a diapason to our talk, like a drone to a bagpipe. The wainscot was adorned with quacks' bills, instead of pictures; never an empiric in the town but had his name in a lacquered frame, containing a fair invitation for a fool and his money to be soon parted. Thus he that wants physic for a clap, or a wet-nurse for a child, may be furnished here at a minute's warning.

After we had squeezed ourselves through a crowd of bum-firking Italians, we fell into a throng of strait-laced monsters in fur and thrum-caps, with huge logger heads, effeminate waists, and buttocks like a Flanders mare, with slovenly mien and swinish looks, whose upper lips were gracefully adorned with turd-coloured whiskers. These, with their gloves under their arms, and their hands in their pockets, were grunting to each other like hogs at their peas. These, my friend told me, were the water-rats of Europe, who love nobody but themselves, and fatten upon the spoils, and build their own welfare upon the ruin of their neighbours.

We had no sooner jostled through this cluster of Commonwealth's-men, but we were got amongst a parcel of lank-haired formalists, in flat crowned hats and short cloaks, walking with as much state and gravity as a snail o'er the leaf of a cabbage, with a box of tobacco-dust in one hand, and the other employed in charging their nostrils from whence it drops into their moustaches, which are always as full of snuff as a beau's wig is full of powder. Every sentence they spoke was graced with a shrug of the shoulders, and every step they took was performed with as much leisure as a cock strides. These, my friend told me, were Spaniards. Says he, 'you may know them by their smell, for they stink as strong of garlic as a Bologna sausage.'

These were confusedly jumbled among people of sundry nations such as our neighbouring antics the French, who talk more with their heads and hands than with their tongues. They commonly speak first and think afterwards, step a minuet as they walk, and sit as gracefully on an Exchange bench as if in a great saddle. Their bodies always dance to their tongues, and they are so great lovers of action that they were ready to wound every pillar with their canes as they passed by, either in tierce, carte, or seconde.

There, likewise, were the Lord's vagabonds, the Jews, who were so accursed for their infidelity that they are generally the richest people in all nations where they dwell. Like the wicked Spaniards, they were such great consumers of the wicked weed in snuff that their upper lips looked as if they excreted through their nostrils and had forgot to use bum-fodder. 'These,' says my friend, 'are the hawks of mankind, the spies of the universe, the only trade-politicians, subtle knaves, and great merchants.'

Here were also a few amber-necklace sellers, as my friend called them; men with fur caps, long gowns and grave countenances, seeming wise in their carriage, retaining something of the old Grecian grandeur in their comely deportment. Among them there was one very handsome young fellow, which my companion bid me take particular notice of, 'for,' says he, 'that spark in the red gown was very familiar with some of our sweet-lipped ladies of the City. He was very much admired and courted by several topping benefactresses at this end of the town, to receive their favours, till the fool, proud of his happiness, must needs boast of their kindnesses to the disreputation of his humble servants; so they all discarded him with such hatred and contempt that he is now become the scorn and ridicule of every woman in the City.'

'Pray,' said I, 'what tall, sober-looked gentleman is that, in so grave a dress, in the long black wig and formal hat that stands as level in the brim as a pot-lid? He seems to be wonderfully reverenced by a great many much finer than himself.' 'That man,' says my friend, 'is the greatest merchant we have in England, and those fellows that keep astern, and now and then come upon his quarter with their topsails lowered, are commanders of ships who are soliciting for employment. He that plies him so close, they call Honour and Glory, who lately bore command in the Service. He was originally a poor fisherman, but did a very notable exploit (by the help of his man Jack) that recommended him to a commission. But either for want of discretion or honesty, he is turned out, and I suppose rather than return to his nets, he is willing to enter into the merchant service.'

In the next walk we went into were a parcel of swordsmen in twisted wigs and laced hats, with broad faces and flattish noses, saluting one another commonly by the title of Captain. But they looked as if they had been a long while out of commission, for most of them were out of repair, some like gentlemen without estates, and others like footmen out of places, many of them picking their teeth, often plucking out large tobacco-boxes to cram a wad in their mouths, as if most of their food was minced meat.

The other sort were a kind of lean, carrionly creatures with reddish hair and freckly faces, being very much given to scratching and shrugging, as if they held lousiness no shame and the itch no scandal;

stooping a little in the shoulders as if their backs had been used to a pedlar's pack. Amongst them was a poor parson who came to the wrong place to look for a benefice. These, I found, were a compound of Scotch and Irish, who looked as if they rather came to seek for business than dispatch any.

We now came to the back gate of the 'Change, on the east side of which sat a parcel of women, some looking like jilts who wanted cullies, and others like servants who wanted places.

We passed by them, and squeezed amongst coasters and English traders, who were as busy in outwitting one another as if plain dealing was a crime and cozenage a virtue.

'Take notice,' says my companion, 'of that camel-backed spark. He is dignified with the title of My Lord and has as many maggots in his head as there are holes in a colander. Though the rickets have crushed him into that lump of deformity, he has the happiness, or curse, I know not which, to have a very handsome woman for a wife, whose prevailing glances have tempted such custom to her shop that he can afford to spend three or four hundred pounds a year in a tavern without doing himself a prejudice. This she very generously allows him to do out of her gettings, as some censorious people are apt to imagine as a gratuity for his toleration for her liberty of conscience. She is never without a shopful of admirers, whom she poisons with her eyes, and bubbles as she pleases. Give her her due, she's as beautiful as an angel, but as subtle as the Devil; as courteous as a courtesan, but sharp as a needle; very free, but very jiltish; very inviting, yet some say very virtuous.'

'Now,' says my friend, 'we are got amongst the Plantation traders. This may be called Kidnappers' Walk, for a great many of these Jamaicans and Barbadians, with their kitchen-stuff countenances, are looking as sharp for servants as a gang of pickpockets for booty. But we have given these their characters already in the *Trip to Jamaica*, therefore we shall speak but little of them here. I'll warrant you, if they knew the author was among them, they'd hustle him about, as the Whigs would a Jacobite at the election of a Lord Mayor, or the Quakers would a drunken Ranter that should disturb 'em at their Meeting.

'Pray,' said I, 'what is the meaning of this inscription in golden capitals over the passage, "My Lord Mayor's Court"?' My friend replied that it was the nest of City cormorants who, by scraping a little out of many men's estates, raise great ones to themselves, by which they teach fools wit, and bring litigious knaves to repentance.

Within that entry is an office of intelligence, pretending to help servants to places, and masters to servants. They have a knack of bubbling silly wenches out of their money, who loiter hereabouts, upon this expectancy, till they are picked up by the Plantation kidnappers and spirited away into a state of misery and whoredom.

'Now,' says my friend, 'let us walk on the middle of the 'Change and view the statue. This,' says he, 'is the figure of King Charles II, and those are stockjobbers who are hovering about him, and are, by report, a pack of as great knaves as ever he had in his dominions. The rest are a mixed multitude of all nations, and not worth describing. Now I'll conduct you upstairs, where we'll first take a view of the fair ladies, and so adjourn to the tavern and refresh ourselves with a bottle.'

Accordingly we went up, where women sat in their pinfolds begging of custom with such amorous looks, and after so affable a manner, that I could not but fancy they had as much mind to dispose of themselves as the commodities they dealt in. My ears on both sides were so baited with 'Fine linen, sir!' 'Gloves and ribbons, sir!' that I had a milliner's and a sempstress' shop in my head for a week together. 'Well,' says my friend, 'what do you think of all these pretty ladies?' I answered, I thought of them as I did of the rest of their sex; I supposed they were all ready to obey the laws of nature and answer the end of their creation. Says he, 'You have guessed right, for this place is the merchants' seraglio, a nursery of young wagtails for the private consolation of incontinent citizens; for most that you see here come under Chaucer's character of a sempstress, and so we'll leave them.

'She keeps a shop for countenance
And swyves for mountenance.'

IV

BEING NOW WELL tired with the day's fatigue, our thirsty veins and drooping spirits called for the assistance of a cordial flask. In order to gratify our craving appetites with this refreshment, we stood awhile debating what tavern we should choose to enrich our minds with unadulterated juice. My friend recollected a little sanctified Amminadib in Finch Lane, whose purple nectar had acquired a singular reputation among the staggering zealots of the sober fraternity, who are allowed of late to be as good judges of the comfortable creature as a Protestant priest, or a Latitudinarian fuddle-cap, who (as rooks play) drinks wine on Sundays.

To this salutiferous fountain of Nature's choicest juleps our inclinations led us, though we knew the little ruler of the mansion intended it chiefly for watering the lambs of grace, and not to succour the evil offspring of a reprobate generation.

When we had entered our land of promise, which overflowed with more healthful riches than either milk or honey, we found all things were as silent as the mourning attendance at a rich man's funeral. There was no ringing of bar-bell, bawling of drawers, or rattling of pot-lids, but a general hush ordered to be kept through the whole family as a warning to all tipplers at their entrance how they make a noise to awake the spirit, lest it move the master and drawers to stand still when you call 'em, and refuse to draw you any more wine for fear the inward man should break out into open disorder.

In the entry we met two or three blushing saints who had been holding forth so long over the glass that had it not been for their flapping umbrellas, puritanical coats, and diminutive cravats, shaped like the rose of a parson's hatband, I should have taken them by their scarlet faces to be good Christians. They passed by us as upright and as stiff as so many figures in a raree-show, as if a touch of the hat had been committing a sacrilege, or ceremonious nod a rank idolatry.

A drunken-looked drawer, disguised in a sober garb, like a wolf in sheep's clothing, or the Devil in a friar's habit, showed us into the kitchen, which we told him we were desirous of being in, as crickets covet ovens, for the sake of their warmth. Several of Father Ramsey's slouching disciples sat hovering over their half-pints, like so many coy gossips over their quarterns of brandy, as if they were afraid anybody should see 'em. They cast as many froward looks upon us swordsmen as so many misers would be apt to do upon a couple of sponging acquaintances, staring as if they took us for some of the wild Irish that should have cut their throats in the beginning of the Revolution.

However, we bid ourselves welcome into their company, and were forced, for want of room (the kitchen being well filled), to mix higgledy-piggledy, as the rooks among the jackdaws upon the battlements of a church steeple. They leered at us under their bongraces with as much contempt as so many primitive Christians at a couple of pagans.

We, like true Protestant topers, scorning the hypocrisy of tippling by half-pints, as if we drank rather to wash away our sins than our sorrows, appeared barefaced, called for a quart at once, and soon discovered our religion by our drinking. They, like true Puritans, gifted with abundance of holy cheats, were unwilling to be catched over more than half a pint, though they'll drink twenty at a sitting.

The wine proved extraordinary, which, indeed, was no more than we expected when we found ourselves surrounded with so many spiritual mumchances, whose religious looks show them to be true lovers of what the righteous are too apt to esteem as the chiefest blessing of Providence.

We had not sat long, observing the humours of the drowsy saints about us, when several amongst them began to look as cheerful as if they had drowned the terrible apprehensions of futurity and thought no more of damnation than a whore of a twelvemonth's standing.

The drawer now was constantly employed in replenishing their scanty measures; for once warmed they began to drink so fast that 'twas the business of one servant to keep them going. Notwithstanding their great aversion to external ceremony, one plucked off his hat and asked his next neighbour, 'What dost think, friend, this cost me? But before thou tellest me, let me drink, and I hope thou understandest my meaning.' This, I suppose, was the canting method of paying more than ordinary veneration to some particular thoughts which, by this stratagem, were rendered intelligible to each other. For I took notice this allegorical method of drinking some obliging health was observed through the whole society with the reverence of uncovered heads, under a crafty pretence of examining into the price of each other's hats. And when they were desirous to elevate their lethargic spirits with the circulation of a bumper, one fills it and offers the prevailing temptation to his left-hand companion, in these words, saying: 'Friend, does the spirit move thee to receive the good creature thus plentifully?' The other replies, 'Yea, do thou take and enjoy the fruits of thy own labour, and by help of grace I will drink another as full.' Thus did the liquorish saints quaff it about as merrily, after their precise canting manner, as so many country parsons over a tub of ale when freed from the remarks of their censorious parishoners, till, like reprobate sinners who have not the fear of Providence before their eyes, they were deluded by Satan into a wicked state of drunkenness.

By this time the subtle spirits of the noble juice had given us a fresh motion to the wheels of life and corroborated those springs which impart vigour and activity to the whole engine of mortality, insomuch that my friend must needs be so frolicsome as to tune his pipes and entertain us with a song, in order to try whether those who were deaf to reason and good manners had any ears towards music with their wine. These are usually held to be such inseparable companions that the true relish of the one can never be enjoyed without the assistance of the other. And because the words happened in some measure applicable to that present juncture, I have thought it not amiss to insert 'em.

Song

Why should Christians be restrained
    From the brisk enlivening juice,
Heaven only has ordained
    (Through love to man) for human use?
Should not claret be denied
    To the Turks, they'd wiser grow;
Lay their Alkoran aside
    And soon believe as Christians do.

Chorus

For wine and religion, like music and wine,
As they're good in themselves, do to goodness incline,
And make both the spirit and flesh so divine
That our faces and graces both equally shine.
Then still let the bumper round Christendom pass,
For Paradise lost may be found in a glass.

Just as my friend had ended his sonnet, in came the little lord of the tippling tenement, about the height of a ninepin, with his head in a hat of such capacious dimensions that his body was as much drowned under the disproportioned brims of this unconscionable castor as a pigmy under the umbrage of a giant's bongrace, or a mouse crept into a close-stool pan. He was buttoned into a plain vestment that touched no part of his body but his shoulders; his coat being so large and his carcase so little that they hung about him like a malkin upon a cross-stick in a country pea field. His arms hung dangling like a mob's Taffy mounted upon a red herring on St David's Day, and his legs were so slender they bid defiance to any parish stocks.

He waited a little while for the motion of the Spirit, and when he had composed his countenance, and put himself into a fit posture for reproof, he breaks into this following oration: 'Pray, friend, forbear this profane hollering and hooting in my house. This wicked noise thou makest among my sober friends is neither pleasing to them nor me, and since I find the wine is too powerful for thy inward man, I must needs tell thee I will draw thee no more of it. I therefore desire thee to pay for what thou hast had, and depart my house, for I do not like thy ways, nor does anybody here approve of thy ranting doings.'

We were not much surprised at this piece of fanatical civility, it being no more than what we expected; but the manner of his delivery rendered his words so very diverting that we could not forbear laughing him into such a passion, that the looks of the little saint discovered as great a devil in his heart as a pious disciple of his bigness could be well possessed with. Then, according to his request, we paid our reckoning and left him in a condition of vinegar and crabs' eyes mixed; that is, upon a great ferment.

From thence, pursuant to my friend's inclinations, we adjourned to the sign of the Angel in Fenchurch Street, where the vintner, like a double-dealing citizen, condescended as well to draw carmen's comfort as the consolatory juice which Nature has bestowed upon more deserving mortals. There my friend had the good fortune to meet some of his acquaintances, with whom we joined and made up together as pretty a tippling society as ever were drawn into a circumference round the noble centre of a punch-bowl, though our liquor was the blood of the grape, in which we found such delectable sweetness that so many thirsty pigs round a troughful of ale-grounds could not have expressed more satisfaction in their grunts than we did in our merry songs and catches.

Time, taking the advantage of our carelessness, had pruned his wings, and fled with such celerity that the noon of night was brought upon our backs before we had measured out a sufficiency of the noble creature to our craving appetites. And as we were contending with the drowsy master for the other quart, who should come in and put an end to our controversy but a tall, meagre, carrionly cony-fumble, and with him his crazy crew of cornigerous halberdiers, who looked together like Judas and his complices, or a parcel of Tom turd-men with their long poles coming to gauge a vault. When he had given us a fair sight of his painted authority, he stamped it down upon the boards before him with as much threatening violence as a Jack Adams in a music-house, at the end of every strain, when dancing with a quarterstaff. Then, with as much pride as a loobily mayor of a country corporation, he opened his mouth, like Balaam's ass, and thus spoke:

'Look you, d'ye see me, gentlemen? 'Tis an unseasonable time of night for people to be tippling. Every honest man ought to have been in bed an hour or two ago.' 'That's true,' said I, 'for nobody ought to be up so late, but constables and their watches.' At this some of the company tittered, which gave great offence to the choleric conservator of Her Majesty's peace, who commanded us instantly to be gone, or he would commit us to the Compter. A wine-cooper in the company, being well acquainted with this shred of authority, used importunate solicitations for the liberty of drinking another quart, saying, 'Pray, Mr Constable, don't be thus severe with us. 'Twas but last night you and I were drinking at a later hour together. I therefore hope you won't deny us the privilege yourself has so lately taken.' This bitter reflection, tossed into the very mouth of a magistrate, had such an unsavoury relish that he could not swallow it, but commanded his blackguards to take us to the Poultry Compter, who presently fell on us, like so many footpads. They first secured our weapons, and then led us along by the elbows in triumph to the rats' castle, where we were forced to do penance till the next morning in obedience to the will of a cucumber-cormorant; a tailor, good Lord! at whom I had flung a remnant of hard words, which made the cross-legged nit-cracker more particularly my enemy.

After we had passed through a spacious porch, where knaves in a forenoon may be seen in clusters as thick as pickpockets round Tyburn at an execution, or beggars at a hall-gate upon a festival-day, we came to a frightful grate, more terrible than the scene of Hell in Circeii, where, after three knocks of authority were given at the gate, a single-headed

Cerberus in a fur cap let fall from the back of a barricade a chain that made a more terrible rattling in our ears than the tongue of a scold, or a clap of thunder. Then, with a key much bigger than St Peter's, in which there was enough iron to have made a porridge pot, and consisted of more wards than are parishes in the City, he opened the wicket of the poor man's purgatory, into which they thrust us, one upon another, like so many swine into a hog sty. The turnkey was so civil as to offer us beds, but upon such unconscionable terms that a salt sinner might have hired a feathered convenience in a bawdy-house, with a downy bedfellow into the bargain, for less money than they exacted for the sheets. So, like good husbands, we thanked him for his love, but refused his courtesy.

After we had taken two or three turns in a paved yard, viewing the strength and loftiness of our garrison by starlight, we began to reflect upon the mischance we had fallen under, and looked as simple as so many knights errant trepanned into an enchanted castle. As we were thus ruminating upon our present circumstances, we heard the laughing of many voices, mixed with the confused wranglings of a different society. We asked the under-turnkey the meaning of this promiscuous noise. He told us the prisoners on the Common Side were driving away sorrow and making themselves merry with some of their pastimes. Upon this we made it our choice to be of their society, and accordingly desired admittance amongst 'em, as a means to pass away the tediousness of the night with some diversion, and also that we might judge the better of confinement, and the hardships of a prison.

When we first entered this apartment, under the title of the King's Ward the mixture of scents that arose from mundungus tobacco, foul sweaty toes, dirty shirts, the shit-tub, stinking breaths, and uncleanly carcases, poisoned our nostrils far worse than a Southwark ditch, a tanner's yard, or a tallow-chandler's melting-room. The ill-looking vermin, with long rusty beards, were swaddled up in rags, some with their heads covered with thrum-caps and others thrust into the tops of old stockings. Some quitted the play they were before engaged in and came hovering round us, like so many cannibals, with such devouring countenances as if a man had been but a morsel with 'em, all crying out, 'Garnish, garnish,' as a rabble in an insurrection, crying 'Liberty, liberty.' We were forced to submit to the doctrine of non-resistance and comply with their demands, which extended to the sum of two shillings each. Having thus paid our initiation fees, we were bid welcome into the King's Ward, and to all the privileges and immunities thereof.

This ceremony being ended, the lousy assembly of tatterdemalions, with their fingers in their necks, returned to their sports, and were as merry as so many beggars in a barn. Some of them formed a High Court of Justice, by which a criminal was to be tried for cracking his lice between his teeth and spitting out the bloody skins about the ward, to the great nuisance of the good subjects of England under confinement in the Poultry. The culprit moved the court to allow him counsel, which was granted. There happening to be amongst them a fat Yorkshire attorney who was committed for foul practice, and extorting undue fees, the offender at the bar chose him as his advocate. He, indeed, was very industrious in the defence of his client, till a couple of rogues, who were privately appointed to manage the design, came on a sudden with their hands charged full of sir-reverence out of the excreting-tub, mixed with soot and tallow, and as the poor pleader was gaping to the court, with abundance of intention they slapped it into his mouth, as poulterers do paste when they cram capons. What, by the strength of his jaws he bit off with his teeth, and would not suffer to be internally applied, they anointed his face with, till they made him stink like a Tom turd-man and look as beautiful as a chimney-sweeper.

This put the court, as well as the other spectators, into an excessive laughter, to see the poor lawyer spit, splutter, spew, and run about swearing and cursing, raving and crying, like a Bedlamite that had broke his chains; they having hid the bucket of water so that he had nothing either to gargle his mouth, or recover his face to its natural complexion. Everybody was glad to escape his fury by keeping at a distance. None came within reach of his arms or the scent of his breath, which, you may be sure, stunk as bad as a house-of-office. At last he seized a young fellow who had no hand in the matter, and blowed upon him like a bear upon a dog, till he had almost poisoned him, and so besmeared him with kisses that they looked as like one another in the face as the two images of St Dunstan's dial. In revenge for this, the young sufferer retired to the stink-tub, as a good fortress well stored with ammunition. There he fished for pellets, which he cast so thick upon his adversary that he made him look and stink like a bogged bailiff. Now and then a random shot hit a bystander, which had like to have begot him more enemies. What the lawyer could gather from the ground and pick off his garment, he most manfully returned, and fighting cunning, being much upon the dodge, an unlucky bullet flew over his shoulder and shot a broken perfumer just in the face, whose nostrils, being used to odoriferous scents, were the more offended at the unsavoury misfortune. It came with such angry force from an unprovoked enemy that the major part of his face was eclipsed by the stinking messenger of war.

Both sides maintained the battle with great bravery till their ammunition was quite spent, which forced them to end their quarrel in a few hard words. But notwithstanding they gave equal testimonials of their undaunted courage, yet I must needs tell you, they came both off, saving your presence, in a very shitten condition.

When the foul mutiny was thus ended, which began with a sir-reverence, a general search was made after the bucket of water in order to wash off the impurities with which, in the heat of passion, they had woefully defiled each other. After a sedulous enquiry, they found the hidden element, which, in cleaning their hands and faces, they had soon dyed of a beastly complexion.

By this time most of the pediculous inhabitants of these uncomfortable confines, being well tired with the pastimes of the night, were sitting naked in their cabins, overhauling their shirts and pressing their eight-legged enemies to death between their thumb-nails wheresoe'er they found them. Every now and then there came a frightful figure from aloft, clawing his own flesh for madness he was so lousy. He turned his buttocks o'er the edge of a wooden convenience, let fly an unsavoury shot, and away scoured up again. At last descended a fellow in a mourning surplice, and in his hand a wooden porridge-dish, whose hair stood as if, Medusa-like, it had been turned into snakes. Whither should he trot but to the pail of water where the dunghill-scented combatants had washed off their mire, and then quaffs off a couple of bumpers very savourily. But as soon as it was done, he found it left an unpalatable relish behind it, which made poor drowsy Barnaby fall a-spitting and cursing: 'The plague damn the pump. It is grown so rotten and makes the water taste so strong of the tree that we shall all be poisoned.' The unlucky deception of the innocent mistaken wretch raised, amongst my friends and I, a great deal of merriment, as, like the rest of mankind, we were under a natural propensity to laugh at mischief. The fellow had got drunk in the cellar, and went to bed before the prisoners began their revels, and knew nothing of the feud that had been raised by the droppings of the fundament, which occasioned him to be thus deceived.

Now the whole family were grown as silent as so many hogs when their bellies are full, nothing being heard but snoring, except now and then a crack from the stretching of a louse's skin, or an ingrateful sound from the untuneable drone of a filthy bagpipe, which is never heard but by the assistance of a stinking breath. With this sort of music were our ears entertained all night, and that my eyes might be obliged with answerable satisfaction, I thought it now the only time to look about me. I observed men lay piled in cabins one upon another, like coffins in a burying-vault, possessing only the same allowance above ground as the dead have under, their breadth and length, that's all. Other poor curs, that wanted the convenience of kennels (being supernumerary to the sleeping-huts), were lain upon benches, as if they had been bred up courtiers' footmen. Others coiled underneath like dogs, and slept as sound as Low Country soldiers. Some lay round the fire, almost covered with ashes, like potatoes roasting, with their noses in conjunction with one another's arses, like hogs upon a dunghill. These, I suppose, were tender mortals bred up at the forge, and as great enemies to cold weather as the mad fellow that walks about the town naked. Another was crept into a corner and had whelmed over his head the ash-tub, and so made a nightcap of an ale-firkin, to defend his head from the coldness of the weather.

With these sort of observations we passed away the dull hours of confinement till the morning, and were all as glad to see daylight again as a man would be to see the sun, who had tumbled by accident into a neglected coal-pit. Our fellow sufferers began now to awake, stretch and yawn, and hawk up their soot-coloured phlegm, congealed in their filthy stomachs, with unwholesome belch and nasty Oronoko. Every one stunk, as he roused from his warm den, like a fox newly kennelled. Now, I must confess, I was forced to hold my nose to the grate and snuff hard for a little fresh air, for I was e'en choked with the unwholesome fumes that arose from their uncleanly carcases. Had the burning of old shoes, draymen's stockings, the dipping of card matches, and a full close-stool pan been prepared in one room, as a nosegay to torment my nostrils, it could not have proved a more effectual punishment.

At last I heard the keys begin to rattle, which, though they were indifferent music overnight, they were very pleasing to our ears in the morning. The turnkey now, according to my wishes, let us into the yard, where we drew a little new breath and belched into the world those pestilential fumes which our bodies had imbibed from the three fatal sisters, filth, poverty and laziness.

We now thought it necessary to fortify our stomachs with a morning's draught, and accordingly descended into the cellar for that purpose, where every captive that had either money or credit was posting with all speed.

Now we were happily come into the conversation of the ladies, who (poor creatures), in tattered garments and without head-clothes, looked as if they were just delivered from the rude hands of an unmerciful rabble. One among the rest, who had something more than ordinary in her person to recommend her to our notice, I drank to, and begged the favour of her company, which, without much importunity, she granted. And after a little talk, I took the freedom to ask her what she was in for. She hesitated a little, and at last told me she was at the suit of a tallyman in Houndsditch, for things to the value of four pounds, and that he offered to kiss it out, but she would not let him, for which reason he arrested her, and had run her up to an execution. 'But, I suppose, madam,' said I, 'you have heartily repented since that you refused the offer.' 'No, sir,' she replied, 'rather than I would satisfy the desires of such unmerciful rogues as either tallyman, pawnbroker, or bailiff, I would prostitute myself to the honest porters in the Town. For I'd have you know, sir, I scorn to defile my body with such vermin, such inhuman knaves, that can't be content to cheat people out of their money, but must cozen them out of their liberty too. Here are but thirteen poor wretches of us on the Common Side, and twelve of 'em were brought in upon the tally account. And if Providence show us no more mercy than our creditors, here they may keep us as examples of their cruelty, to frighten others in their books to turn either whore or thief to get money to be punctual in their payments. This many have been forced to do, to my certain knowledge, to satisfy the hungry demands of those unconscionable usurers.'

I was mightily pleased with the woman's talk because I thought it reasonable to believe there was abundance of truth in't. For people that are poor to pay such unreasonable extortion as cent per cent, it's a scandal to the laws and a shame to Christianity that such indigent wretches should be so heavily oppressed, contrary to all charity and justice, to satisfy the unreasonable interest, or else the unmerciful revenge, of such unconscionable misers.

I rose up and peeped a little to survey this subterranean boozing-ken, and found it divided by as many partitions as the Temple house-of-office, though, I confess, it smelt not quite so sweet. The walls were varnished with the slime of snails, and had nothing to cover their nakedness in the coldest of weather but a tiffany cobweb, wherein hung spiders, as big as bumble-bees, that had not been molested with a broom since they were first enlivened. The tables and benches were of sturdy oak, handed down through many ages to posterity, and looked of that venerable antiquity as if they had been faithful servants to some great man so long since as the first year of Jubilee. Like undutiful children, we trod and spat upon the bare skin of our first parent, Earth, for 'twas floored like a barn, though it stunk like a stable, for everybody pissed as they sat, without the use of a chamber-pot.

By this time came down the constable who committed us, with a countenance as white as the head of a Romford calf, and both his sleeves armed with Spanish needles of all sorts and sizes, with here and there a remnant of basting thread and stitching silk hanging upon his coat and stockings. His shoes, behind in the quarters, were polished with the sweat of his heels to a jet-colour, to show his profession requires him to be slipshod. By virtue of his painted rolling-pin, he removed us from the plagues of Scotland, and carried us before our betters, Sir Milk and Maycril, to answer what Mr Stablecunt could allege against us. When His Worship had set his band to rights, and dressed his countenance with abundance of gravity, he betook himself to his elbow-chair, placed within a bar to keep unmannerly transgressors at their due distance, and also to secure his corns from the careless affronts of whispering constables, who are commonly proud to be seen standing between Justice and the People.

Our business was soon dispatched. 'Twas a case so familiar to His Worship that he had it at his fingers' end, without consulting *Keble*, for all the charge delivered against us was tippling at an unseasonable hour, and refusing to go home according to the command of authority. But Mr Buckram being highly displeased at some aggravating words I had given him overnight, told His Wisdom I threatened him, and said I would make him pay five pounds an hour for detaining me. 'How!' says Sir Serious. 'Pray what are you, that you value your time at so precious a rate, or that you dare speak such affrightening words to the face of the Queen's representative?' I replied, 'An't it please Your Worship, I am a gauger and was out last night about the Queen's business as well as Mr Constable; and the Queen, for aught I know, has sustained two or three hundred pounds damage by my being detained from my duty, for which, as I hope to make matters appear, Mr Constable must be answerable, for I assure him I will give a report of the matter to the Commissioners.'

This put His Gravity to his hums and haws. 'I must confess, Mr Constable,' said he, 'you did not do well to commit one of Her Majesty's officers. It was very unadvisedly done of you. Well, gentlemen, paying your fees, you may go about your business, I have nothing further to say to you.'

Had it not been for the assistance of a few brains and a little confidence, I had been bound over to the Sessions. But, I bless my stars, a lucky providence prevented the misfortune and restored us to our former liberty. We were now glad we had shaked off the yoke of confinement at so easy a rate, without paying for either drunkenness, swearing, or the like, which are as commonly accumulated upon transgressors under our circumstances as are canvas, stay-tape and buckram in a tailor's bill. As we had been fellow sufferers together, there was no parting without a glass. So we went to the Rose Tavern in the Poultry, where the wine, according to its merit, had justly gained a reputation. There in a snug room, warmed with brush and faggot, over a quart of good claret, we laughed at our night's adventure, and cursed the constable. And so that all others who fall into his clutches may do the like, I have here furnished them with an anathema proper for their purpose.

> May rats and mice
> Consume his shreds,
> His patterns and his measures.
> May nits and lice
> Infest his beds,
> And care confound his pleasures.

> May his long bills
> Be never paid,
> And may his helpmate horn him.
> May all his ills
> Be public made,
> And may his watchmen scorn him.

> May cucumbers
> Be all his food,
> And small beer be his liquor;.
> Lustful desires
> Still fire his blood,
> But may his reins grow weaker.

When old may he
Reduced be
From constable to beadle,
And live until
He cannot feel
His thimble from his needle!

After we had drunk a refreshing glass, my friend and I took leave of our companions and concluded to take a turn in Guildhall, which he told me was a fine place, and my Lord Mayor's chosen dining-room upon his day of triumph. As I came out of the tavern, bumpkin-like, I could no more forbear staring at Bow steeple than an astrologer could looking at a blazing star, or a young debauchee at a fine woman. But I wondered the projector of such a noble pyramid should form so mean a model for the church, which, compared together, is just the reverse of St Andrew's, Holborn, the one being like a woman with a beautiful face joined to a deformed body, and the other like an old pigmy's head upon a young giant's shoulders. 'But, pray,' said I, 'what is the meaning of this terrible monster upon the top, instead of a vane or weathercock?' 'Why, that', says my friend, 'is a brazen dragon, exalted as an emblem of the Church's persecution. The Dissenters once looked devilishly asquint at it, but now they dread it no more than More of More Hall did the Dragon of Wantley.'

From thence we jostled through a parcel of busy citizens, who blundered along with as much speed towards the 'Change as lawyers in term-time towards Westminster Hall, till we turned down King Street and came to the place intended. This I entered with as great astonishment, to see the giants, as the Morocco ambassador did London, when he saw the snow fall. I asked my friend the meaning and design of setting up those two lubberly preposterous figures, for I suppose they had some peculiar end in't. 'Truly,' says my friend, 'I am wholly ignorant of what they intended by 'em, unless they were set up to show the City what huge loobies their forefathers were, or else to fright stubborn apprentices into obedience. For the dread of appearing before two such monstrous loggerheads will sooner reform their manners, or mould 'em into a compliance with their masters' will, than carrying 'em before my Lord Mayor, or the Chamberlain of London. For some of them are as much frighted at the names of Gog and Magog as little children are at the terrible sound of Raw-Head and Bloody-Bones.'

'Pray,' said I, 'what are yon cluster of people doing, that seem all as busy as so many fools at the Royal Oak lottery?' 'Truly,' said my friend, 'you are something mistaken in your comparison. If you had said knaves, you had hit it, for that's the Sheriff's Court, and I must give 'em that character, for I never knew one fool among them, though they have to do with a great many. All those tongue-padders, who are chattering within the Bar, are picking the pockets of those that stand without. You may know the sufferers by their pale faces; the passions of hope, fear, and revenge, hath put them into such disorder, they are as easy to be distinguished in a crowd by their looks as an owl from a hawk, or a country esquire from a town sharper.'

'He's a very comely gentleman,' said I, 'that sits upon the bench and puts on so pleasing a countenance, as if, like a god, he viewed with pleasure the jars and discords of contending mortals that fret and fume beneath him.'

My friend replied, 'He might well look merrily who sits the playing of so many great games and is sure always to be on the winning side. For you must know,' says he, 'these courts are like public gaming-tables, the steward's the box-keeper, the counsel and attorneys are the sharpers, and the clients are the fools that are bubbled out of their money.'

'Pray, what is that crowd doing at the other end of the hall?' 'That,' says my friend, 'is a Court of Conscience, whose business is to take care that a debtor of a sum under forty shillings shall not pay money faster than he can get it. 'Tis a very reasonable establishment, without jesting, for the prevention of poor people's ruin, who lie at the mercy of a parcel of rascally tallymen, and suchlike unconscionable traders, who build their own welfare upon the miseries and wants of others. There are several other courts held here, besides what we now see sitting, but this I think does the most good of any of 'em, except to the lawyers, and they look upon it with as evil an eye as the Devil looked over Lincoln.'

'Pray,' said I, 'whose graceful pictures are those, that are so great an ornament to the place?' My friend replied, they were the grave sages of the law. 'Sure,' said I, 'he was no skilful artist that painted 'em. Do you see how black he has made some of the palms of their hands?' 'Pooh, pooh!' says my friend. 'I find you are no judge of painting. Why, it must be so. That's nothing but the shadow! Don't you see, the light strikes full upon the back of the hand, and consequently the inside must appear dark?' 'That's true,' said I. 'I thank you for making me so much the wiser. I must confess it is an art I have no knowledge in. Pray, whose pictures are those at the upper end?' 'Those,' replied my friend, 'are the King and the late Queen Mary. And those in black gowns, with the Purse before them, are such as have been Chancellors.' 'Bless me!' said I, 'painting is a fine art. How steadfastly all those in black look upon the King. But, to my thinking, all those that come after in red, squint with one eye upon His Majesty, and the other wishfully on the Purse and Mace.'

'Away, away!' says my friend. 'That's nothing but your foolish fancy. I shall apply the old proverb to you, "As the fool thinketh, the bell clinketh". We have seen all we can see here at this time, I'll go and show you St Paul's, and by that time, I reckon, you'll have got a good stomach to your dinner.'

According to my friend's proposal, we steered our course towards the famous cathedral, and as we passed along Cheapside, we met an old fellow with a nose (bless my eyesight!) that 'twas as long almost as a rolling-pin, and I am sure as big at the end as a football, beset with carbuncles and rubies. No Oliver's nose could have appeared more glorious. It looked as fresh as the gills of an angry turkey-cock and was so rare a fence for his mouth that whoever fights him must first knock off the gnomon of his face, or he could never propose to do his teeth any damage. 'I wonder,' said I, 'he should be so foolish to walk the streets in public. Certainly, if he would keep it private and only show himself in Bartholomew Fair amongst the Arabian monsters, he might make his nose worth two or three hundred pounds a year to him.' Says my friend, 'It's nothing now to what it is sometimes. You see it in the wane. He's forced to have it pared every full moon, it grows so fast. I see by its redness it has been done lately. I'll warrant you, he has had a pound or two of steaks cut off it within this day or two.' 'I vow,' said I, ''tis very strange, methinks my nose begins to swell at the very thoughts of him. Sure, this is Tom Jolly the song was made on, is it not?'

'No,' says my friend. 'This is a good honest fellow, a tallyman, who is so true a toper of claret he will sit twelve hours in a tavern before he can fill his nose. But, when he has replenished it, he staggers home, and the bottle end being spongy, he squeezes it again into his mouth. So he has the pleasure of drinking his claret the second time, and will live longer, they say, by sucking his nose than a bear can by licking his paws.' 'Marry,' said I, 'that may well be, for if you tell me the truth, his nasal runlet affords much the better liquor!'

We had not gone much further but we met with a fellow stark naked from the waist upward, armed with a lusty cudgel. I concluded he must be either fool or madman to expose his bare flesh to the sharp pinches of so cold a season. But, however, I enquired of my friend if he knew the meaning of his ridiculous whimsy. He replied he had heard he was a man of good parts and learning, and from thence did believe he was a kind of self-willed philosopher, who had a mind to broach some new principles, and make people believe he first left off his clothes to keep himself warm, and ever since has refused to put 'em on for fear he should catch cold by wearing 'em. 'But I fancy he has made but few proselytes. He has gone in this manner many years, till his skin is by the weather as hard as the upperleather of a drayman's shoe. I met him, the last snowy day we had, going into the fields (instead of a mouthful) to take his bellyful of fresh air, for he esteems it much better walking then, than at midsummer.'

By this time we were come to Cheapside Conduit, palisaded in with chimney-sweepers' brooms, and guarded with such an infernal crew of soot-coloured funnel-scourers that a countryman, seeing so many black attendants waiting at a stone hovel, took it to be one of Old Nick's tenements, and asked a shopkeeper why they would suffer the Devil to live in the heart of the City. These we passed and entered into Paul's Churchyard, where our eyes were surprised with such a mountainous heap of stones that I thought it must require the assistance of a whole nation for an age to remove 'em from the quarry, and pile 'em upon one another in such admirable order, and to so stupendous a height.

We turned to the right, where booksellers were as plenty as pedlars at a fair, and parsons in their shops as busily searching after the venerable conceits of our wormeaten ancestors, as if they came thither, for want of brains or a library, to patch up a seasonable discourse for the following Sunday.

'Pray,' says my friend, 'take notice of that old lantern-jawed peripatetic, so thoughtfully perambulating in his warehouse of Roman saints, religious heathens, and honest sociable moralists. He looks as like a modern politician as if, through the whole course of his life, he had studied nothing but Machiavelli. In all seasons of the year you may find him walking in his shop, and (like a Spanish farrier that shoes horses in his cloak) he is never to be seen without his hanging-coat; it is his comfortable companion at all times, and in all business. As the Satyr in the *Fables* could with the same breath blow hot and cold, so is his Irish mantle possessed of the like qualities, for he wears it in the winter to keep him warm, and in the summer as an umbrella to screen his withered carcase from the scorching sunbeams. Though he has but a small head, he has a great deal more brains than a goose, and never gave anybody occasion to call him fool, that ever dealt with him. He's so far a true-bred Englishman as to be a great enemy to the interest of France, for he rails mightily against taverns and never drinks wine but when he's treated. He's a little too cunning to be honest, and too miserly to be generous. He loves nothing more than his money, and hates nothing so much as to part with it. Calls generosity, folly; charity, extravagance; overreaching, wisdom; niggardliness, discretion; and unconscionable extortion, but a lawful interest. Since Winchester quarts were first thrown out of fashion, he never was known to drink strong drink but once, and then treated by his apprentice who had found at the door a piece of money, and being upon his master's ground, he claimed the right, and after some little contest about the matter, they agreed to spend it.'

It now being about three o'clock, we concluded to go into Paul's, an account of which I shall give in my next.

V

IN OUR LOITERING perambulation round the outside of St Paul's, we came to a picture-seller's shop, where as many smutty prints were staring the church in the face as a learned debauchee ever found in Aretino's *Postures*. I observed there were more people gazing at these loose fancies of some lecherous engraver than I could see reading sermons at the stalls of all the neighbouring booksellers. Among the rest of the spectators, an old citizen had mounted his spectacles upon his nose, and was busily peeping at the bawdy representation of the gentleman and the milkmaid.

'Pray, father,' said I, 'what do you find in that immodest picture worth such serious notice?' 'Why, I'll tell you, young man,' says he, 'I cannot without wonder behold in this painting the madness and vanity of you young fellows, with what confidence you can take a bear by the tooth, without the dread of the danger.' 'I rather believe,' said I, 'you gratify some sensual appetite by giving titillation to your vicious thoughts, from the obscenity of the action.' To which he replied, 'Indeed, Mr Inquisitive, you are much mistaken; but if thy head had been where his hand is, I should have viewed it with much more pleasure to have thought in what a pretty condition thy nose had been.' And away he shuffled, with compassion towards his corns, as stiff as a Yorkshire bullock into Smithfield Market, very merry at his jest, and chattering to himself like a magpie that had bilked a gunner.

We walked a little further, and came amongst the music-shops, in one of which were so many dancing-masters' apprentices fiddling and piping of borees and minuets, that the crowd at the door could no more forbear dancing into the shop than the merry stones of Thebes could refuse capering into the walls, when conjured from confusion into order by the power of Amphion's harmony. Amongst 'em stood a little red-faced blade, beating time upon his counter, with as much formality as if a Bartholomew Fair consort, with the assistance of a Jack-pudding, had been ridiculing an Italian sonnet in the balcony to draw people into the booth, for he was as prodigally pert in giving his instructions to the rest as a young pedagogue tutoring a disciple in the hearing of his father. We added two to the number of fools, and stood a little, making our ears do penance, to please our eyes with the conceited motions of their heads and hands, which moved to and fro with as much deliberate stiffness as the two wooden horologists at St Dunstan's, when they strike the quarters.

We left these jingle-brains to their crotchets, and proceeded to the west end of the cathedral, where we passed by abundance of apples, nuts, and gingerbread. We came to a melancholy multitude drawn into a circle, giving very serious attention to a blind ballad-singer, who was mournfully setting forth the wonderful usefulness of a godly broadside, proper to be stuck up in all righteous and sober families, as a means to continue the grace of God before their eyes, and secure even the little lambs of the flock from the temptations of Satan. After he had prepared the ears of his congregation with a tedious preamble in commendation of his divine poem, being mounted upon a stone, above his blue-apron auditory, he began with an audible voice to lyric it over in a psalm tune, to the great satisfaction of the penitent assembly. They sighed and sobbed, shook their heads and cried, showing a greater sorrow and contrition for their sins (which I believe, indeed, were great) than the pious assembly at Meg's dancing-school when the Reverend Doctor Burgess holds forth upon death and judgement. At last he came to the terrible words of Hell and Damnation, which he sung out with such an emphasis that he put the people a-trembling as if they had all been troubled with a tertian ague. Liking not the harsh sound of such inharmonical bugbear words, they began to sneak off, like a libertine out of a church when the parson galls the old sore of his conscience by pressing too hard upon his vices. Many charitable Christians bought his religious sonnets because he made 'em himself, wondering how a blind man should see to pen such marvellous good things, and remember to sing them by heart without the help of his eyesight.

From thence we turned through the west gate of St Paul's Churchyard, where we saw a parcel of stone-cutters and sawyers so very hard at work that I protest, notwithstanding the vehemence of their labour and the temperateness of the season, instead of using their handkerchiefs to wipe the sweat off their faces, they were most of them blowing their nails. 'Bless me!' said I to my friend, 'sure this church stands in a colder climate than the rest of the nation, or else those fellows are of a strange constitution, to seem ready to freeze at such warm exercise.' 'You must consider,' says my friend, 'this is work carried on at a national charge, and ought not to be hastened on in a hurry, for the greatest reputation it will gain when it's finished will be that it was so many years in building.' From thence we moved up a long wooden bridge, that led to the west portico of the church, where we intermixed with such a train of promiscuous rabble that I fancied we looked like the beasts driving into the Ark, in order to replenish a new succeeding world.

The first part that I observed of this inabruptable pile were the pillars that sustained the covering of the porch. 'I cannot but conceive,' said I, 'that legs of such vast strength and magnitude are much too big for the weight of so small a body it supports.' In answer to which, my friend repeats me this following fable:

'There was a little carpenter, and he hewed himself a mighty strong stool out of the whole timber, to sit and smoke a pipe on at his door. A passenger coming by, seeing such a disproportion between the man and his seat, took an occasion to ask him why he had made such a huge clumsy stool for such a pigmy of a man. He replied, he liked it himself, and cared not whether anybody else did or not; adding, he intended it to serve the children's children of his grandchildren. And besides, "The stronger it is," says he, "if anybody finds fault, the better able it is to bear their reflections."'

From thence we entered the body of the church, the spaciousness of which we could not discern for the largeness of the pillars. 'What think you now?' says my friend. 'Pray how do you like the inside?' 'I'll tell you,' said I. 'I must needs answer you as a gentleman did another, who was a great admirer of a very gay lady, and asked his companion whether he did not think her a woman of extraordinary beauty. He answered, truly, he could not tell, she might be so for aught he knew, for he could see but very little of her face for patches. "Pooh, pooh," says the other, "you must not quarrel at that, she designs them as ornaments." To which his friend replied, since she has made them so large, fewer might have served her turn, or if she must wear so many, she might have cut 'em less. And so I think by the pillars.'

We went a little further, where we observed ten men in a corner, very busy about two men's work, taking as much care that everyone should have his due proportion of the labour as so many thieves in making an exact division of their booty. The wonderful piece of difficulty the whole number had to perform, was to drag along a stone of about three hundredweight, in a carriage, in order to be hoisted upon the mouldings of the cupola. But they were so fearful of dispatching this facile undertaking with too much expedition that they were longer in hauling on't half the length of the church than a couple of lusty porters, I am certain, would have been in carrying it to Paddington, without resting of their burden.

From thence we approached the choir, on the north side, which had been very much defaced by the late fire, occasioned by the carelessness of a plumber who had been mending some defective pipes of the organs. This unhappy accident has given the Dissenters so fair an opportunity to reflect upon the use of music in our churches, that they scruple not to vent their spleen by saying: ''Twas a judgement from Heaven upon their carvings and their fopperies, for displeasing the ears of the Almighty with the profane tootings of such abominable catcalls.' But, some of the most learned amongst them, and in particular Mr Baxter, were of a different opinion as to the use of grave music in holy places. He so highly extolled and commended to all Christians the usefulness of it that, in his *Christian Directory*, he expressed these words: 'As spectacles are a comfortable help to the reading of the divine Scripture, so music serves to exhilarate the soul in the service of Almighty God.'

Afternoon prayers being now ready to begin, we passed into the choir, which was adorned with all those graceful ornaments that could anyways add a becoming beauty and venerable decency to so magnificent a structure, which indeed, considered abstractedly from the whole, is so elegant, awful, and well-composed a part, that nothing but the glorious presence of Omnipotence can be worthy of so much art, grandeur and industry as shines there to the honour of God and the fame of human excellence.

When prayers were over, which, indeed, were performed with that harmonious reverence, and exhilarating order, sufficient to reclaim the worst of men from following the untuneable discord of sin, and bring them over to the enlivening harmony of grace and goodness, we then returned into the body of the church, happily intermixed with a crowd of good Christians who had concluded, with us, their afternoon's devotion.

We now took notice of the vast distance of the pillars from whence they turn the cupola, on which, they say, is a spire to be erected, three hundred foot in height, whose towering pinnacle will stand with such stupendous loftiness above Bow Steeple dragon, or the Monument's flaming urn, that it will appear to the rest of the holy temples like a cedar of Lebanon among so many shrubs, or a Goliath looking over the shoulders of so many Davids.

As we were thus gazing with great satisfaction at the wondrous effects of human industry, raising our thoughts by degrees to the marvellous works of Omnipotence, from those of his creatures, we observed an old country fellow leaning upon his stick, and staring with great amazement up toward Heaven, through the circle from whence the arch is to be turned. Seeing him fixed in such a ruminating posture, I was desirous of knowing his serious thoughts, in order to discover which, I asked him his opinion of this noble building, and how he liked the church. 'Church!' replied he, ''tis no more like a church than I am. 'Ad's heart! It's more by half like a goose pie I have seen at my landlord's, and this embroidered hole in the middle of the top is like the place in the upper crust where they put in the butter.' I could not forbear laughing at the oddness of Slouch's notion, and hoping to hear something further from him that might give us a little diversion, we continued his company.

'Prithee,' said I, 'honest countryman, since thou dost not believe it to be a church, what place dost thou take it to be?' 'Why,' says he, 'I'll warrant you now, thou think'st me to be such an arrant fool I can't tell, but thou art mistaken. My vather was a trooper to Oliver Cromwell, and I have heard him say, many a time, he has set up his horse here, and do you think the Lord will ever dwell in a house that the Roundheads converted to the use of a stable?' 'That was done,' said I, 'by a parcel of rebellious people, who had got the upper hand of the government, and cared not what murders, sacrilege, treason, and mischief they committed. But it was a church before it was converted to that heathenish use, and so it is now.' 'Why then,' says Roger, 'I think, in good truth, the Cavaliers are as much to blame in making a church of a stable, as the Roundheads were in making a stable of a church, and there's a Roland for your Oliver, and so goodbye to you.' Away he trudged, like the true offspring of schismatical and rebellious ancestors, expressing in his looks no little malice and contempt towards the magnificence of the building, which they have been always ready to deface when they have had any opportunity.

We now began to stifle our sober and more elevated thoughts and contemplations, and form in ourselves a suitable temper to a different undertaking. This was to observe some disconsolate figures which were wandering about the church, like mice in an empty barn, or snails in a vintner's cellar, as if their melancholy cogitations had tempted them foolishly to look for what they were assured they should not find. Some of them were as pale as if troubled with the hypochondria, and fancied themselves to be walking in some subterranean cavern, far remote from that transitory world in which they had once been sinners. These had their eyes cast down as if they had great regard to their footsteps, and were under some melancholy apprehension (if they took not great care) of slipping into that bottomless pit from whence there is no redemption.

Others, walking with their arms crossed, directed their eyes altogether upwards, as if they were so deeply fallen in love with the beauty of the building that their senses were ravished with each masterly stroke of the skilful artificers. Amongst the rest, here and there, was a lady, who looked as wild and wanton as if (though she was admiring the church) she thought more on a gallant than she did on her devotions, and would rather sing a song than say her prayers, or see a play than hear a sermon.

The next that we remarked upon were a kind of a cuckoldly row of penurious citizens, consisting in number of about half a dozen, who, I suppose, had taken sanctuary in the church to talk treason with safety, or because it was cheaper walking there than sitting in a coffee-house. Their heads, tongues, hands and eyes were all eagerly in motion, showing they were extraordinarily intent upon some wonderful projection. At last I conjectured from words which I overheard, they were some of the shallow-brained cullies who were drawn in by the Land Bank, and were fumbling out a method of licking themselves whole, by cheating of other people. These, I thought, like the money-changers, ought to have been whipped out of the Temple.

There was nothing offered worth our further attention, except a parcel of wenches fit for husbands, playing at whoop-and-hide among the pillars, who were full able enough, and I suppose willing, in an evening to help the young workmen home with their tools, if they would venture to thrust 'em into their custody. This revelling of girls I thought was very indecent, and ought to be carefully prevented, lest the new church be polluted far worse than the old one, and instead of a stable, be defiled with worse beasts than horses.

From thence we made our egress on the south side, quitted the consecrated bounds of this holy leviathan, and crossed a dirty kennel to take a view of a parcel of cleanly beau apprentices, who were walking in their masters' shops with their periwigs just combed out of buckle, well dredged with the barber's powdering puff, the extravagant use of which made them appear so particoloured that their upper parts looked like millers. And their coats, from the waist downwards, hung in as many folds as a waterman's doublet, to show they had more cloth in the skirts of one tunic than any of their ancestors wore in a whole suit. But this much may be said in excuse of 'em, they might the better afford it because they were woollen-drapers.

By this time we were come to an arch, where we turned in, on the left hand of which many scutcheons were hung out, as if funerals were more in fashion at this end of the town than any part I had yet seen. Had I been skilled in heraldry I might have blazoned the vanity of a great many noble families who are apt to boast of their coats of arms, though there are blots which denote treason in one, cowardice in another, illegitimacy in a third, and murder in a fourth, &c. Yet, the vulgar understanding them not, they are sometimes reverenced for that painted distinction which they ought to be ashamed of. I asked my friend the meaning of all these gaudy hieroglyphics being hung out in so private a thoroughfare. 'You are mistaken,' says he, 'this is a place of great business, for most persons who travel in dead men's shoes are necessitated to come this way, and ask leave of those who never knew one of their family, whether they shall enjoy that which nobody has any right to but themselves. And that shop where you see so many good colours flung away upon paper, like so much gold upon gingerbread, belongs to a heraldic painter, who, indeed (give him his due), is as honest a man as ever guided pencil and has taken as much pains, at his own expense, to detect a knave, and prevent the public's being cheated, as ever his neighbour did to subdue a stubborn conscience, and make it pliable to his own and the nation's interest. This is his office who upon just grounds laid open the funeral interloper; the robber, instead of preserver, of the dead. He was the cozener of the living, the corrupter of gentlemen's coachmen, the invader of tradesmen's properties, the undervaluer of poor men's labour, the fool of an embalmer, and the knave of an undertaker.'

'Pray,' said I, 'whose great house is that on the right hand, which, though it looks so stately, appears as plain as a physician's coach, or a gouty stateman's horse-litter?' 'Why that,' replied my friend, 'was a large trap set by the government to catch the popular weasel, so much talked of, who stood so long tottering in the beginning of the Revolution, between hawk and buzzard, but at last he snapped at the bait and was taken. And from a man of a discontented conscience, he is become as well satisfied since, as if *de jure* and *de facto* had never been a point in question. This is the seat of him, to his everlasting praise be it spoken, who served his followers as Saul did the gentiles, and became a convert to the new faith in fashion, there being this difference to be considered, the one got a better name and a worse living, the other a better living but a worse name. He has been baited fifty-times worse than ever the tiger was, for every scribbling mongrel in the town had a fair snap at him, till at last they uncased him, but all to little purpose. His case is so well amended that there are but three dangers which he stands in fear of, viz., the coming of King James, the scolding of his wife, and a consumption.

'That place,' says he, 'on the left hand is a spiritual purgatory to torment fornicators and adulterers, where they bring many sinners to penance but very few to repentance, and oftener excommunicate people out of the church for not going thither.' 'That, methinks,' said I, 'is like forcing a man to forbear such victuals which he cannot endure to eat, or debarring him of such company which he always hated to keep.' 'This liberty of conscience,' says my friend, 'has been a devilish thorn in their sides, for in the joyful days of Church persecution, they used to have two or three brace of Dissenters for breakfast, but now the office is dwindled into such a vacancy of business, their neighbouring vintner despairs of ever being made an alderman, for the White Horse Alehouse has run away with most of his customers.'

'Pray,' said I, 'whither does that passage lead where those country fellows stand gaping and staring about?' 'That,' replied my friend, 'is Doctors' Commons, and they are come to Town about the probate of some last dying will and testament, administration, caveat, or some such business. It's a wonder none of the spiritual cormorants has seized them yet, for they are generally as quick-sighted as hawks, and love as dearly to prey upon a country curmudgeon as a hound does upon horseflesh. In that court live the learned readers of the law civil, who made such a terrible bustle with the poor word, Abdication. But after all their debates and consultations they could not, with the assistance of all their magic, conjure up any other puzzling crambo so proper for their purpose, and at last did approve that the word might stand instead of a better.'

We adjourned from thence back into Paul's Churchyard, and turned westward into a famous street, wherein a noble postern was presented to our view. The stateliness of its appearance made me inquisitive of my friend what they called this edifice; to what purpose it was built, and to what use converted. He told me it was called Ludgate, raised both as an ornament and a security to the City. And through a charitable compassion to unfortunate citizens, it was made a commodious prison for freemen, furnished with such conveniences, and so plentifully supplied with provisions by the gifts of good people, and other certain allowances, that many live better in it than ever they did out on't, and are so fallen in love with their confinement that they would not change it for liberty.

After we had shot the arch, we turned up a street, which my companion told me was the Old Bailey. We walked on till we came to a great pair of gates. It being a remarkable place, according to my usual custom I requested my friend to give me some further knowledge of the matter. He informed me it was Justice Hall, where a Doomsday Court was held once a month to sentence such canary-birds to a penitential psalm, as would rather be choked by the product of hempseed, for living roguishly, than exert their power in lawful labour to purchase their bread honestly. 'In this narrow part of the street,' says my friend, 'into which we are now passing, many such a wretch has taken his last walk, for we are going towards that famous university where, if a man has a mind to educate a hopeful child in the daring science of padding, the light-fingered subtlety of shop-lifting, the excellent use of jack and crow for silently drawing bolts and forcing barricades, with the knack of sweetening, or the most ingenious dexterity of picking pockets, let him but enter him in this college on the Common Side, and confine him close to his study but for three months, and if he does not come out qualified to take any degree of villainy he must be the most honest dunce that ever had the advantage of such eminent tutors.'

From thence my friend led me through a place called Giltspur Street, and brought me to a spacious level, which he told me was distinguished by the name of Smithfield Rounds, which entertained our nostrils with such a savoury scent of roasting meat, and surprised my ears with the jingling noise of so many jacks, that I stared about me like a country bumpkin in Spitalfields amongst so many throwsters' mills. And seeing such a busy number of cooks at work, I thought myself in the kitchen to the universe, and wondered where the gluttons could live who were to devour such vast quantities of sundry sorts of food, which run so merrily round before large fires in every greasy mansion. We soon delivered our squeamish stomachs from the surfeiting fumes that arose from their rotten roasted pork, which made the Rounds stink like a Hampshire farmer's yard when singeing of a bacon hog.

From thence we proceeded to the rails, where country carters stood armed with their long whips to keep their teams (upon sale) in a due decorum. These were drawn up into the most sightly order imaginable, with their forefeet mounted on a dunghill and their heads dressed up to as much advantage as an Inns of Court sempstress, or a mistress of a boarding-school. Some had their manes frizzled up, to make 'em high withered, so that they looked as fierce as one of Hungess's wild boars. Others had their manes plaited, as if they had been ridden by the nightmare, and the fellows that attended them made as uncouth figures as the monsters in the Temple. Amongst these cattle, here and there, was the conductor of a dung-cart, in his dirty surplice, wrangling about the price of a beast, as a wary purchaser; and that he might not be deceived in the goodness of the creature, he must see him stand three fair pulls at a post, to which the traces of the poor jade are tied, that he may exert his strength, and show the clown his excellence, for which he strokes him on the head, or claps him on the buttocks, to recompense his labours.

We went a little further, and there we saw a parcel of ragged rapscallions, mounted upon scrubbed tits, scouring about the Rounds, some trotting, some galloping, some pacing, and others stumbling; blundering about in such confusion that I thought them like so many beggars on horseback riding to the Devil, or a parcel of French Protestants upon Dover Road, scrambling post-haste up to Piccadilly.

'Pray, friend,' said I, 'what are these eagle-looked fellows, in their narrow-brimmed white beavers, jockey-coats, a spur on one heel, and bended sticks in their hands, that are so busily peeping into every horse's mouth, and sauntering about the Market like wolves in a wilderness, as if they were seeking whom they should devour?' 'Those blades,' says my friend, 'are a subtle sort of Smithfield fox called horse-coursers, who swear every morning by the bridle, they will never from any man suffer a knavish trick, or ever do an honest one. They are a sort of English Jews, that never deal with any man but they cheat him, and have a rare faculty of swearing a man out of his senses, lying him out of his reason, and cozening him out of his money. If they have a horse to sell that is stone-blind, they'll call a hundred gods to witness he can see as well as you can. If he is downright lame, they will use all the asseverations that the Devil can assist 'em with, that it's nothing but a Spring halt. If he be as rotten as a Town stallion who has been twenty times in the powdering-tub, they will warrant, upon their souls' damnation, he's as sound as a roach. And if he be twenty years old, they'll swear he comes but seven next grass, if they find the buyer has not judgement enough to discover the contrary.'

'I perceive,' said I, 'this is a market for black cattle as well as horses.' 'Yes,' replied my friend, 'if we had come in the morning you would have seen the butchers as busy in handling the flanks and arses of sheep and oxen as now the jockeys are in fumbling about the jaws of horses. But now the market is almost over; yet you may see some Welsh runts and Scotch carrion, which wait for the coming of Shoreditch butchers, who buy 'em up for the Spitalfields weavers, and the poorer sort of Huguenots, who have taken possession of that part of the town and like the Scots, have no great kindness for fat meat, because they never used to eat any in their own country.

'Come,' says my friend, 'now we are here we'll take a turn quite round, and then we shall escape nothing worth observing.' In order to complete our circular walk we moved on, but had as many stinking whiffs of Oronoko tobacco blown into our nostrils as would have cured an afflicted patient of the toothache, or put a nice lady into a gentle salivation.

By this time we came to an arch, about the middle of the row, where a parcel of long-legged loobies were stuffing their lean carcases with rice-milk and furmety, until it ran down the corners of their mouths back into their porringers, so that each of them was a true copy of Martin Barwel's feeding the cat with custard. We passed by these devouring gang of milksops, and came to the corner of a narrow lane, where 'Money for Old Books' was written upon some part or other of every shop, as surely as 'Money for Live Hair' upon a barber's window. We took a short turn into it, and so came back, where we saw a couple of poor scholars with disconsolate looks, in threadbare black coats, selling their authors at a penny a pound, which their parents perhaps had purchased with the sweat of their brows. And there was a parson almost in every shop, searching the shelves with as much circumspection to find out a book worth purchasing as ever cock used upon a dunghill of rubbish when he's scraping after an oat worth pecking at.

Being now pretty well tired with our day's journey, we concluded to refresh ourselves with one quart of claret before we walked any further. We were near the sign of Honour's fountain, the Crown, the representation of which royal diadem I thought no vintner would presume to distinguish his house by, unless he had wine in his cellar fit to bless the lips of princes. To experience the truth of this notion, we stepped in, where the jolly master, like a true kinsman of the Bacchanalian family, met us in the entry with a manly respect and bid us welcome. We desired he would show us upstairs into a room forward. Accordingly, in his own proper person, like a complaisant gentleman-usher, he conducted us into a large stately room, where, at first entrance, I discerned the master-

strokes of the famed Fuller's pencil, the whole room being painted with
that commanding hand. His dead figures appeared with such lively
majesty that they begot reverence in us, the spectators, towards the awful
shadows; our eyes were so delighted with this noble entertainment that
every glance gave new life to our weary senses.

We now begged him to oblige us with a quart of his richest claret,
such as was fit only to be drunk in the presence of such heroes, into
whose company he had done us the honour to introduce us. He accordingly gave directions to his drawer, who returned with a quart of such
inspiring juice that we thought ourselves translated into one of the houses
of the Heavens, and were there drinking immortal nectar, amongst gods
and goddesses. My friend, like myself, was so wonderfully pleased at this
obliging usage, that he was very importunate with me to scribble a few
lines in commendation of our present state of happiness, which, to gratify
his desire, I performed, and have here presented to the reader.

Who can such blessings, when they're found, resign?
An honest vintner, faithful to the vine?
A spacious room, rare painting, and good wine?

Such tempting charms what mortal can avoid?
Where such perfections are at once enjoyed,
Who can be dull, or who be ever cloyed?

If you would love, see there fair Pallas stands,
How chaste her looks! How fine her breasts and hands!
Her awful mien each gen'rous heart commands.

If you to wit or music would aspire,
Gaze at the Nine, that blest harmonious choir,
They'll kindle in your thoughts new sparks of fire.

If to the war-like Mars you'd be a friend,
And learn to bravely conquer, or defend,
See Ajax and Ulysses there contend.

If neither love nor arms your fancy suit,
Nor would you be wise, musical or stout,
Here's wine will make you truly blest without!

By this time we had tippled off our salubrious juice, and business denying us leisure to renovate our lives with t'other quart, we took our leave, with a promise to recompense his respectful usage, some better opportunity. We had not gone above ten strides from the door, but we saw a cluster of tun-bellied mortals, with malignant aspects, armed with sturdy oak of an unlawful size, looking as sharp upon every passenger, as if, cannibal-like, they were just ready to devour 'em. I enquired of my friend what he took those ill-favoured crew to be, whose bulldog countenances and preposterous bodies rendered them in appearance betwixt men and monsters. 'These fellows,' says my companion, 'which you seem to be so much amazed at, are nothing but serjeants who are waiting to give somebody a clap on the shoulder. This corner is their plying place, and is as seldom to be found without a rogue as Gray's Inn Walks without a whore, or Newgate Market without a basket-woman.'

We moved from thence, till we came to the corner of a lane where a parcel of nimble-tongued sinners leapt out of their shops and swarmed about me like so many bees about a honeysuckle. Some got me by the hands, some by the elbows, and others by the shoulders, and made such a noise in my ears that I thought I had committed some egregious trespass unawares, and they had seized me as a prisoner. I began to struggle hard for my liberty, but as fast as I loosed myself from one, another took me into custody. 'Wounds!' said I, 'what's the matter? What wrong have I done you? Why do you lay such violent hands upon me?' At last a fellow with a voice like a speaking-trumpet came up close to my ears and sounded forth, 'Will you buy any clothes?' 'A pox take you,' said I, 'you are ready to tear a man's clothes off his back, and then ask him whether he'll buy any. Prithee let mine alone, and they will serve me yet this six months.' But they still hustled me backwards and forwards like a taken pickpocket in a crowd, till at last I made loose and scampered like a rescued prisoner from a gang of bailiffs, my friend standing all the while looking on, and laughing at me.

'Pray,' said I, 'what's the meaning of these unmannerly clip-nits using passengers with this shameful incivility? Certainly 'tis a greater penance for a man to walk through this confounded wardrobe than 'tis to run the gauntlet. But what is the reason,' said I to my friend, 'they did not treat you after the same manner?' 'You must know,' says he, 'they can distinguish a countryman as well by his looks as you can a parson by his robes. Being a parcel of unlucky vermin, they tease a stranger to the town, as much to make themselves sport as to promote the sale of their

goods, and if they had got you up a little higher, they would have handed
you quite through the lane, for it's like a gulf, when you're a little way
entered the current will carry you through. The masters of those shops
will give as much wages for one of those tongue-padding sweeteners,
who stand sentinel at their doors as an illiterate mountebank will allow
to a good orator, i.e. fifty shillings, or three pounds, a week. They are
like the jackal to the lion, they catch the prey for their masters, and if
they but get you into one of their shops, they as certainly cheat you
before you come out again, as you go in with money in your pocket.
They will out-wheedle a gipsy, out-swear a common gamester, out-lie an
affidavit man, and out-cozen a tallyman. They will make up new clothes
and sell them for second-hand, and get more money by 'em than the
topping'st tailor in Town ever got by a young heir, when he made his
clothes upon credit. They are a pack of the sharpest knaves about
London, and are as great a grievance to the public as the Royal Oak
lottery.'

'Why then,' said I, 'since they have served me so affrontively, and
you have given me such a hopeful character of 'em, I'll lend them a few
of my good wishes to revenge myself of their rudeness to me.

> 'May the cockroach and the moth
> Eat such holes in their cloth
> That the prime cost may never return in;
> But must all be laid by
> For a black rusty dye
> Fit for deadmongers' coachmen to mourn in!

> 'May their second-hand stocks
> Of coats, breeches and cloaks
> Hang by till they're quite out of fashion;
> And, like usurers' bags,
> May they rot into rags
> And provoke the damned knaves to a passion!

'May their tailors never trust,
Nor their servants prove just,
And their wives and their families vex 'em.
May their foreheads all ache
And their debtors all break,
And their consciences daily perplex 'em!

'With their whores may they sport
Till their noses fall short,
And have none but a quack to come nigh 'em;
And in fluxing become
Lame, deaf, blind and dumb,
That a man may walk quietly by 'em!'

Having thus taken our farewell of those hempen-looked tormentors, we strolled along till we came into a corner, where the image of a bear stood out upon a signpost, perked up on his arse, with a great faggot-bat in his claws so that he looked like one of the City waits playing upon the double-curtal. Beneath the effigies of His Ugliness a parcel of swine lay couchant in the dirt, attended with a guard of lousy ragamuffins with one hand in their necks and the other in their codpieces, looking like some of the Devil's drovers who had brought his hogs to a fair market, and smelling as frowzy, together with their swine, as so many flitches of rusty bacon in hot weather, or Bruin's bedchamber in the beargarden.

We jogged on from thence, to relieve our noses from their sweaty feet and nasty jackets, that out-stunk a dog kennel, and crossed over, fetlock deep in mud and filthiness, to the sheep-pens, where a parcel of dirty mongrels did the drudgery of their worse-looked masters, and reduced each straggling innocent to his proper order and decorum. Butchers were here as busy as brokers upon 'Change, and were groping their wares with as much caution, to know whether they were sound and wholesome, as a prudent sportsman would a new she-acquaintance of a loose conversation. Money, in every house, seemed to be a plentiful commodity; for every russet-coloured clown was either paying or receiving, to the great uneasiness of such who passed by and wanted it. We walked on till we came to the end of a little stinking lane, which my friend told me was Chick Lane, where measly pork and neck-beef stood out in wooden platters, adorned with carrots, and garnished with the leaves of marigolds, and where carriers and drovers sat in public view, stuffing their insatiate appetites with greasy swines' flesh, till the fat drivelled down from the corners of their mouths, as spittle from the lips of a changeling.

Having now seen all the market could afford, we crossed the Rounds and went into a lofty cloister, which my friend told me was the Lame Hospital, where a parcel of wretches were hopping about by the assistance of their crutches, like so many Lincoln's Inn Field mumpers drawing into a body to attack the coach of some charitable lord. Women were here almost as troublesome as the Long Lane clickers, and were so importunate with us to have some dealings with them that we had much ado to forbear handling their commodities. I looked about me and could not forbear taking notice of two things, viz., the prettiness of the place, and the homeliness of the women. 'Sure,' said I, 'the noblemen never come hither to choose themselves mistresses, for, I protest, I can scarce see one among them handsome enough to make a wife for a Moorfields conjurer.'

As many names were pencilled out upon the walls as if there had been the genealogy of the Twelve Tribes, or a public register of all the topping cuckolds in the City. I asked my friend the meaning of this long catalogue of esquires and worships. He told me, 'They were the names of the benefactors, ostentatiously set up, that every passenger might see what a number of charitable Lord Mayors and Aldermen we have had in our famous metropolis. And, indeed, it was politically done by the Governors, for it is a great encouragement for others who glory in their good deeds to do the like. If it was not for seeing their names in great letters, to vainly beget amongst men an opinion of their piety, they would no more dispose of a groat to charitable uses than they would give a portion to a daughter who had pleased herself in the choice of a husband, without the consent of her father. You may imagine by the number of the names, it is largely endowed, there being several branches belonging to the same foundation, as Kingsland Hospital, and St Thomas's in Southwark.' 'And pray,' said I, 'what are these hospitals for?' My friend answered, 'For the receiving of sick and lame soldiers and seamen, and other poor wretches that can make interest, and here they keep 'em upon water gruel and milk porridge till they are dead or well, and turn 'em either into this wide world, or the next, about their business.'

We went from thence through a narrow entry, which led us by a parcel of diminutive shops, where some were buying gloves, some smoking tobacco, others drinking brandy, and from thence into a famous piazza, where one was selling of toys, another turning of nutcrackers, a third, with a pair of dividers, marking out such a parcel of tringam-trangams, to understand the right use of which is enough to puzzle the brains of an Aesculapius. From thence we passed into another cloister, whose rusty walls and obsolete ornaments denoted a great antiquity, where abundance of little children, in blue jackets and kite-lanterned caps were very busy at their several recreations.

'This,' says my friend, 'was originally founded by Edward the Sixth for the education of poor children, but has been largely improved since by additional gifts, and is one of the noblest foundations in England. No youths can have the advantage of a better education than is here allowed them. They are afterwards provided for according as they're qualified, being sent either to sea, trades, or the university.

There is a ridiculous story reported, and credited by many people, which is that a gentlewoman, possessed of great riches when she came to die, gave her whole estate to this hospital, leaving behind her a poor sister for whom she neglected to make any provision. She, having the expectancy of the estate after the other's decease, and finding herself unhappily disappointed, reflecting upon her unfortunate condition and the unkindness of her sister, broke her heart. And upon her deathbed she rashly pronounced the curse of some distemper always to attend the hospital. Ever since that time it has always been subject to the itch. But I look upon this tale to be very fabulous; for, indeed, it would be very wonderful that so many hundred children, though looked after with all the cleanliness imaginable, should at any time be all free from those distempers to which they are chiefly incident.'

After we had taken a turn round the cloister we made our egress towards Newgate Street, in order to pay a visit to Physicians' College, and some other neighbouring places; an account of which I shall defer till my next.

VI

WE NOW PROCEEDED to survey Physicians' College, which we found illustrated with so lofty and large a portico that when we had entered it we were no more in proportion to the spacious lantern o'er our heads than a cricket to a biscuit-baker's oven, or Tom Thumb to a pudding-bowl.

'Pray,' said I, 'what is the cause of that great painted tub that stands upon wheels? It looks as if it were designed as a whimsical cottage for some maggot-brained Diogenes. I hope there are no such fantastical humorists among this learned society?' 'No, no,' replied my friend, 'you are much beside the cushion; that engine is a kind of water syringe, designed to cure such houses by injection that are under an inflammation. From this a learned physician of these times took up a new notion of curing a gonorrhea, till by the practice of his upstart measures he has poxed half the town, to the great satisfaction of his fraternity, but so much to the plague and terror of his patients that it is believed fallen noses will be as much in fashion about Soho and Piccadilly in a little time, as scars amongst prize-fighters, or short snouts amongst ladies' lapdogs.' 'Pray,' said I, 'explain your allegory. I do not readily understand what you mean by your syringe, &c.' 'Why, if you must have it in plain terms,' says he, 'that which I termed so, is a device to cast water into houses that by accident have taken fire, from whence, I suppose, the doctor undertook to extinguish after the like manner all venereal fires that had unhappily taken hold of the instruments of generation.'

'There are a couple of fine statues, placed opposite to each other, pray who do they represent?' 'The one,' says my friend, 'is the King's, and the other's that worthy, charitable good Christian, Sir John Cutler's, who, as a means, I suppose, the better to secure his own health and long life, by the faithful assistance of this anti-mortal society, was in his lifetime so great a benefactor to this learned corporation that when the fire in '66 had consumed their college in Amen Corner, and the ground being holden but by lease, he lent them money to purchase this foundation, and to build thereon this stately edifice. They, through the mistaken hopes they had of his generosity, received it from him as a gift, and to express their gratitude for so bountiful a donation, publicly returned him thanks for what the muddling Croesus never intended to give 'em, dedicating several books to him, wherein, like poor poets, they expressed their unparalleled veneration to so liberal a patron. At last their flatteries so provoked the penurious temper of the money-loving gentleman, that he thanked them kindly for their thanks, and praised them highly for their praises; but told them plainly, he feared there was a misunderstanding between them, for he had not given them a groat, as he knew on, but only assisted them at an unhappy juncture with the loan of some money, to recover their ancient grandeur, then buried in ashes. And he expected in a little time they would make a just return of it. This disappointment so astonished the Galenian fraternity that they looked as disconsolate one upon another as so many broken gamesters at a hazard table, hoping His Worship would take it into his further consideration, and not give them so bitter a pill to purge out the grateful relish of so sweet an expectancy as they had hitherto been under. A little time after this conference had passed between 'em, the pale-faced Master of the Ceremonies conducted the old gentleman to the next world, in mercy to his surviving relations who have since demanded the money from the college, the dread of refunding which hath put some of them into as loose a condition as if they had lately fed upon nothing but their own physic.'

'What privileges,' said I, 'extraordinary are granted to them in their charter, above what are held by other physicians, who are not of their society?' 'Many,' replied my friend, 'and these in particular, viz., no person, though a graduate in physic of Oxford or Cambridge, and a man of more learning, judgement and experience than one half of their members, shall have the liberty of practising in, or within seven miles of, London, without licence under the College seal, or in any other part of England, if they have not taken some degree at one of the universities. They have also power to administer an oath which they know by experience is as practicable to be broke the next day as 'tis to be taken. They can likewise fine and imprison offenders in the science of physic and all such who presume to cure a patient, when they have given 'em over, though by more excellent methods than ever were known to their ignorance.

'They have also the privilege of making by-laws, for the interest of themselves and the injury of the public, and can purchase lands in right of the corporation, if they could but find money to pay for 'em. They have authority to examine the medicines in all apothecaries' shops, to judge of the wholesomeness and goodness of many drugs and compositions they never yet understood. They are likewise exempt from troublesome offices, as jurymen, constables, &c., being no ways obliged to keep watch or ward, except with a rich patient, where they are assured to be well paid for their labour. They have also the liberty to kill as many as they please, provided they do it *secundum artem*, and no law shall call them to account. They are freed from the bearing of arms, or providing of ammunition, except pill, bolus, or potion, or such as destroy the body of sick persons they know not how to cure. Any member of the College may practise surgery, if he will but take the pains to understand it.

'They lately committed a more able physician than themselves without bail or mainprize, for malpractice in curing a woman of a dangerous ulcer in her bladder by the use of cantharides, which they affirm not fit for internal application, though the patient's life was saved by taking it; which shows they hold it a greater crime to cure out of the common method, than it is to kill in it. And in prosecuting their antagonist for the contempt of Galen and Hippocrates, they charged him for the doing that good which they themselves wanted either the will or knowledge to perform, and thus made themselves all fools in attempting to prove the other a knave, who procured his discharge at the Queen's Bench Bar, without a trial, and now sues them for false imprisonment; having also informed against 'em in the Crown Office, as common disturbers.

'They rail mightily in their writings against the ignorance of quacks and mountebanks, yet, for the sake of lucre, they license all the cozening pretenders about town, or they could not practise. This shows it is by their toleration that the people are cheated out of their lives and money. And yet they think themselves so honest as to be no ways answerable for this public injury, as if they could not kill people fast enough themselves, but must depute all the physical knaves in the town to be Death's journeymen. Thus do they license what they ought carefully to suppress, and practise themselves what they blame and condemn in others. And that the town may not be deceived by apothecaries, they have made themselves medicine-mongers, under a pretence of serving the public with more faithful preparations. In order to persuade the world to a belief of this, they have published bills where, in the quacks' dialect, they tell you the poor shall be supplied for nothing; but whoever is so needy as to make a challenge of their promise empty-handed, will find, according to the mountebanks' saying, "No money, no cure!" The disposal of their medicines they leave to a boy's management, who scarce knows

mercurius dulcis from white sugar, or mint-water from aqua fortis.
People are likely to be well served, and prescriptions truly observed, by
such an agent.'

From thence my friend conducted me to Bridewell, being Court day,
to give me the diversion of seeing the lechery of some town ladies
cooled by a cat-o'-nine-tails. But in our passage thither meeting with
some remarkable accidents, I think it may contribute something to the
reader's satisfaction to give a rehearsal of them.

As we came down Ludgate Hill, a couple of town bullies (as I
suppose, by their behaviour) met each other. 'Damn ye, sir,' says one,
'why did you not meet me yesterday morning according to appointment?'
'Damn you, sir, for a cowardly pimp,' replied the other. 'I was there and
waited till I was wet to the skin, and you never came at me.' 'You lie
like a villain,' says t'other; 'I was there, and stayed the time of a
gentleman, and draw now, and give me satisfaction like a man of honour,
or I'll cut your ears off.' 'You see,' says the valiant adversary, 'I have
not my fighting sword on, and hope you are a man of more honour than
to take the advantage of a gentleman.' 'Then go home and fetch it,' says
Don Furioso, 'like a man of mettle, and meet me within the hour in the
Queen's Bench Walks in the Temple, or the next time I see you, by
Jove's thunderbolts, I will pink as many eyelet-holes in your skin as you
have buttonholes in your coat, and therefore have a care how you
trespass upon my patience.' 'Upon the reputation of a gentleman, I will
punctually meet you at your time and place,' replied the other, and so
they parted.

> Bullies, like dunghill cocks, will strut and crow,
> But few or none dare stand a sparring blow.
> So does the peevish mongrel take delight
> To bark and snarl, show teeth, but dare not bite;
> Oft mischief makes, but still the danger shuns;
> If matched, he fawns, or else turns tail and runs.
> So cowards often do their swords unsheath,
> But cowed and daunted with the fear of death
> Thus tamely show their blades, as fearful curs their teeth.

We moved on till we came to Fleet Bridge, where nuts, gingerbread,
oranges and oysters, lay piled up in movable shops that run upon wheels,
attended by ill-looking fellows, some with but one eye, and others

without noses. Over against these stood a parcel of trugmoldies in straw hats and flat-caps, selling socks and furmety, nightcaps and plum-pudding. Just as we passed by, a feud was kindling between two rival females who, from the brimstone of lust, had blown up such a fire of jealousy between 'em that one called the other adulterous bitch, and charged her with lying with her husband and robbing her of his love. Then falling into tears, she expressed herself further in these words: 'Have I lent you the money out of my pocket, the gown off my back, and my petticoat off my arse, to be thus ungratefully rewarded? You know, hussy, I have given you the very bread out of my mouth, but before you shall take my bedfellow from my belly, you whore, I'll tear your eyes out.' And then with teeth and nails she made a violent assault upon her rival, who roared out for help, crying out that she was quick with child. The mob, hearing her plead her belly, were moved to compassion, and so parted 'em, their coifs having received the greatest damage in the fray.

Just as the squabble was ended, before the rabble was dispersed, who should be stumbling along upon his hidebound prancer, but one of the horse-mountebanks, who, seeing so rare an opportunity to hold forth to a congregation already assembled, spurred up his foundered Pegasus, and, halting in the middle of the crowd, plucked out a packet of universal hodgepodge, and thus began an oration to the listening herd:

'Gentlemen, you that have a mind to be mindful of preserving a sound mind in a sound body, that is, as the learned physician, Doctor Honorificicabilitudinitatibusque has it *manus sanaque in cobile sanaquorum*, may here at the expense of sixpence, furnish himself with a parcel, which though 'tis but small, yet containeth mighty things of great use, and wonderful operation in the bodies of mankind, against all distempers, whether homogeneal or complicated; whether derived from your parents, got by infection, or proceeding from an ill-habit of your own body.

'In the first place, gentlemen, I here present you with a little inconsiderable pill to look at; you see not much bigger than a corn of pepper. Yet is this diminutive panpharmacon so powerful in effect, and of such excellent virtues, that if you have twenty distempers lurking in the mass of blood, it shall give you just twenty stools, and every time it operates it carries off a distemper, but if your blood's wholesome, and your body sound, it will work with you no more than the same quantity of gingerbread. I therefore call it, from its admirable qualities, *Pillula Tondobula*, which signifies in the Greek, the Touchstone of Nature. For by taking this pill, you will truly discover what state of health or infirmity your constitution is then under.

'In the next place, gentlemen, I present you with an excellent outward application, called a plaster, good against all green wounds, old fistulas and ulcers, pains and aches in either head, limbs or bowels, contusions, tumours or Queen's evil, sprains, fractures or dislocations, or any hurts whatsoever, received either by sword, cane or gunshot, knife, saw or hatchet, hammer, nail or tenterhook, fire, blast or gunpowder, &c. It will continue its virtue beyond credit, and be as useful seven years hence as at this present moment, that you may lend it to your neighbours in the time of distress and affliction, and when it has performed forty cures 'twill be ne'er the worse, but still retain its integrity. *Probatum est.*

'The next unparalleled medicine contained in this my little sixpenny beneficence is an admirable powder, good to fortify the stomach against all infections, unwholesome damps, malignant effluvia that arise from putrid bodies, and the like. It also is a rare cordial to strengthen and cheer the heart under any misfortune and will procure such an appetite, being drunk a little before dinner, that a man of an ordinary stomach may eat a pound of Suffolk cheese, and twice the quantity of rye bread, and still have as good an appetite to a sirloin of roast beef as if he had not eaten a bit in a fortnight. This most excellent preparation is also the most powerful antiverminous medicine ever given in England, Scotland, France, or Ireland, and if either yourselves, or your children are troubled with that epidemical distemper, worms, which destroy more bodies than either plague, pestilence or famine, give or take this, infused in a little warm ale, instead of wormseed and treacle, and you will find these devouring vermin, these death's agents, that burrow in our bodies as rabbits in a warren, come creeping out at both ends, like lice out of a beggar's doublet when he hangs it in the sunshine. It is also a most rare dentifrice, and cleanses all foul, and fastens all loose, teeth to a miracle. This powder I call my *Pulvis Lubberdatus*, because in my travels I first gave it amongst the Dutch, when I was a student at Leyden, where, gentlemen, I would have you to know, I took my degrees, although I expose myself to the world's censures by appearing thus public, for the good of my own country which at all times, it's well known, I have been very ready to serve.

'The last, and most useful medicine prepared throughout the whole universe, is this my Orvietan whose virtues are such, it will, equally with the unicorn's horn, expel the rankest poison. It is absolutely necessary for all persons to carry in their pockets, for who knows how the passions of love, fear, anger, despair, jealousy, or the like, by the subtle insinuation of Satan who is watchful of all opportunities, may prevail upon you to offer violence to your most precious lives, by taking ratsbane, mercury, arsenic, opium and the like. Why, who, I say would be without a medicine to relieve themselves under such misfortunes, which would not only hurry 'em to death, but to damnation. It is also the best sudorific, in all colds and fevers that ever can possibly be taken, working out the distemper by gentle perspiration, and fortifies the heart against all fainting and swooning, also the brains against all dizziness and swimming, and is, upon the word of a physician, the greatest cordial the most eminent doctor can prescribe or patients take.

'I do assure you, gentlemen, the College of Physicians offered to admit me as a member of their society if I would have made but a discovery only to themselves of this most excellent and admirable secret. "No, hold you me there a little, gentlemen," said I, "I shall then make you as wise as myself, and should I do that, pray who would be a fool then?" Why, truly myself, for I would have you to know, gentlemen, I have more manners than to reflect upon such a learned society.'

This piece of impudence so tickled the ears of the brainless multitude that they began with as much eagerness to untie their purses, and the corners of their handkerchiefs, and to be as free of their pence, as they usually are to buy apples by the pound, or to purchase the sight of a puppet-show, that it was as much as ever the doctor could do to deliver out his physic fast enough. His industrious lies took as well with the mob as a treasonable ballad, or a disgusted statesman's pamphlet upon the turn of a government. Thus they continued flinging away their money, showing there were fools of all ages, from sixty to sixteen, many of them looking as if they could scarce command as much more till next Saturday night they received their wages; till at last, either the doctor broke the crowd of their money, or the crowd the doctor of his physic, I know not which. Then away he trotted on horseback with their pence, and left his patients to trudge away on foot with his packets.

'Pray,' says my friend, 'what do you think? Is it not a shame to our English physicians to suffer such a parcel of ignorant, illiterate and impudent vagabonds to cozen poor innocent wretches out of their money, publicly in the streets, who want it themselves to purchase bread and necessaries? I can't imagine what can be urged as an excuse for the tolerating such rascals to drain the pockets of the poor by preposterous lies, jumbled into a senseless cant, to persuade the people to believe them really that, to which they are only a scandal. Therefore, as a means to dissuade the public from their foolish opinion of these empirical vagabonds or their medicines, which are only prepared from a parcel of perished drugs ground promiscuously together, without art or rule, and so made up into sundry sorts of species to allure the ignorant, I have here given a true portraiture of such a scandalous fellow, who makes it his business to cheat the common people by his lying assertions and fallacious insinuations not only out of their money, but often out of their health, which is far more valuable.

A Character of a Quack

> A shame to art, to learning, and to sense,
> A foe to virtue, friend to impudence,
> Wanting in Nature's gift, and Heaven's grace,
> An object scandalous to human race.
> A spurious breed by some Jack Adams 'got,
> Born of some common, monstrous God-knows-what.
> Into the world no woman sure could bring
> So vile a birth, such an un-manlike thing.
> Trained from his cradle up in vice's school,
> To tumble, dance the rope, and play the fool.
> Thus learned, he strolls with some illit'rate quack,
> Till, by long travels, he acquires the knack
> To make the sweepings of a drugster's shop
> Into some unknown universal slop
> On which some senseless title he bestows,
> Though what is in't, nor buy'r or seller knows.
> Then lazy grown, he doth his booth forsake,
> Quitting the rope or hoop, and so turns quack.
> Thus by base means to live, does worse pursue
> And gulls the poor of life and money too.

From thence we took a turn down by the Ditch Side, I desiring my friend to inform me what great advantages this costly brook contributed to the town, to countervail the expense of seventy-four thousand pounds, which, I read in a very credible author, was the charge of its making. He told me he was wholly unacquainted with any, unless it was now and then to bring up a few chaldron of coals to two or three peddling fuel merchants, who sell them never the cheaper to the poor for such a convenience. 'And as for those cellars you see on each side, designed for warehouses, they are rendered by their dampness so unfit for that purpose that they are wholly useless, except for lightermen to lay their tails in, or to harbour frogs, toads and other vermin. The greatest good that ever I heard it did was to the undertaker, who is bound to acknowledge he has found better fishing in that muddy stream than ever he did in clear water.'

We then turned into the gate of a stately edifice which my friend told me was Bridewell. At my first entrance, it seemed to me rather a prince's palace than a house of correction, till, gazing round me, I saw in a large room a parcel of ill-looking mortals stripped to their shirts like hay-makers, pounding a pernicious weed, which I had thought from their unlucky aspects seemed to threaten their destruction. 'These,' said I, to my friend, 'I suppose, are the offenders at work. Pray what do you think their crimes may be?' 'Truly,' said he, 'I cannot tell you; but if you have a mind to know, ask any of them their offence, and they will soon satisfy you.'

'Prithee, friend,' said I to a surly bull-necked fellow who was thumping as lazily at his wooden anvil as a ship-carpenter at a log in the Queen's Yard at Deptford, 'what are you confined to this labour for?' My hempen operator, leering over his shoulder, cast at me one of his hanging looks which so frightened me that I stepped back, for fear he should have knocked me on the head with his beetle. 'Why, if you must know, Mr Tickle-tail,' says he, taking me, as I believe, being in black, for some country pedagogue, 'I was committed hither by Justice Clodpate, for saying I had rather hear a blackbird whistle "Walsingham" or a peacock scream against foul weather, than a parson talk nonsense in a church, or a fool talk Latin in a coffee-house. And I'll be judged by you, that are a man of judgement, whether in all I said there be one word of treason to deserve a whipping-post.' The impudence of this canary-bird so dashed me out of countenance, together with this unexpected answer, that, like a man surfeited with his mistress's favours, I had nothing to say, but heartily wished myself well out of their company. And as we were turning back to avoid their further sauciness another calls to me, 'Hark you, master in black, of the same colour with the Devil, can you tell me how many thumps of this hammer will soften the hemp so as to make a halter fit easy if a man should have occasion to wear one?' A third cried out, 'I hope, gentlemen, you will be so generous to give us something to drink, for you don't know but we may be hard at work for you.'

We were glad, with what expedition we could, to escape their impudence, and so turned from the work-room to the Common Side, or place of confinement where they are locked up at night, through the frightful grates of which uncomfortable apartment a ghastly skeleton stood peeping, whose terrible aspect was so surprising that I thought some power immortal had imprisoned Death, that the world might live forever. I could not speak to him without dread or danger, lest when his lips opened to give me an answer he should poison the air with his contagious breath, and communicate to me the same pestilence which had brought his infected body to such a dismal anatomy. Yet moved with pity towards so languishing an object, I began to enquire into the causes of his sad appearance. He, after a penitential look that called for mercy and compassion, with much difficulty raised his feeble voice a degree above silence, and told me he had been sick six weeks under that miserable confinement, and had nothing to comfort him but bread and water, with now and then the refreshment of a little small beer. I asked him further what offence he had committed that brought him under this unhappiness. To which he answered, he had been a great while discharged of all that was charged against him, and was detained only for his fees, which, for want of friends, being a stranger in the town, he was totally unable to raise. I asked him what his fees amounted to. He told me five groats. Bless me! thought I, what a rigorous, uncharitable thing is this, that so noble a gift, intended when first given to so good an end, should be thus perverted! And what was designed to prevent people's falling into misery through laziness or ill-courses should now be so corrupted by such unchristian confinement as to starve a poor wretch because he wants money to satisfy the demands of a mercenary Cerberus, when discharged of the prison by the court! Such severe, nay barbarous, usage is a shame to our laws, an unhappiness to our nation, and a scandal to Christianity.

From thence we turned into another court, the buildings being, like the former, magnificently noble. There straight before us was another grate, which proved the women's apartment. We followed our noses and walked up to take a view of the ladies, who we found were shut up as close as nuns but, like so many slaves, were under the care and direction of an overseer, who walked about with a very flexible weapon of offence, to correct such hempen journeywomen as were unhappily troubled with the spirit of idleness. These smelt as frowzy as so many goats in a Welsh gentleman's stable, or rather a litter of piss-tail children under the care of a parish nurse, and looked with as much modesty as so many Newgate Saints canonized at the Old Bailey. They were all as cheerful over their shameful drudgery, notwithstanding their miserable circumstances, as so many jolly Crispins in a garret o'er St Hugh's bones, or Vulcans in a cellar o'er the merry clinks of the sledge and anvil. Some seemed so very young that I thought it very strange they should know sin enough, at those years, to bring them so early into a state of misery. Others were so old that one would think the dread of the grave, and thoughts of futurity, were sufficient to reclaim 'em from all vice, had they been trained up never so wickedly. Some between both, in the meridian of their years, were very pretty, but seemed so very lewd that, Messalina-like, they might be tired, but never satisfied.

'Pray, sir,' says one of them, 'how do you like us? You look very wishfully upon us. What do you think of us?' 'Why, truly,' said I, 'I think you have done something to deserve this punishment, or else you would not be here.' To which she replied, 'If you'll believe me, without blushing I'll tell you the truth. I happened to live with an old scrivener, and when my mistress was out of the way he used to tickle my lips with a pen-feather. And at last she catched us, and had me before Justice Overdo, who committed me hither, where I have had more lashes on my poor back than ever my belly deserved since I first scattered my virginity.'

'Don't believe her, master,' cries another, 'she's as arrant a strumpet as ever earned her living at twopence a bout, and was committed hither for lying so long upon her back that her rump grew to the bottom sheet, so that she could not rise again. She's one of Posture Moll's scholars and can show you how the watermen shoot London Bridge, or how the lawyers go to Westminster.'

'What do you think,' replies the other, 'this buttocking brimstone came hither for? I'll tell you, master,' says she, 'because I believe you have no good guess with you, viz., 'twas for picking a countryman's pocket of his pouch and hiding it in her oven. But when she came to be searched, the fool, having forgot to take up the strings, was discovered in her roguery, and sent here to be lashed. Does she not deserve it, sir, for trusting her money in a box that has neither lid nor bottom to it?'

I could not but wonder to hear this impudence from women, more especially when I considered they were under such shame, misery and punishment, which a man might reasonably imagine would work upon the most corrupt minds, and make them abominate those base practices which brought 'em to this unhappiness.

Being now both tired with, and amazed at, the confidence and loose behaviour of these degenerate wretches, who had neither sense of grace, knowledge of virtue, fear of shame, or dread of misery, my friend re-conducted me back into the first quadrangle, and led me up a pair of stairs into a spacious chamber, where the Court was sitting in great grandeur and order. A grave gentleman whose awful looks bespoke him some honourable citizen, was mounted in the judgement seat, armed with a hammer, like a 'Change broker at Lloyd's Coffee House when selling goods by inch of candle, and a woman under the lash in the next room, where folding doors were opened so that the whole Court might see the punishment inflicted. At last down went the hammer, and the scourging ceased. I protest, till I was undeceived, I thought the offenders had been Popish penitents who, by the delusion of their priests, were drawn thither to buy lashes by auction. The honourable Court, I observed, were chiefly attended by fellows in blue coats, and women in blue aprons. Another accusation being then delivered by a flat-cap against a poor wench, who had no friend to speak in her behalf, proclamation was made, viz.: 'All you who are willing E___th T____ll should have present punishment, pray hold up your hands.' Which was done accordingly, and then she was ordered the civility of the house, and was forced to show her tender back and tempting bubbies to the grave sages of the august assembly, who were moved by her modest mien, together with the whiteness of her skin, to give her but gentle correction.

Finding little knowledge to be gained from their proceedings, and less pleasure and satisfaction from their punishments, my friend and I thought it better to retire, and leave them to flog on till the accusers had satisfied their revenge and the spectators their curiosity.

'Now,' says my friend, 'pray give me your thoughts of what you have seen, whether you think this sort of correction is a proper method to reform women from their vicious practices, or not.' 'Why, truly,' said I, 'if I must deliver my opinion according to my real sentiments, I only conceive it makes many whores, but that it can in no measure reclaim 'em. And these are my reasons:

'First. If a girl of thirteen or fourteen years of age, as I have seen some here, either through the ignorance or childishness of their youth, or unhappiness of a stubborn temper, should be guilty of negligence in their business, or prove headstrong, humoursome, or obstinate, and through an ungovernable temper take pleasure to do things in disobedience to the will of their master or mistress, or be guilty of a trifling wrong or injury through inadvertence, they have power at home to give them reasonable correction, without exposing 'em to this shame and scandal, never to be washed off by the most reformed life imaginable. This unhappy stain makes them always shunned by virtuous and good people, who will neither entertain a servant, nor admit of a companion, under this disparagement, the one being fearful of their goods, and the other of their reputation. So the poor wretch, by her necessity, is at last driven into the hands of ill persons and forced to betake herself to bad conversation, till she is insensibly corrupted and made fit for all wickedness.

'Secondly, I think it a shameful indecency for a woman to expose her naked body to the sight of men and boys, as if it were designed rather to feast the eyes of the spectators, or stir up the beastly appetites of lascivious persons, than to correct vice or reform manners. Therefore I think it both more modest and more reasonable they should receive their punishment in the view of women only, and by the hand of their own sex.

'Thirdly, as their bodies by nature are more tender, and their constitution allowed more weak, we ought to show them more mercy, and not punish 'em with such dog-like usage, unless their crimes are capital.'

'I believe,' replied my friend, 'you are aiming to curry favour with the fair sex. This lecture to a Town lady, if you had a mind to be wicked, would save you money in your pocket, though indeed, what you have urged seems no more than reasonable. I think I have now showed you all this place affords, so we'll take our leaves of it. But I hope you will give us a few lines upon it, and then we'll seek some new diversion.' I could not but gratify my friend's request, and what I did to oblige him, I here present unto the reader.

On Bridewell

'Twas once the palace of a prince,
    If we may books confide in;
But given was, by him long since,
    For vagrants to reside in.

The crumbs that from his table fell,
　　Once made the poor the fatter;
But those that in its confines dwell,
　　Now feed on bread and water.

No ven'son now whereon to dine,
　　No fricassees nor hashes;
No balls, no merriment, nor wine;
　　But woeful tears and slashes.

No prince or peers to make a feast,
　　No kettledrums or trumpets,
But are become a shameful nest
　　Of vagabonds and strumpets.

Where once the king and nobles sat
　　In all their pomp and splendour,
Grave City grandeur nods its pate
　　And threatens each offender.

Unhappy thy ignoble doom
　　Where greatness once resorted,
Now hemp and labour fills each room
　　Where lords and ladies sported.

　　We now departed Bridewell, and willing to refresh ourselves with the
smoking of one pipe, turned into a neighbouring coffee-house where,
glancing upon an old *Flying Post*, we put ourselves in mind of my Dame
Butterfield's invitation to her Essex calf and bacon, with her six brass
horns to accommodate sportsmen with the delightful harmony of hunting.
And believing a relation of this unusual feast might be welcome to the
public, my friend and I agreed to move with the stream, and give
ourselves a country walk to the place appointed. I am sensible it is
something of a digression, or rather a deviation from the title, but though
the feast was in the country, yet the guests were Londoners, and therefore
what we shall observe among 'em may be reasonably admitted.
　　Fearing old Time should slide insensibly away and cut short our
intended pastime, we smoked our pipes with greater expedition in order
to proceed on our journey, which we began about eleven o'clock. And

marching through Cheapside we found half the people we either met or overtook equipped for hunting, walking backwards and forwards, as I suppose, to show one another their accoutrements. The City beaus were in boots as black as jet, which shone, by much rubbing, like a stick of ebony, their heels armed with spurs (those travelling weapons to defend the rider from the laziness of his horse) so carefully preserved bright in a box of cotton that they dazzled in the eyes of each beholder like a piece of looking-glass in the sunshine. Their waists were hooped round with Turkey leather belts, at which hung a bayonet or short scimitar, in order to cut their mistresses' names upon the trees of the forest. In the right hand was a whip, mounted against the breast like the sceptre of a king's statue upon the 'Change, and their heads were adorned with twisted wigs and crowned with edged castors. They were all over in such prim and order that you could scare distinguish them from gentlemen. Amongst 'em were many ladies of the same quality, tied up in safeguards so beknotted with twopenny taffeta that a man might guess, by their finery, their fathers to be ribbon weavers.

We crowded along, mixed among the herd, and could not but fancy the major part of the citizens were scampering out of town to avoid the horse-plague. We moved forward without any discontinuance of our perambulation, till we came to the Globe at Mile End, where a precious mortal made us a shorthand compliment, and gave us an invitation to a sirloin of roast beef, out of which corroborating food we renewed our lives, and after strengthening our spirits with a flask of rare claret, we took leave of my honest landlord, and so proceeded.

By this time the road was full of passengers, everyone furnished with no small appetite to veal and bacon. Citizens in crowds, upon pads, hackneys and hunters, all upon the tittup, as if he who rode not a gallop was to forfeit his horse. Some spurred on with such speed and cheerfulness as if they intended never to come back again; some double, some single. Every now and then dropped a lady from her pillion, or another from her side-saddle, some showing the Milky Way to bliss, others their bugbears to the company, which, though it made them blush, it made us merry. Sometimes a beau would tumble and daub his boots, which to show his neatness he would clean with his handkerchief.

Horses, coaches, carts, wagons and tumbrels filled the roads, as if the whole town had been going to encamp; all occupied by men, women and children, rich, poor, gentle and simple, having all travelling conveniences suitable to their quality. In this order did we march, like Aaron's proselytes to worship the calf, till we came to the new-raised fabric called Mob's Hole, where the beast was to be eaten. The house was so surrounded with the mobility that it looked like the cow-keeper's Welsh camp, consisting of a number of both sexes of all sorts and sizes, sufficient, instead of one, to have eaten all the calves in Essex. We pressed hard to get into the house, which we found so full that, when I was in, what with the smell of sweat, stinking breaths and tobacco, I thought there was but a few gasps between this place and eternity. Some were dancing to a bagpipe, others whistling to a bass-viol, two fiddlers scraping 'Lilliburlero,' my Lord Mayor's delight, upon a couple of cracked crowds, and an old Oliverian trooper farting upon a trumpet.

My friend and I, being willing to get as far out of the noise as we could, climbed up into a garret, where we found a single lady in her safeguard rectifying her commode from the abuses of the wind. I thought myself obliged in civility to make some little use of so fair an opportunity, and accordingly welcomed her to Mob's Hole, and at last talked her into so compliant a humour that I perceived she was as willing to give us her company as we could be to ask it, till we had brought ourselves in danger of entailing that trouble and expense upon ourselves, which, to tell you the truth, we thought it was prudent to avoid. So by a cooler sort of treatment than we first began with, we gave her delicious ladyship some reasons to believe she might go a little further and fare better. Accordingly she took her leave and squeezed downstairs, to show her marmoset looks and inviting airiness upon the parade where ragtag and bobtail were promiscuously jumbled amongst City quality from beau to booby, and the merchant's lady to the thumb-ringed ale-wife.

Being now left by ourselves, in a room not much bigger than a hogshead, furnished with nothing but a little bedstead, and that of an uneasy height to sit on, we found, notwithstanding our tedious walk of seven long miles, at our journey's end we had little likelihood of a resting-place, but must either be forced to lie down like dogs, or lean like elephants, and have as much difficulty to get a little drink as, by reason of their number, a rabble do at a conduit that runs wine upon a state holiday.

When, with abundance of pains, and as much patience, we had liquored our throats with two or three slender-bodied mugs of country guzzle, we jostled down two narrow pair of stairs, and increased the numberless troop of grazing animals, who were differently disposed to divers exercises, some cramming down veal and bacon to allay the fury of their cormorant appetites, having no table-cloth but grass, or seats but ground; others projecting better for their ease had made a table of a horse-block, and blowed their noses in the same napkins with which they wiped their fingers. Some had climbed into an arbour on the top of an old tree, where they sat whooping and hollering like so many owls, but could get nobody near 'em to bring 'em either drink or victuals. Some ladies sat in their coaches masked, wanting, I suppose, to give some cully a cast home, as they could not pay the coachman. Others were on horseback, barefaced, conducted thither by their fathers' apprentices, and many hundreds of both sexes on foot, some smoking, some drinking, others cursing and swearing through want of that refreshment which the more industrious spectators had very painfully procured.

In the interim, as we were thus walking to take notice of the sundry humours and transactions of the buzzing multitude, came four merry dames in a coach, and alighted by me. One was tricked up like an old maid, with a gold chain about her neck, patches on her wrinkled face, and her ill-shaped carcase splendidly set off with very gay apparel; her eyes looking angry with a hot rheum cast up into her head by the staleness of her virginity. The rest wore motherly countenances, and looked as if they had understood trap this twenty years. I welcomed them to Mob's Hole and began to entertain 'em with some talk applicable to the present juncture. At last the old gentlewoman, whom I supposed a maid, took the freedom to ask me what it was o'clock by my watch.

'Truly, madam,' said I, 'I have not one about me, but if you please to turn about, and look at the sun with those virgin's eyes of yours, a lady of your judgement may understand the hour of the day by its distance from the horizon.' Says another of 'em, 'Maybe the gentleman's watch is down and he is ashamed to show it us.' To which I replied, 'Indeed, madam, if it be, I can see nothing in your ladyship's face that will wind it up again.' 'Why, sir,' says the third, 'can faces be used to wind up watches?' 'Yes, madam,' answered I, 'such a one as I carry about me, which is made without wheels and will give such a lady as you are a better time of day, when it's standing, than other watches do when they are moving.' 'Bless me! sir,' says the fourth, 'yours is the strangest watch that ever I heard of. I wish you would be so kind as to let a body see it.' 'Truly, madam,' says I, ''tis without a case, and unfit to be plucked out in public company, or otherwise I would be very willing to oblige you.' She replied, 'I am sorry to hear it is so much out of order, but if it wants nothing but a case you don't know but I may present you with one I think 'twill fit.' I found I should be out-talked upon this subject, and was glad to make an excuse to avoid their further conversation.

From thence we went into the kitchen, built up of furzes in the open air, to behold their cookery, where the major part of the calf was roasting upon a wooden spit. Having lost two or three great slivers off his buttocks, his ribs pared to the very bone, with holes in his shoulders, each large enough to bury a Seville orange, he looked as if a kennel of hounds had every one had a snap at him. Under him lay the flitch of bacon of such an Ethiopian complexion that I should rather have guessed it the side of a blackamoor. It looked more like a cannibal's feast than a Christian entertainment. My appetite was so far from coveting a taste that I had a full meal at the very sight of their dainties, and I believe for the future I shall have as great a kindness for veal and bacon as an Anabaptist preacher has for the Church Liturgy.

Being soon glutted with the view of this unusual piece of cookery, we departed from the kitchen, and, hearing a great bustle in the upper room of an outhouse, we went upstairs to see what was the matter, where we found a poor fiddler scraping over the tune of "Now Ponder Well You Parents Dear", and a parcel of country people dancing and crying to't. The remembrance of the uncle's cruelty to the poor innocent babes, and the robin redbreast's kindness, had fixed in their very looks such signs of sorrow and compassion that their dancing seemed rather a religious worship than a merry recreation.

Having thus given ourselves a prospect of all the place afforded, we returned to Stratford, where we got a coach, and from thence to London.

VII

WHEN OUR STRATFORD tub, by the assistance of its carrionly tits of different colours, had outrun the smoothness of the road, it entered upon London stones with as frightful a rumbling as an empty hay-cart. Our leather convenience, being bound in the braces to its good behaviour, had no more sway than a funeral hearse or a country wagon, so that we were jumbled about like so many peas in a child's rattle, running, at every kennel jolt, a great hazard of a dislocation. This we endured till we were brought within Whitechapel Bars, where we alighted from our stubborn caravan, with our elbows and shoulders as black and blue as a rural Joan that had been under the pinches of an angry fairy. Our weary limbs, being rather more tired than refreshed by the thumps and tosses of our ill-contrived engine, were as unfit to move upon a rugged pavement as a gouty sinner is to halt o'er London Bridge with his boots on.

'For my part,' said I, 'if this be the pleasure of riding in a coach through London streets, may those that like it enjoy it, for it has so loosened my joints in so short a passage that I shall scarce recover my former strength this fortnight. And indeed, of the two, I would rather choose to cry mousetraps for a livelihood, than be obliged every day to be dragged about town under such uneasiness, and if the quality's coaches are as troublesome as this, I would not be bound to do their penance for their estates.' 'You must consider,' says my friend, 'you have not the right knack of humouring the coach's motion, for there is as much art in sitting in a coach finely as there is in riding the great horse, and many a younger brother has got a good fortune by his graceful lolling in his chariot, and his genteel stepping in and out when he pays a visit to her ladyship. There are a great many such qualifications amongst our true French-bred gentlemen, that are admired amongst our nicer ladies nowadays, besides the smooth dancing of a minuet, the making of a love song, the neat carving up a fowl, or the thin paring of an apple.'

'Pray, friend,' said I, 'don't let us trouble ourselves how the ladies choose their husbands, or what they do with their gallants, but consider how we shall get to the other end of town, for my pedestals are so crippled with our whimsical peregrination that I totter like a foundered horse, or an old sinner when his corns are tender.' To this, says my friend, 'You have expressed such a dislike to a coach that I know not which way to get you thither if you cannot walk it, except you can make your supporters carry you down to the Bridge, and there we may take water at the Old Swan and land at Salisbury Court. Then we shall be properly placed to proceed in our further ramble.'

I accordingly submitted to my friend's advice and hobbled down to the waterside with as much uneasiness as a badger walks upon even ground, or a bear down a hill. There a jolly grizzle-pated Charon handed us into his wherry, whipped off his short-skirted doublet, whereon was a badge to show whose fool he was, then fixed his stretcher, bid us trim the boat, and away he rowed us. But we had not swum above the length of a West Country barge before a scoundrel crew of Lambeth gardeners attacked us with such a volley of saucy nonsense that it made my eyes stare, my head ache, my tongue run, and my ears tingle.

One of them began with us after this manner: 'You couple of treacherous sons of Bridewell bitches, who are pimps to your own mothers, stallions to your sisters, and cock-bawds to the rest of your relations! You were begot by huffling, spewed up, and not born, and christened out of a chamber-pot! How dare you show your ugly faces upon the river of Thames and fright the Queen's swans from holding their heads above water!' To this our well-fed pilot, after he had cleared his voice with a 'hem', most manfully replied, 'You lousy starved crew of worm-pickers and snail-catchers! You offspring of a dunghill and brothers to a pumpkin, who can't afford butter to your cabbage, or bacon to your sprouts! You shitten rogues, who worship the fundament because you live by a turd! Who was he that sent the gardener to cut a hundred of asparagus and dug twice in his wife's parsley-bed before the good man came back again? Hold your tongues, you nitty radish-mongers, or I'll whet my needle upon my arse and sew your lips together.'

This verbal engagement was no sooner over, but another squabbling crew met us, being mostly women, who, as they passed us, gave us another salutation: 'You tailors, who pawned the gentleman's cloak to buy a wedding dinner, and afterwards sold his wife's clothes for money to fetch it out again! "Here, Timothy, fetch your mistress and I three ha'p'orth of boiled beef. See first they make good weight, then stand hard for a bit of carrot."' To this our orator, after a puff and a pull-up, being well skilled in the water dialect, made this return: 'You dirty salt-arsed brood of night-walkers and shoplifters! Which of you was it that tied her apron about her neck because she would be kissed in a night-rail, and reckoned her gallant a shilling for fouling of linen, when she had never a smock on? Have a care of your cheeks, you whores! We shall have you branded next sessions that the world may see your trade in your faces. You are lately come from the hemp and hammer. "Oh, good Sir Robert, knock! Pray, good Sir Robert, knock!"'

The next boat we met was freighted with a parcel of city shopkeepers who, being eager, like the rest, to show their acuteness of wit and admirable breeding, accosted us after this manner, viz.: 'You affidavit scoundrels, pluck the straws out of the heels of your shoes! You oats journeymen, who are you going to swear out of an estate at Westminster Hall, though you know nothing of the matter? You rogues, we shall have you in the pillory when rotten eggs are plenty! You are in a safe condition, for you may travel anywhere by water and never fear drowning!' Thus they ran on, till our spokesman stopped their mouths with this following homily: 'You cuckoldly company of whiffling, peddling, lying, overreaching, ninny-hammers! You were forced to desire some handsome bachelor to kiss your wives and beg a holiday for you, or else you would not have dared to come out today! Go, make haste home, that you may find the fowls at the fire! If I had as many horns on my head as you are forced to hide in your pockets, what a monster should I be? You little think what your wives are providing for you when you come home! Don't be angry, friends, it's many an honest man's fortune!'

Said I, 'This is a rare place for a scold to exercise her faculties and improve her talent, for I think everybody we meet is an academy of ill-language. I observe 'tis as great a penance for a modest man to go a mile upon the river as 'tis for him to run the gauntlet through an alley where the good housewives are picking oakum; bad words being as much in fashion amongst such gossips as curses at a gaming ordinary, and good words used as seldom as plain dealing among courtiers.'

By this time we were come to our proposed landing-place, where a stately edifice (the front supported by lofty columns) presented itself to our view. I enquired of my friend what magnificent Don Croesus resided in this noble and delightful mansion. He told me, nobody as he knew on, except rats and mice, and perhaps an old superannuated Jack-pudding to look after it and to take care that no decayed lover of the drama should get in and steal away the poets' pictures, and sell 'em to some uphol-sterer for Roman Emperors. I suppose there is little else to lose, except scenes, machines or some such gimcracks. 'For this,' says he, 'is one of the theatres, but now is wholly abandoned by the players and, 'tis thought, will in a little time be pulled down, if it is not bought by some of our Dissenting brethren and converted to a more pious use, that may in part atone for the sundry transgressions occasioned by the levity which the stage of late has been so greatly subject to.'

Here we took our leaves of the Lady Thames, wondering she should have so sweet a breath, considering how many stinking pills she swallows in a day. For each neighbouring tail, in contempt of her pride, defiles her peaceful surface, which unsavoury droppings the courteous dame with patience wears to adorn her smooth countenance instead of patches.

Being now landed upon terra firma, we steered our course up Salisbury Court, where every two or three steps we met some old figure or another that looked as if the Devil had robbed 'em of all their natural beauty (which, being in our Maker's image, we derive from our Creator), and had infused his own infernal spirit into their corrupt carcases, for nothing could be read but devilism in every feature. Theft, whoredom, homicide and blasphemy, peeped out at the very windows of their souls. Lying, perjury, fraud, impudence and misery were the only graces of their countenance.

One with slip-shoes, without stockings, and a dirty smock (visible through a crepe petticoat) was stepping from the alehouse to her lodgings with a parcel of pipes in one hand, and a gallon pot of guzzle in the other, yet with her head dressed up to as much advantage as if the members of her body were sacrificed to all wickedness to keep her ill-looked face in a little finery. Another, I suppose taken from the oyster-tub and put into whore's allurements, made a more cleanly appearance but became her ornaments as a cow would a curb-bridle, or a sow a hunting-saddle. Every now and then a fellow would bolt out and whip nimbly cross the way, being equally fearful, as I imagine, of both constable and serjeant, and looked as if the dread of a gallows had drawn its picture in his countenance.

Said I to my friend, 'What can these people be, who are so stigmatised in their looks that they may be known as well from the rest of mankind as Jews from Christians? They seem to me so unlike God's creatures that I cannot but fancy them a colony of hell-cats planted here by the Devil as a mischief to mankind.' 'Why, truly,' says my friend, 'they are such an abominable race of degenerate reprobates that they admit of no comparison on this side Hell's dominions. All this part, quite up to the Square, is a corporation of whores, coiners, highwaymen, pickpockets, and housebreakers, who, like bats and owls, skulk in obscure holes by daylight, but wander in the night in search of opportunities wherein to exercise their villainy.'

When we had taken a gentle walk through this abominable Sodom, where all the sins invented since the fall of Lucifer are daily practised, we came into the common road, Fleet Street, where the rattling of coaches, loud as the cataracts of the Nile, robbed me of my hearing, and put my head into as much disorder as the untuneable hollers of a rural mob at a country bull-baiting.

'Now,' says my friend, 'we have a rare opportunity of replenishing our boxes with a pipe of fine tobacco; for the greatest retailer of that commodity in England lives on the other side of the way, and if you dare run the hazard of crossing the kennel, we'll take a pipe in the shop, where we are likely enough to find something worth our observation.' 'Indeed,' said I, 'you may well style it a hazard, for whenever I have occasion to go on the wrong side of the post I find myself in as much dread of having my bones broke by some of these conveniences for the lame and lazy as an unlucky apprentice to a crabbed master is of a sound beating after a stolen holiday.' However, when we had waited with patience for a seasonable minute to perform this dangerous service, we at last ventured to shoot ourselves through a vacancy between two coaches, and so entered the smoky premises of the famous fumigator. There a parcel of ancient worshippers of the wicked weed were seated, wrapped up in Irish blankets to defend their withered carcases from the malicious winds that only blow upon old age and infirmity, every one having fortified the great gate of life with English guns, well charged with Indian gunpowder.

Their meagre jaws, shrivelled looks, and thoughtful countenances, might render them philosophers; their bodies seemed very dry and light, as if they had been as hard-baked in an oven as a sea-biscuit, or cured in a chimney like a flitch of bacon. They fumbled so very often at a pan of small coal that I thought they had acquired the salamander's nature, and were sucking fire through a quill for their nourishment. They behaved themselves like such true lovers of this prevailing weed that, I dare engage, custom had made their bodies incapable of supporting life by any other breath than smoke. There was no talking amongst 'em but a puff was the period of every sentence, and what they said was as short as possible, for fear of losing the pleasure of a whiff, as 'How d'ye do?' Puff. 'Thank ye.' Puff. 'Is the weed good?' Puff. 'Excellent.' Puff. 'It's fine weather.' Puff. 'God be thanked.' Puff. 'What's o'clock?' Puff, &c.

Behind the counter stood a complaisant spark, who, I observed, showed as much breeding in the sale of a pennyworth of tobacco, and the change of a shilling, as a courtier's footman when he meets his brother-skip in the middle of Covent Garden. And he is so very dextrous in discharge of his occupation that he guesses from a pound of tobacco to an ounce, to the certainty of one corn; and will serve more pennyworths of tobacco in half an hour than some clouterly mundungus-sellers shall be able to do in half four and twenty. He never makes a man wait the tenth part of a minute for his change, but will so readily fling you down all sums, without counting, from a guinea to three pennyworth of farthings, that you would think he had it ready in his hand for you, before you asked him for it. He was very generous of his small beer to a good customer, and I am bound in justice to say this much in his behalf, that he will show a man more civility for the taking of a penny than many stiff-rump mechanics will do for the taking of a pound.

By this time the motion of our lungs had consumed our pipes, and our boxes being filled, we left the funking society in a stinking mist, parching their entrails with the drowsy fumes of the pernicious plant, which, being taken so incessantly as it is by these immoderate skeletons, renders them such slaves to a beastly custom that they make a puff at all business, are led astray by following their noses, burn away their pence, and consume their time in smoke.

We soon departed hence, my friend conducting me to a place called White Friars, which he told me was formerly of great service to the honest traders of the City, who, if they could by cant, flattery and dissimulation, procure large credit amongst their zealous fraternity, would slip in here with their effects, take sanctuary against the laws, compound their debts for a small matter, and oftentimes get a better estate by breaking than they could propose to do by trading. But now a late Act of Parliament has taken away its privilege, and since knaves can neither break with safety nor advantage, it is observed there are not a quarter so many shopkeepers play at bo-peep with their creditors as when they were encouraged to be rogues by such cheating conveniences.

We thus entered this debtors' garrison, where till of late, says my friend, Old Nick broached all his wicked inventions, making this place the very theatre of sin, where his most choice villainies were daily represented. As we passed through the gateway, I observed a stall of books, and the first that I glanced my eye upon happened to be dignified and distinguished by this venerable title: *The Comforts of Whoring and the Vanity of Chastity, together with a Poem in Praise of the Pox.* Bless me! thought I, sure this book was printed in Hell and writ by the Devil, for what diabolical scribbler upon earth could be the author of such unparalleled impudence! I was so surprised with the title that I was quite thoughtless of inspecting into the matter, but marched on till we came into the main street of this neglected asylum, so very thin of people, the windows broken, and the houses untenanted, as if the plague, or some such judgement from Heaven, as well as executions on earth, had made a great slaughter amongst the poor inhabitants.

We met but very few persons within these melancholy precincts, and those by the airiness of their dresses, the forwardness of their looks, and the affectedness of their carriage, seemed to be some neighbouring lemans, who lay conveniently to be squeezed by the young fumblers of the law; who are apt to spend more time upon Phyllis and Chloris than upon Coke and Littleton.

Having taken a survey of these infernal territories, where vice and infamy were so long protected, and flourished without reproof, to the great shame and scandal of a Christian nation, I shall therefore bestow a few lines upon this subject, which I desire the reader to accept of:

On White Friars

The place where knaves their revels kept,
    And bid the laws defiance,
Where whores and thieves for safety crept,
Is of her filthy swarms clean swept.
Her lazy crew that skulked for debt
    Have lost their chief reliance.

The vermin of the Law, the Bum,
    Who gladly kept his distance,
Does safely now in triumph come,
And if he finds the wretch at home,
He executes the fatal doom
    Without the least resistance.

Villains of ev'ry black degree
  Were on this spot collected.
Oaths, curses, lies and blasphemy
Passed currently from he to she,
Made Virtue stare to hear and see
  What vices here were acted.

A soil where sin could only grow,
  And dev'lish dark opinion,
A looking-glass on earth to show
How fiends and devils live below,
That mankind might the discords know,
  That dwell in Hell's dominion.

The streets were stained and houses lined
  With bloodshed, sin and sorrow.
So wicked, it was hard to find
One Christian with an upright mind,
But seemed to be a place designed
  To perish like Gomorrah.

The sodden sinners here that lived
  With pox, looked pale as tallow.
By whom no god was e'er believed,
Or man amongst 'em ever thrived,
But that cursed wretch who daily strived
  To be the basest fellow.

To thieve, pick pockets, whore and cheat,
  Were all their chiefest study,
And he or she that was unfit
For any roguery or deceit,
Such a poor rascal had not wit,
  And she a silly dowdy.

Pox, poverty, dirt, rags, and lice,
  By most were carried about 'em.
They were too nasty to be nice,
And all their daily exercise

Were whoring, drinking, cards, and dice,
    No living here without 'em.

No orders did they mind, or hours,
    But free of all restriction,
Each tippling-house kept open doors
At midnight, for sots, rogues and whores,
To curse and wrangle at all hours
    And vent their malediction.

But now the wicked scene withdraws
    And makes an alteration.
It's purged and cleansed by wholesome laws
And is become a sober place
Where honesty may show its face
    Without disrepution.

My friend conducted me from thence through the little wicket of a great pair of gates, which brought us into a stately part of that learned society, the Temple. 'This,' says my friend, 'is called the King's Bench Walks, and here are a great many sorts of people, that are now walking to waste their time, who are well worth your notice. We'll therefore take two or three turns amongst 'em and you will find 'em the best living library to instruct mankind that ever you met with.'

'Pray,' said I, 'what do you take that knot of gentlemen to be, who are so merry with one another?' 'They,' replied my friend, 'are gamesters, waiting to pick up some young bubble or other as he comes from his chamber. They are men whose conditions are subject to more revolutions than a weathercock, or the uncertain mind of a fantastical woman. They are seldom two days in one and the same station. They are, one day, very richly dressed, and perhaps out at elbows the next; they have often a great deal of money, and are as often without a penny in their pockets. They are as much Fortune's bubbles as young gentlemen are theirs, for whatever benefits she bestows upon 'em with one hand she snatches away with t'other. Their whole lives are a lottery; they read no books but cards; all their mathematics is to truly understand the odds of a bet. They very often fall out, but very seldom fight, and the way to make 'em your friends is to quarrel with them. They are men who have seldom occasion to pare their nails, for they most commonly keep them

short by biting them. They generally begin every year with the same
riches, for the issue of their annual labours is chiefly to enrich the
pawnbroker. They are seldom in debt, because nobody will trust 'em, and
they never care to lend money because they know not where to borrow
it. A pair of false dice and a pack of marked cards sets 'em up; and an
hour's unfortunate play commonly breaks 'em. They are nearly related
to madmen, for they have generally more raving fits in a day than a
Bedlamite. At such times they are as profuse in their oaths as a young
scholar is of his Latin. They generally die intestate, and go as poor out
of the world as they came into it.

> 'As mariners with hopes their anchors weigh,
> But if cross-winds or storms they meet at sea
> They damn their stars, and curse the low'ring day.
>
> 'So gamesters, when the luck of one prevails
> Above another, then the loser rails,
> Damns Fortune, and in passion bites his nails.'

'You have given me a very pretty character of 'em. But pray what
sort of blades are those in antiquated piss-burnt wigs, whose clothes hang
upon their backs as if they were not made for 'em; who walk with
abundance of circumspection?' 'I'll tell you,' says my friend, 'they are
a kind of hangers-on upon the warden of the Fleet, and the marshal of
the Queen's Bench. They pretend to have an interest with them in the
procuring of liberty for prisoners removed by habeas corpus. Thus,
cunningly, they dive into your circumstances, and report 'em to the
warden or marshal, who then knows the better how to deal with you, and
screw you up to the utmost doit you are able to afford him. They are a
kind of solicitors in this sort of business, who, whilst they are pretending
to serve you, are subtly contriving a treacherous way to pick your pocket.
And if any person makes his escape, they are very diligent in their
enquiries after him, and if they make discovery do privately dispatch
intelligence to the keepers aforesaid, for which they are rewarded. These
are a parcel of as honest fellows as ever cut the throat of a friend, or
robbed their own father. For a crown, or half a piece, they will give any
bailiff a cast of their office in dogging or setting even those of their own
acquaintance to whom they profess the greatest friendship. They are also
very serviceable agents in a bad cause. If they can say or swear anything

that will do your business a kindness, they will at any time, for a small fee, strain a point to your assistance. They are generally tradesmen, brought into poverty by negligence and their own profuseness, and by poverty and imprisonment have arrived to the unhappy knowledge of these shameful undertakings. They are men whose liberty is owing to a long confinement, or the keeper's clemency, and whenever they die the warden or marshal make dice of their bones, to secure themselves from the suit of their creditors.

> 'Sure none like man will their own kind annoy!
> Hawks will not hawks, wolves will not wolves destroy.
> But these inhuman sharks, worse beasts than they,
> On their own fellow creatures basely prey.
> Surely at last such destined are to starve,
> Who can no better life than this deserve.'

'I observe,' said I, 'there are another sort of men that appear something like gentlemen, with meagre jaws and dejected countenances; each walking singly, and looking as peevish as if the blind jilt and he, through a mutual dislike, were frowning on each other.'

'Those, you must know,' says my friend, 'are gentlemen in distress. Some, coming to their estates so early, before they had sense enough to preserve 'em, have been bubbled by the Town parasites, taverns, whores and sharpers, till reduced to misery and made the sad examples of their own extravagance. They are now waiting with a hungry belly to fasten upon some old acquaintance, for a dinner, who dreads the sight of one of 'em as much as a debtor does a bailiff; but because he knew his family and him in prosperity, thinks himself obliged now and then to give him a meal, or relieve him with the gift of a shilling, which he takes with as humble an acknowledgement as a poor parson does a dinner from his patron, or a tradesman the payment of a bill from a courtier's steward.

> 'How vain is Youth? How ripe to be undone,
> When rich betimes, and made a man too soon?
> Humour his folly, and his pride commend,
> You make him both your servant and your friend,
> But if with counsels you the wretch shall aid,
> He tells you to advise is to upbraid.

That good your admonitions are, 'tis true,
But still no more than what before he knew.
Prays you to hold your tongue, he scorns to learn of you.

'There's another sort among them who were born gentlemen and bred up in idleness, whose parents had the care, by way of prevention, to spend their estates themselves and leave their issue nothing to trust to. These, some of them, are pensioners to the petticoat, some boretto-men at the Groom-Porter's, and some flatterers and smoothers, who support themselves by bringing others into the like unhappiness. Those amongst them of the meekest spirits are relation-punishers who have patience enough to bear a reproof at dinner without spoiling their appetites.

'Unhappy wretch, by chance and bounty fed,
To nothing born, and yet to nothing bred,
Thou'rt Fortune's pensioner, whom men receive
Sometimes for sport and sometimes to relieve.
Mechanics in thy company look great
And magnify by thee their happier state.
Each man that knows thee doubly guards his purse.
Thou'rt like infection shunned, and what is worse
Not only a burden to the world, but to thyself a curse.'

As my friend and I were walking upon the Grand Parade, I observed abundance of masked ladies with rumpled hoods and scarves, their hands charged with papers, bandboxes and rolls of parchment, frisk in and out of their staircases, like coneys in a warren bolting from their burrows. Said I to my friend, 'Do you think all these women are Madam Blackacres, and come hither about Law business, that we see tripping backwards and forwards so very nimbly?' 'No, no,' replied my companion, 'these are ladies that come to receive fees, instead of giving any. They have now extraordinary business upon their hands with many of the young lawyers, though nothing in relation to the Law. For you must know these are nymphs of delight, who only carry papers in their hands for a blind. They are such considerable dealers they can afford to give credit for a whole vacation, and now, in term-time, they are industrious in picking up their debts. You are now, I'll assure you, in one of the greatest places of trade in Town for dealing in that sort of commodity; for most ladies who, for want of fortunes, despair of husbands, and are willing to give themselves up to man's use, in spite of matrimony, come hither to be truly qualified for their mercenary undertaking. And by the time any condescending nymph has had a month's conversation with the airy blades of this honourable society, she will doubtless find herself as well fitted for the employment as if she had had a twelvemonth's education under the most experienced bawd in Christendom; and if you ever chance to meet with any of our trading madams, and ask her who debauched her it's ten to one but her answer will be, "A Gentleman of the Temple." But whether those sins are justly laid to their charge, or whether it is only the ambition of the jilt to have you think she sacrificed her virginity to the use of so worthy a society, I won't presume to determine. Though, I confess, I think it reasonable to believe that our forward ladies are more apt to dedicate their honours to an Inns of Court than elsewhere, for three reasons. First, as they are the flower of our gentry. Secondly, as the greatness of their number affords variety of choice. And thirdly, as they have the best conveniences for consummating debauchery without the dread or danger of detection.

> 'Could Youth those early hours to study bend
> Which on the tempting sex he vainly spend,
> How sparkling would his happy genius shine!
> How strong his nerves, his knowledge how divine!
> To Adam's first perfection he'd attain
> And by degrees lost Paradise regain.
> But that which plagues and bitters human life
> Is woman, whether mistress or a wife,
> Mother of sin, disease, of sorrow, and of strife.'

'Pray,' said I, 'what noun-substantive flat-cap of a house is this, so very different from all the rest of the buildings?' My friend told me 'twas the Queen's Bench Office, 'where,' says he, 'they sell broken Latin much dearer than physicians do their visits, or apothecaries their physic. Time, you know, has been always valued as a precious commodity by all men, but here they sell their minutes at as extravagant a rate as great men do their courtesies, and won't let four fingers and a thumb run once cross a slip of paper but by virtue of a hocus-pocus custom, called the Fees of the Office, they'll conjure two or three half-crowns out of your pocket, and won't put their tongues to the trouble of giving you either a why or a wherefore for it.'

Being wonderfully pleased with the prospect of the Thames, the beauty of the buildings, and the airiness and spaciousness of the Court, I began to look about me with no little satisfaction; and, gazing round, I espied the sundial subscribed with this motto, "Be Gone About Your Business". 'Pray,' said I to my companion, 'what wonderful mystery lies hid in those words, for surely so learned a society would never have chosen a sentence for this purpose but what should be very significant; and I cannot, for my life, understand the meaning on't? For certain they intended something extraordinary by it, not intelligible to a common capacity.' 'Truly,' said my friend, ''tis something that nobody could ever find out, for I never could hear it would admit of any other application or construction than what is rendered by the literal sense.' 'No,' said I, 'then I think whoever placed it here deserves to be bogged for putting such an affront upon so honourable a society. For I remember when I was a schoolboy those very words were the burden of a ballad.' 'Pooh, pooh,' says my friend, 'you only jest with me.' 'Upon my word,' said I, ''tis very true, and I can myself repeat some stanzas of it, which are these:

> 'Fie! You great looby, John,
> Pray now let me alone!
> If you won't let me rest
> Now a body is dressed,
> *Be gone about your business.*

> 'Never stir, let me go,
> Don't you rumple me so.
> Hold your hand, you great cur!
> If you think I'm a whore,
> *Be gone about your business.*

> 'Nay, I vow and protest,
> I will not be in jest.
> Why you ugly damned devil
> If you will not be civil
> *Be gone about your business!*

'Oh dear! Nay, I vow,
Why where are you now?
O Lord, I'm undone,
You will kill me anon!
Go on about your business.'

'Certainly,' says my friend, 'if the benchers had ever heard this merry
ditty, they would not have thought it consistent with their gravity to have
chosen the chorus for a motto. I cannot but conceive they have showed
a blind side in putting so imperative fustian in so public a place, as if
they designed to conjure loiterers out of the Walks, as a juggler does his
balls from under his cups with a "Presto, be gone!" I think it's a great
dishonour to so learned a society that they could find no apt phrase to
serve so poor a purpose, but were so sadly puzzled at so ordinary a task
as to use so bald and naked a sentence, such a threadbare scrap of
English too, which is now become the common jest and ridicule of every
mean mechanic.'

From thence we went towards the Hall, and turned in at a dark entry
that brought us into a cloister, or piazza, where a parcel of grave blades
gowned and banded, with green snapsacks in their hands, were so busily
talking alphabetically about A marrying B, and how they begat two sons,
C and D, and how C, being the elder brother, married E, by whom he
had two daughters, F and G, &c. I thought they were examining the
genealogy of the criss-cross-row, so I listened all the while with great
attention, expecting I should have heard the original rise of every
individual mark or letter, and how they begot one another, from A to Z
throughout the alphabet, till my friend told me 'twas their method of
stating a case, which made me blush at my ignorance. Heads, tongues,
feet and hands were all moving, which occasioned me to fancy their
reading so much Law-French had inspired them with the Gallic grace of
so much action in their talk.

We left them debating the weighty difference between John-a-nokes
and John-a-stiles and marched forward, till we came into the Inner
Temple, as my friend informed me, where we had a fine prospect of a
stately hall and pleasant fountain. Here we also found walking sundry
sorts of peripatetics, some, I believe, through good husbandry, having
chosen the broad stones for the prevention of the rough gravel wearing
out of their shoe soles, others for the ease of their corns. Some country
clients, with grey coats and long staves, I suppose, desired to walk there

by their lawyers whilst their business was dispatched, so that they should
not spoil their chamber-floors with their hobnails. Here and there
amongst 'em was a creeping old fellow, with so religious a countenance
that he looked as if he had spent more pounds in law than ever he read
letters in the Gospel, and had paid in his time as much money for
declarations, pleas, orders and executions, subpoenas, injunctions, bills,
answers and decrees, as ever it cost him in the maintenance of his family.

   'Now,' says my friend, 'I believe we are both tired with the labours
of the day. Let us therefore dedicate the latter part purely to our pleasure,
take a coach and go see May Fair.' 'Would you have me,' said I,
'undergo the punishment of a coach again, when you know I was so
great a sufferer by the last that it made my bones rattle in my skin, and
has brought as many pains about me as if troubled with the rheumatism?'
'That was a country coach,' says he, 'and only fit for the road; but
London coaches are hung more loose, to prevent your being jolted by the
roughness of the pavement.' This argument of my friend's prevailed upon
me to venture my carcase a second time to be rocked in a Hackney
cradle. So we took leave of the Temple, turned up without Temple Bar,
and there took coach for the general rendezvous aforementioned.

   By the help of a great many slashes and hey-ups, and after as many
jolts and jumbles, we were dragged to the Fair, where the harsh sound
of untuneable trumpets, the caterwauling scrapes of thrashing fiddlers, the
grumbling of beaten calves'-skin, and the discording toots of broken
organs, set my teeth on edge, like the filing of a handsaw, and made my
hair stand as bolt upright as the quills of an angry porcupine.

   We ordered the coach to drive through the body of the Fair, that we
might have the better view of the tinsel heroes and the gazing multitude,
expecting to have seen several corporations of strolling vagabonds, but
there proved but one company, amongst whom merry-andrew was very
busy in coaxing the attentive crowd into a good opinion of his fraternity's and his own performances. And when, with abundance of labour,
sweat and nonsense, he had drawn a great cluster of the mob on his
parade, and was just beginning to encourage them to walk in and take
their places, his unlucky opposite, whose boarded theatre entertained the
public with the wonderful activity of Indian rope-dancers, brings out a
couple of chattering homunculi dressed up in scaramouch habit.
Everything that merry-andrew and his second did on the one side was
mimicked by the little flat-nosed comedians on the other, till the two
diminutive buffoons, by their comical gestures, had so prevailed upon the

gaping throng that though merry-andrew had taken pains, with all the wit he had, to collect the straggling rabble into their proper order, yet, like an unmannerly audience, they turned their arses upon the players and devoted themselves wholly to the monkeys, to the great vexation of Tom-fool and all the strutting train of imaginary lords and ladies.

At last out comes an epitome of a careful nurse, dressed up in a country jacket, and under her arm a kitten for a nursling, and in her contrary hand a piece of cheese. Down sits the little matron, with a very motherly countenance, and when her youngster mewed she dandled him and rocked him in her arms with as great signs of affection as a loving mother could well show to a disordered infant. Then she bit a piece of cheese, and after she had mumbled it about in her own mouth, then thrust it with her tongue into the kitten's, just as I have seen some nasty old sluts feed their own grandchildren.

Beyond these were a parcel of scandalous boozing-kens, where soldiers and their trulls were skipping and dancing about to most lamentable music, performed upon a cracked crowd by a blind fiddler. In another hut a parcel of Scotch pedlars and their maggies were dancing a Highlander's jig to a hornpipe. Over against 'em was the Cheshire booth, where a gentleman's man was playing more tricks with his heels in a Cheshire round than ever were shown by the mad coffee-man at Sadler's Music House. These intermixed with here and there a puppet-show, where a senseless dialogue between Punchinello and the Devil was conveyed to the ears of a listening rabble through a tin squeaker, which was thought by some of 'em as great a piece of conjuration as ever was performed by Dr Faustus.

We now began to look about us, and take a view of the spectators, but could not, amongst the many thousands, find one man that appeared above the degree of a gentleman's valet, nor one whore that could have the impudence to ask above sixpence wet and sixpence dry for an hour of her cursed company. In all the multitudes that ever I beheld, I never in my life saw such a number of lazy, lousy-looked rascals, and so hateful a throng of beggarly, sluttish strumpets, who were a scandal to the Creation, mere antidotes against lechery, and enemies to cleanliness.

As we were thus rambling through the Fair, a coach overtook us, wherein were a couple of more tolerable punks, whose silken temptations and more modest deportment gave them a just title to a higher price than the white-apron bang-tails, who were sweating in the crowd, could pretend to. An arch country bumpkin, having picked up a frog in some of the adjacent ditches, peeping into the coach as he passed by, was very much affronted that they hid their faces with their masks. ''Ad's blood,' says he, 'you look as ugly in those black vizards as my toad here, e'en get you all together,' and tossed it into the coach. At this the frightened ladybirds squeaked out, opened the coach doors, and leaped out amongst the throng to shun their loathsome companion.

The adjacent mob being greatly pleased at the countryman's unluckiness, set up a laughing holler as loud as an huzza, to make good the jest, which occasioned the coachman to look back. Knowing nothing of the matter, and seeing his fares out of the coach, he thought they were about to bilk him. He alighted out of his box, and in a great fury seized one of them by the scarf, accosting them in these words: 'Zounds you bitches! What, would you bilk me? Pay me my fare, or by Gog and Magog you shall feel the smart of my whipcord before you go a step further.' The harlots endeavoured to satisfy their angry charioteer that they were women of more honour than to attempt so ill an action, telling him, as well as their surprise would give them leave, the occasion of their alighting. This would not convince the choleric whore-driver, who refused either to quit his hold, or suffer them to go again into his coach till they had paid him eighteenpence, which he demanded as his fare. But, in the sequel of the matter, they had it not to give him, presuming to have met with some cully in the Fair that might have answered their purpose; so that rather than to stand a vapulation, one of them took notice of his number, and gave him her scarf as a pledge. Notwithstanding this, he refused to carry them back, I suppose for fear they might call upon some bully or other that might make him deliver up his security without any other redemption than a thrashed jacket. Thus were the unfortunate madams dismounted of their coach, and were forced to mob it on foot with the rest of their sisters.

There being nothing further that occurred, or anything to be seen worth notice, only a Turkey ram with as much wool upon his tail as would load a wheelbarrow, and a couple of tigers, grown now so common they are scarce worth mentioning, I shall therefore conclude the account we give you of May Fair in these following lines:

'Tis a sad rendezvous of the wicked'st of wretches,
Poor rogues without money, and whores without patches,
A Sodom for sin, where the worst Jack-a-dandy
May swyve through the Fair for a gallon of brandy.

VIII

FOR WANT OF glasses to our coach, having drawn up our tin sashes, pinked like the bottom of a colander that the air might pass through the holes and defend us from stifling, we were conveyed from the Fair, through a suffocating cloud of dusty atoms, to St James's Palace, in reverence to which we alighted and discharged our grumbling essedarius, who stuck very close to our backsides and muttered heavily, according to their old custom, for t'other sixpence, till at last, moving us a little beyond our patience, we gave an angry positive denial to his unreasonable importunities, and so parted with our unconscionable carrion-scourger, who we found, like the rest of his fraternity, had taken up the miserly immoral rule, Never to be satisfied.

We passed through a lofty porch into the first Court, where a parcel of hobnailed loobies were gazing at a whale's rib with great amazement; being busily consulting what creature it could be that could produce a bone of such unusual magnitude. Who should come by in this interim, but a Fingalian conjurer, posting to (as my friend supposed) Duke Humphrey's Walk in the Park to pick his teeth and loiter away his supper-time. But seeing the country hobbies stand gaping at this puzzling rarity, he put himself amongst the rest to deliver his judgement of this amazing object. 'I pray you, sir,' says one of the countrymen to him, 'what sort of bone do you take this to be?' To which the Dear Joy, after taking a little snuff, most judiciously replied, 'By my shoul, begorra, I believe it is the jaw-bone of the ass wid which Shampson killed the Philischines, and it ish nailed up here dat nobody should do any more mischief wid it.' 'I wonder,' said another of the plough-jobbers, 'how he could use it, 'tis such a huge unwieldy weapon?' 'By my shoul,' replied Teague, 'let Shampson look to dat his own shelf, for it ish none of my business.'

From thence we went through the Palace into the Park about the time when the Court ladies raise their extended limbs from their downy couches, and walk into the Mall to refresh their charming bodies with the cooling and salubrious breezes of the gilded evening. We could not possibly have chosen a luckier minute to have seen the delightful Park in its greatest glory and perfection, for the brightest stars of the Creation sure that ever shone by no other power than human excellence were moving here, with such an awful state and majesty that their graceful deportment bespoke 'em goddesses. Such merciful looks were thrown from their engaging eyes upon every admiring mortal; they were so free from pride, envy or contempt, that they seemed, contrary to experience, to be sent into the world to complete its happiness. The wonderful works of Heaven were here to be read in beauteous characters. Such elegant compositions might be observed among the female quality, that it's impossible to conceive otherwise than that such heavenly forms were perfected after the unerring image of Divine excellence. I could have gazed forever with inexpressible delight, finding in every lovely face and magnificent behaviour something still new to raise my admiration, with due regard to Heaven for imparting to us such shows of celestial harmony, in that most beautiful and curious creature, WOMAN.

Woman (when good) the best of saints,
    That bright, seraphic lovely she!
Who nothing of an angel wants
    But truth and immortality.

Whose silken limbs, and charming face,
    Keeps Nature warm with amorous fire,
Was she with wisdom armed and grace,
    What greater bliss could man desire?

How smoothly would our minutes slide,
    How sweetly lovers must accord,
Had she but wit herself to guide,
    Or prudence to obey, her lord!

Few troubles would our lives annoy,
    Could man on wav'ring beauty trust.
But her misguidance mars the joy,
    Through want of wisdom to be just.

Adam no Paradise had lost
    Had Eve not disobedient been.
Her wand'ring inclination cost
    The price of happiness, for sin.

How blessed a marriage-state would be,
    Were but her temper and her love
From lust and revolution free,
    How great a blessing would she prove!

But pride of being great and gay
    Tempts her to deviate, by degrees,
From Virtue's paths, and run astray
    For gaudy plumes and lolling ease.

Thus once defiled, she soon grows lewd,
    Like angels fallen from purity,
Pursuing ill, disdaining good,
    And envies what she cannot be.

Could beauty in her dressing-glass
    The charms of innocence but see,
How Virtue gilds her awful face,
    She'd prize the darling rarity.

For she that's lovely, just and kind,
    Does blessings to a husband bring;
But if her honour's once resigned,
    Though fair, she's but a pois'nous sting.

    Though I was greatly affected with the majestic deportment of the female sex, each looking with a presence as well worthy of Diana's bow, or Bellona's shield, as the golden apple of Venus, yet I could by no means reconcile myself to the sheepish humility of their cringing worshippers, who were guilty of so much idolatry to the fair sex that I thought the laws of the Creation were greatly transgressed, and that man had dwindled from his first power and authority into pusillanimity and luxury, and had suffered deceitful Woman to cozen him of his prerogative. The men looked so effeminate, and showed such cowardly tameness by their extravagant submission, as if they wanted courage to exercise that freedom which they had a just title to use. It seemed to me as if the world was turned topsy-turvy, for the ladies looked like undaunted heroes, fit for government or battle, and the gentlemen like a parcel of fawning, flattering fops, that could bear cuckoldom with patience, make a jest of an affront, and swear themselves very faithful and humble servants to the petticoat, creeping and cringing in dishonour to themselves, to what were decreed by Heaven their inferiors, as if their education had been amongst monkeys, who (as it is said) in all cases give pre-eminence to their females.

Having thus seen what the Mall afforded, we stepped over its boarded bounds into Duke Humphrey's Walk, as my friend informed me, where he showed me an abundance of our neighbouring bull-factors, distinguishable by their flat noses and broad faces, who were walking away their leisure hours beneath the umbrage of the lime-trees and crawling about backwards and forwards, like so many straggling caterpillars in a grove of sycamores, who, for want of other food, are ready to devour the very leaves that bred them. So these looked as sharp as if they were ready to swallow their best friends for want of other subsistence.

'This Walk,' says my friend, 'is a rare office of intelligence for a woman as rich as lewd to furnish herself with a gallant that will stick as close as a crab-louse to her *nunquam satis*, if she will but allow him good clothes, three meals a day, and a little money for usquebaugh. If she likes him when she has him, she need not fear losing him as long as she's worth a groat, for they are very constant to anybody that has money, and he will measure out his affections by her generosity, and she will surely find (at her own cost) that nothing but her poverty will make him look out for a new mistress.

'The worthy gentlemen who chiefly frequent this sanctuary are non-commissioned officers. I mean not such who have lost their commissions, but such as never had any, and yet would be very angry should you refuse to honour them with the title of Captain, though they never so much as trailed a pike towards the deserving it.'

From thence we took a walk upon the Parade, which my friend told me used in a morning to be covered with the bones of red herrings, and smelt as strong about breakfast-time as a wet-salter's shop at midsummer. 'But now,' says he, 'it's perfumed again with English breath, and the scent of Oronoko tobacco no more offends the nostrils of our squeamish ladies, who may now pass backwards and forwards free from all such nuisances; and, if with child, without the danger of being frighted at a terrible pair of Dutch whiskers.'

From thence we walked up to the Canal, where ducks were frisking about the water and standing upon their heads, showing as many tricks in their liquor as a Bartholomew Fair tumbler. Said I to my friend, 'Her

Majesty's ducks are wondrous merry.' He replied, 'Well they may be, for they are always tippling.' We then took a view of the famed figure of the Gladiator, which indeed is well worthy of the place it stands in, for the exactness of its proportion, the true placing and expressing of the exterior muscles, veins and arteries, show such a perfection of art that justly deserves our admiration. Behind this figure, upon the foot of the pedestal, my friend and I sat down to please our eyes with the prospect of the most delightful aqueduct and to see its feathered inhabitants, the ducks, divert us with their sundry pastimes. In this interim, who should come up to the front of the Gladiator but two or three merry buxom ladies, who, I suppose, by their exceptions against the statue, were women of no little experience, but very competent judges of what they undertook to censure. One of them, more forward to arraign the artist than the rest, not knowing we were behind, expressed herself with abundance of scorn and contempt, after this manner: 'Is this the fine proportioned figure I have heard my husband so often brag on? It's true, his legs and arms are strong and manly. But look, look, cousin, what a bauble it has got!' With that my friend starts up. 'You must consider, ladies,' says he, 'in the time when this was made women did not wear their consciences so large as they do nowadays.' At which, like a company of merry wagtails, they ran away tittering and laughing as if they thought us under the same predicament with the statue.

We arose from thence, and walked up by the Decoy, where meanders glide so smoothly beneath their osier canopies that the calm surface seemed to express nothing inhabited this watery place but peace and silence. I could have wished myself capable of living obscure from mankind in this element like a fish, purely to have enjoyed the pleasure of so delightful a flumenous labyrinth, whose intricate turnings so confound the sight that the eye is still in search of some new discovery, and never satisfied with the tempting variety so artificially ordered within so little a compass.

We turned up from thence into a long Lime Walk, where both art and nature had carefully preserved the trees in such exact proportion to each other that a man would guess by their appearance that they all aspire in height, and spread in breadth, to just the same dimensions, and confine their leaves and branches to an equal number. Beneath this regular and pleasant shade were pensive lovers whispering their affections to their mistresses, and breathing out despairing sighs of their desired happiness. Here also were the tender offspring of nobility handed by their fresh-looked nurses, to strengthen and refresh their feeble joints with air and exercise suitable to their childish weakness; and some, having started more forward in their infancy, were accompanied with their tutors, showing such manliness in their presence, and such promises of virtue in their propitious looks at ten or a dozen years of age, that they seemed already fortified with grace, learning and wisdom against the world's corruptions.

The termination of this delectable walk was a knot of lofty elms by a pond side, round some of which were commodious seats for the tired ambulators to refresh their weary pedestals. Here a parcel of old worn-out cavaliers were conning over the Civil Wars, and looking back into the history of their past lives, to moderate the anxiety and infirmities of age with pleasing reflections on their youthful actions.

Amongst the rest, a country curmudgeon was a standing with his backside against a tree, leaning forward on his oaken companion, his staff, and staring towards the top of a high adjacent elm. 'Pray,' said I, 'friend, what is it you are so earnestly looking at?' He answered me, 'At yonder bird's nest.' I further asked him what bird's nest it was. He replied, 'What a foolish question you ask me! Why did you ever know anything but rooks build so near the Queen's Palace?' This innocent return put my friend and me into laughter. I asked him if he did not think they were noble trees. 'Yes, zure,' says he, 'if the Queen's trees should not be noble, pray whose should?' 'I mean,' said I, 'don't they thrive and spread finely?' 'They have nothing else to do,' says he, 'as I know on. Everything thrives that stands upon Crown-land, zure, and so does my landlord.'

Having now seen chiefly what the Park afforded, we sat ourselves down beneath the pleasant umbrage of this most stately arbour, by the pond side, where I composed this following acrostic on Saint James's Park, at the reader's service.

> S ure Art and Nature nowhere else can show
> A park where trees in such true order grow.
> I n silver streams the gentle Isis here
> N o banks o'erflows, yet proudly swells so near
> T he pleasing cup does just brimful appear.

J n Summer's longest days, when Phoebus takes
A pride to pierce the thickest shades and brakes,
M ay beauties walk beneath a verdant screen,
E xempt from dust, and by the sun unseen.
S o thick of leaves each plant, so green the grass,
S ure mortal never viewed a sweeter place.

P revailing ladies meet in lovely swarms,
A nd bless each day its umbrage with their charms.
R ev'rence the Stuarts' name for this hereafter:
K ing James the First clubbed wood, his grandson
                                        Charles found water.

When by an hour's enjoyment we had rendered the beauty of the Park but dull and flat to our palled appetites, we began to think of some new object that ought to feast and refresh our tired senses with pleasures yet untasted. Accordingly we took our leaves of the Park with the same willingness as lovers turn their backs upon their mistresses when (by too vigorous a repetition of kindnesses to engage her affections) they have turned the delight into a servile drudgery. We went through a narrow passage that directed us towards Westminster, in order to take a view of that ancient and renowned structure, the Abbey, to which I was an utter stranger.

When we came in sight of this sacred edifice, I could not behold the outside of the awful pile without reverence and amazement. 'Twas raised to such stupendous height, and beautified with such ornamental statues, that the bold strokes of excelling artists, whilst the building stands, will always remain visible. The whole seemed to want nothing that could render it truly venerable. We passed by that emblem of mortality, the charnel-house, where poets, priests, pimps and porters lay their empty heads together, without envy or distinction, and on the north side entered the magnificent temple with equal wonder and satisfaction. It entertained our sight with such worthy monuments and astonishing antiquities that we knew not which way to direct our eyes, each object was so engaging. We took a general survey of all that's to be seen in the open parts of the church, where almost every stone gives a brief history of the memorable actions due to their pious ashes to whom the tablet appertaineth. By this time the bells began to chime for afternoon prayers, and the choir was opened, into which we went, amongst many others, to pay with reverence

that duty which becomes a Christian. There our souls were elevated by
the divine harmony of the music, far above the common pitch of our
devotions, whose heavenly accents have so sweet an influence upon a
contrite heart that it strengthens our zeal, fortifies the loose imagination
against wandering thoughts, and gives a man a taste of immortal
blessings upon earth, before he is thoroughly prepared for the true relish
of celestial comforts.

When we had given our souls the refreshment of this enlivening
exercise, we made an entrance into the east end of the Abbey, which is
kept locked, and paid a visit to the venerable shrines and sacred
monuments of the dead nobility, where the virtues and magnanimous
actions of our heroic princes are conveyed to their posterity by the
sundry inventions of our ingenious ancestors, as epitaphs, effigies, arms,
emblems and hieroglyphics.

When we had satisfied ourselves with a view of these ancient
curiosities, we ascended some stone steps, which brought us to a chapel
that may justly claim the admiration of the whole universe. Such
inimitable perfections are apparent in every part of the whole composure,
which looks so far exceeding human excellence that a man would think
it was knit together by the fingers of angels, pursuant to the directions
of Omnipotence.

From thence we were conducted by our little guide to King Charles
the Second's effigy, and as much as he excelled his predecessors in
mercy, wisdom and liberality, so does his effigy exceed the rest in
liveliness, proportion and magnificence.

Having now satisfied our curiosity with a sight of what was chiefly
admirable, we came again into the body of the church, where my friend
and I began to consider of some things which we did not think were
consistent with piety, or the glory of that Power to whom the holy pile
is dedicated, which are these:

1   That the parish poor of St Margaret's should be suffered to beg
    within the Abbey, even in prayer-time.
2   That those who are chosen as particular agents in the service of
    God, should be permitted to sing in the Playhouse.
3   That the monuments should lie defaced, some with their hands off,
    and some with their feet off and thrown by them, without
    reparation.

4 That women should have Hebrew, Greek and Latin epitaphs, who never understood a word of the languages.
5 That Ben Jonson should want a tomb, and lie buried from the rest of the poets.
6 That the monument of Squire Thynne, whose death was so remarkable, should be without any inscription.

Having now satisfied our senses with the sight of the sundry curiosities contained within this reverend building, being term-time we steered our course towards Westminster Hall. But just as we came out of the north portico of the Abbey, a company of trainbands was drawn up in the yard in order to give their captain a parting volley. I could not forbear laughing to see so many greasy cooks, tun-bellied lick-spigots, and fat wheezing butchers, sweating in their buff doublets, under the command of some fiery-faced brewer, whose godgel-gut was hooped in with a golden sash, which the clod-skulled hero became as well as one of his dray-horses would an embroidered saddle.

When the true-blue officer (over-thoughtful of hops and grains) had by two or three mistaken words of command hustled his courageous company into close confusion instead of order, he bid 'em make ready, which made half of them change colour, and show as much cowardice in cocking their muskets as if half a dozen Turks had faced 'em and frighted 'em with their whiskers. Then the noble captain, advancing his silver-headed cane formally over his head with both his hands, gave the terrible word Fire! popping down his noddle like a goose under a barn-door, to defend his eyesight from the flashes of the gunpowder. In this interim, such an amazing clap of thunder was sent forth from the rusty kill-devils that it caused fear and trembling amongst all those that made it, for which the little boys gave them the honour of a great holler; and away trudged the foundered soldiers home to their wives, well satisfied.

We then marched forward towards the Palace Yard, which we found as full of Hackney coaches as Gray's Inn Walks of Hackney whores on a Sunday after sermon, standing rank and file in as much order as if they had been marshalled by the Fleet Street deadmonger ready for a funeral. When we had made more turnings and windings amongst the coaches than ever were known in Fair Rosamond's bower, we arrived at the Hall-Gate, withinside of which innumerable crowds of contending mortals were swarmed at every bar, where the black sirens of the law, with silver tongues and gilded palms, were charming the ears of the judges with their rhetorical music. We first gave our attention at the Common Pleas, where my friend and I were much delighted, sometimes with elegant speeches from the Bench, as well as the pleasing eloquence and powerful reasonings at the Bar.

An old yeoman happened to be a witness in one cause, and he had sworn very heartily and knowingly in a matter of great antiquity, so that the counsel on the opposite side asked him how old he was. To this he answered, at first, gravely in these words: 'I am old enough to be your father, and therefore, I hope, young man, you will give that respect to my grey hairs that is due to 'em.' 'That,' replied the counsel, 'is no answer to my question. I desire to know how many years old you account yourself, for I am very apt to believe you have sworn positively to some things that are beyond your knowledge.' 'I would have you consider, sir,' says the old gentleman, 'I am of a very great age. I am in my fourscore and seventeenth year, and yet, I thank God for it, I have memory and sense enough left still to make a knave an answer.' With that the Court burst into a laughter, which dashed the lawyer out of countenance and made him ashamed of making any further interrogatives.

From thence we moved towards the upper end of the Hall, through such a crowd of Jerry Blackacres that we were shoved about like a couple of owls fallen into a company of rooks and jackdaws. As we were thus squeezing along towards the Chancery Bar, a couple of country fellows met, and greeted one another after the following manner. 'How d'ye, neighbour?' says the one, 'is your suit ended yet?' 'No, trowly,' says the other, 'nor can anybody tell when it wool. To spaik the truth, neighbour, I believe my returney's a knave.' 'How shid a be otherwise?' replied the first, 'for thou seeth there are so many of 'em here, that it's impossible they shid live honestly one by another.'

We were now got to the Chancery, where so many smooth tongues were so vigorously contending for equity that we found by their long harangues, and strenuous arguments, it was not to be obtained but with little difficulty. Whilst we were giving our attention to that engaging harmony which flowed with such a careless fluency from their well-tuned instruments of oratory, a cause was called wherein a tailor happened to be a chief witness. The counsel on the other side, knowing his profession, took an occasion to give him this caution: 'I understand, friend, you are by trade a tailor. I would advise you to use more conscience in your depositions than you do in your bills, or else we shall none of us believe you.' 'Truly, sir,' says the tailor, 'our trade, I must confess, does lie under a great scandal; but if you and I were in a room together, and the Devil should come in and ask for a thief and a liar, I wonder which of us should be most frightened?'

We adjourned from thence to the Queen's Bench Bar, where two pleaders, very eager in dispute, were mixing their arguments with some reflections one upon another. A countryman, happening to stand just by us, seemed mightily pleased to hear 'em at such variance. At last, being unable to contain himself any longer, he broke out into these words: 'Well said, i'faith; this I hope will make the old proverb good, that when knaves fall out, honest men will come by their right.' A little after, one of the counsel, in a heat, happened to say rashly, if what he had offered was not law, he'd justify the law to be a lottery. Upon this, said the countryman, 'I wish heartily it was so, for then it would be put down by the late Act of Parliament, and I should fling away no more money at it, for I am sure it has kept me and my family as poor as Job, this fifteen years.'

From thence we walked down by the sempstresses, who were very nicely digitizing and pleating turnovers and ruffles for the young students, and coaxing them with their amorous looks, obliging cant, and inviting gestures, to give so extravagant a price for what they buy, that they may now and then afford to fling them a night's lodging into the bargain.

We now began to take notice of the building, which to me seemed as noble as 'twas ancient; and looking upwards, could do no less than greatly admire the timber roof, being finely built after the Gothic order. But that which was chiefly to be observed in it, was the cleanliness thereof, it being as free from dust and cobwebs as if 'twas raised but yesterday. 'This,' says my friend, 'occasions some people to conjecture it is built with Irish oak, to which is ascribed this miraculous virtue, viz., that no spiders, or any such sort of nauseous or offensive insects, will ever breed or hang about it.' 'And,' said I, 'are you apt to give credit to this vulgar error, and attribute its cleanness to any quality of the wood?' 'No,' says he, 'I am apt to believe all such notions to be vain and fabulous; and that its continuing free from all such nasty vermin proceeds from another reason.' 'Pray,' said I, 'let's hear your conjecture concerning it; for I assure you, I look upon it to be very strange that a wooden roof of such antiquity should be so very free of all that filth which is most commonly collected in all such old fabrics.' 'Why, then,' says he, 'I'll frankly tell you my opinion, which, if it seems incongruous to your reason, I hope you will be so friendly as to excuse my weakness. You must consider,' says he, 'that the young lawyers are unhappily liable to abundance of mischances, and often require the use of mercury to repair their members. Some subtle particles of this, being emitted with their breath, ascend by their volatility to the top of the Hall, where it condenses itself and lies sublimed upon the beams, and so by its poisonous quality renders the roof obnoxious of all vermin. For this is certainly true, that let any person that has taken a mercurial dose but breathe upon a spider, and it will die immediately.' 'This,' said I, 'from a surgeon is well enough, for men of your profession may take the liberty of talking like apothecaries, and not be censured for it. But I think you have fitted me with a piece of as dark philosophy as any to be found in Aristotle's masterpiece.'

Meeting with nothing further, much worth our observation, I think it may not be improper to conclude our remarks of this place with the character of a pettifogger.

He's an amphibious monster that partakes of two natures, and those contrary; he's a great lover both of peace and emnity, and has no sooner set people together by the ears, but is soliciting the Law to make an end of the difference. His mother was a scold, and he was begot in a time when his father used the act more for quietness' sake than procreation. His learning is commonly as little as his honesty, and his conscience much larger than his green-bag. His affection for the Law proceeds from the litigiousness of his ancestors, who brought the family to beggary. Therefore there is nothing he abhors more than poverty in a client. He is never more proud than when he has a fee for a topping counsel, and would make anybody believe Sergeant Such-a-one and he are as great as the Devil and the Earl of Kent. He gets money in term-time by sitting in a tavern, for every client that comes in he makes pay sixpence a glass till he has sold a quart or two at that rate, and puts the overplus in his pocket.

He seems always as busy as a merchant in 'Change time, and if ever a cause is carried that he's concerned in, he tells you it's owing to his management. He's a great lover of veal, through the respect he has for calves'-skin, and admires the wonderful works of the bee, more for the wax than honey. He's a man of such justice that he loves all things should be done according to the law, and calls everybody fool that pays a debt till he has forced the creditor to prove it in some of the courts at Westminster. Unlike the rest of mankind, he hates peace in his neighbourhood, and looks upon it that he sits rent-free if he be but happily seated among wrangling neighbours. Catch him in what company soever, you will always hear him stating of cases, or telling what notice my Lord Chancellor took of him when he begged leave to supply the deficiency of his counsel. He always talks with as great assurance as if he understood what he pretends to know, and always wears a band, in which lies his gravity and wisdom. He concerns himself with no justice but the justice of a cause, and for making an unconscionable bill he outdoes a tailor.

He is so well-read in physiognomy that he knows a knight of the post by his countenance; and if your business requires the service of such an agent, he can pick you up one at a small warning. He is very understanding in the business of the Old Bailey, and knows as well how to fee a juryman as he does a barrister. He has a rare knack at putting in broomstick-bail, and knows a great many more ways to keep a man out of his money than he does to get it him. He's very diligent in business when money's to be got, and runs backward and forward between the lawyer and the client as a rocket upon a string between two posts. Tricks and quirks he calls the cunning part of the law; and that attorney that practises the most knavery is the man for his money.

His study is abroad, his learning all experience, and his library in his pocket, which is always stuffed with as many papers as poet Bayes's in the *Rehearsal*. He puts more faith in the law than he does in the Gospel and knows no other religion than to get money. He thinks nothing a breach of charity but the starving of a good cause and has often that text of scripture in his mouth, viz. 'The labourer is worthy of his hire', which is as much as to say he would not waste time to read a chapter in the Bible without being paid for it. He's also a great newsmonger and all public reports must occur to his knowledge, for his business lies most in a coffee-house, and the greatest of his diversions is in reading the newspapers. He is commonly a great smoker and will walk half a mile to a tobacconist's where he thinks he may have six corns more than ordinary for his penny. Meet him wheresoever in term-time, and ask him, 'Whither go you?' And his answer shall be 'To Westminster.' And indeed you may find him in the Hall much oftener than he that has ten times the business there, for he is one of those that loves to hear how other people's matters go, though it does not at all concern him. There's nothing he abominates more than to be thought negligent, and has no other virtue to boast on truly but his diligence, for no man shall be more watchful in another's ruin than himself. In short, he's a caterpillar upon earth, who grows fat upon the fruits of others' labour; a mere horseleech in the Law, that when once he is well fastened, will suck a poor client into a deep consumption.

Having thus taken notice of most things remarkable in the Hall, we made our exit from thence, and crossed the Palace Yard, on the east side of which lay the relics of Westminster stone clock-case, in a confused heap of ruin. 'There's nothing,' says my friend, 'concerns me more than to see any piece of antiquity demolished. It always puts me in mind of the ignoble actions of the unsanctified rebels in the late domestic troubles, who made it their business to deface old images, and with sacrilegious hands threw down the urns and spoiled the monuments of the dead; a base and inglorious revenge, to gratify their choleric zeal, by robbing their own native country of its ancient beauties; a crime abominated by the most savage and unpolished people in the whole universe. That Christians should be guilty of such barbarity that is held detestable amongst the worst of heathens, is very strange. I speak not this,' says he, 'to reflect upon the destruction of this old steeple, which was wholly useless when they had removed the clock to St Paul's, which, indeed, is far more worthy of so ponderous a bell, that affords so grave a sound, than the place it stood in.

'The common people have a notion (but of no authority as I know on) that this bell was paid for by a fine levied upon some judge, for the unlawful determination of some weighty affair in which he suffered himself to be bribed to partiality, and that it was converted to the use of a clock with this moral intent, that whenever it struck it might be a warning to all succeeding magistrates in the Courts at Westminster how they do injustice. But if it were so, the judges and lawyers in this more religious age are so free from corruption that they need no other motives or memorandums to discharge their trust with unbiased honesty than the unerring dictates of their own good conscience, so that my loud-mouthed namesake might very well be spared to a better purpose, and hang within the hearing of all the cuckolds in the City to call their wives twice a day to prayers, that they may ask forgiveness for the great injury they did their husbands the last opportunity, and also to proclaim, by the gravity of its sound, the greatness of that huge, huge, huge Cathedral, which is big enough to hold more souls than Westminster Abbey, though it is not half so venerable.'

From the Palace Yard we moved on progressively till we came to the tennis court, but I could not for my life imagine what place that could be, hung round with such a deal of network. At last, thinks I, I have heard of such a place as a Plot office. I fancy this must be it, and those are the projectors' nets to catch such Jacobite fools who have no more wit than to be drawn into the design. But however, not well satisfied with my own notion, I thought it proper to enquire of my friend before I told him my sentiments, lest, through an innocent mistake, I should give him just occasion to laugh at my ignorance. He informed me 'twas a convenience built for the noble game of tennis, a very delightful exercise, much used by persons of quality, and attended with these extraordinary good properties; it is very healthful to him that plays at it, and is very profitable to him that keeps it. And rightly considered, it's a good emblem of the world. As thus, the gamesters are the great men, the rackets are the laws, which they hold fast in their hands, and the balls are we little mortals which they bandy backwards or forwards from one to t'other, as their own will and pleasure directs 'em.

We passed by this and went forward to Whitehall, whose ruins we viewed with no less concern than the unhappy fate of such a noble structure must needs beget in each considerate beholder, especially when they reflect upon the honour it had to entertain the best and greatest of princes, in their highest state and grandeur, for several preceding ages; and now at last to be consumed by flames near so much water. Who can do otherwise than grieve to see that order which the hands of artists, at the cost of kings, had improved to such delight and stateliness, lie dissolved in a heap of rubbish? Those spacious rooms where majesty has sat so oft, attended with the transcending glories of his Court, the just, the wise, the brave and beautiful, now are huddled in confusion, and nothing more can boast themselves but dirt and ashes; as if the misfortunes of princes were visited upon their palaces, as well as persons, to manifest to the world more clearly that an overruling power, and not accident, always decrees their sufferings.

After we had taken a survey of the ruins, and spent some melancholy thoughts upon the tattered object that lay in dust before us, we walked on through several out-courts, till we came into a place my friend told me was Scotland Yard, where gentlemen soldiers lay basking in the sun, like so many lazy swine upon a warm dunghill. I stood a little while ruminating on the great unhappiness of such a life, and could not restrain my thoughts from giving a character of that unfortunate wretch who in time of war hazards his life for sixpence a day, and that perhaps ne'er paid him, and in time of peace has nothing to do but to mount the guard and loiter.

A foot-soldier is commonly a man who, for the sake of wearing a sword, and the honour of being termed a gentleman, is coaxed from a handicraft trade whereby he might live comfortably, to bear arms for his king and country whereby he has the hopes of nothing but to live starvingly. His lodging is as near Heaven as his quarters can raise him, and his soul generally as near Hell as a profligate life can sink him, for to speak without swearing he thinks a scandal to his post. He makes many a meal upon tobacco, which keeps the inside of his carcase as nasty as his shirt. He's a champion for the Church, because he fights for religion, though he never hears prayers except they be read upon a drumhead. He's oftentimes seen to stand sentinel over an oyster-tub, in the absence of his flat-cap mistress, who has him more at command than his officer. He often leads a sober life against his will, and whenever he gets drunk it is in a bawdy-house. He can never pass by a brandy shop with two pence in his pocket, for he as naturally loves strong waters as a Turk loves coffee. He is generally beloved by two sorts of companions, viz. whores and lice, for both these vermin are great admirers of a scarlet coat.

No man humbles himself more upon the committing of a fault, for he bows his head to his heels, and lies bound by the hour to his good behaviour. He is a man of undaunted courage; dreading no enemy so much as he does the wooden horse, which makes him hate to be mounted, and rather chooses to be a foot-soldier. He's a man that upon the guard always keeps his word, and obeys his officer, as Indians do the Devil, not through love but fear. He makes a terrible figure in a country town, and makes the old women watch their poultry more than a gang of gipsies. He seldom wants the two good properties of begging and thieving, without which he would be but a poor traveller.

When once he has been in a battle it's a hard matter to get him out of it, for wherever he comes he's always talking of the action, in which he was posted in the greatest danger, and seems to know more of the matter than the General. Scars, though got in drunken quarrels, he makes badges of his bravery and tells you they were wounds received in some engagement, though perhaps given him for his sauciness. He's one that loves fighting no more than other men, though perhaps a dozen of drink and an affront will make him draw his sword; yet a pint and a good word will make him put it up again. Let him be in never so many campaigns in Flanders, he contracts but few habits of a Dutchman, for you shall oftener see him with his fingers in his neck than his hands in his pockets. He has the pleasure once a week, when he receives his subsistence, of boasting he has money in his breeches and, for all he's a soldier, owes no man a groat; which is likely enough to be true, because nobody will trust him. Hunger and lousiness are the two distempers that afflict him, and idleness and scratching the two medicines that palliate his miseries. If he spends twenty years in wars and lives to be forty, perhaps he may get a halbert, and if he survives threescore, an hospital. The best end he can expect to make is to die in the bed of honour, and the greatest living marks of his bravery, to recommend him at once to the world's praise and pity, are crippled limbs, with which I shall leave him to beg a better livelihood.

To a cobbler's awl, or butcher's knife,
    Or porter's knot, commend me!
But from a soldier's lazy life,
    Good Heaven, I pray, defend me.

IX

AS SOON AS we turned out of Scotland Yard into the common road, I espied a famous edifice diametrically opposite to the gate we passed through; the freshness of the bricks and form of which building which showed it was of a modern erection. Perpendicularly over the main door or entrance was placed a golden anchor, which occasioned me to enquire of my friend to what public use this noble fabric was converted. In answer to this said he, 'This is the place where so many letters have been directed, which were put into the *Gazette* concerning the discovery of many abuses and irregularities committed in Her Majesty's Navy, and great encouragements were offered to the authors of those letters to appear and justify what illegal and unwarrantable practices they could charge upon any person or persons commissioned in that service under the Government.' 'And pray,' said I, 'what became of that matter at last about which there was so great a bustle?' 'You must be careful,' says my friend, 'how you ask questions in such affairs, and it behoves me to be as cautious how I answer any. But to divert you from your enquiries, I'll tell you a story.

'A merry cobbler, as he sat stitching in his stall, was singing a piece of his own composition to indulge his cheerful humour, wherein he very often repeated these following words, viz. "The King said to the Queen, and the Queen said to the King." A passenger coming by, who was mighty desirous of knowing what it was the King and Queen said to one another, stood listening a considerable time, expecting the cobbler to have gone on with his ditty, wherein he should have satisfied his longing curiosity. But the musical translator continued a rehearsal only of the same words, till he had tired the patience of his auditor, who at last stepped up to the stall and seriously asked the drolling sole-mender what it was the King said to the Queen, and the Queen to the King. The busy Crispin snatches up his strap and lays it, with all his might, across the shoulders of the impertinent querist, passionately expressing himself in these words: "How, now, Saucebox! It's a fine age we live in when such coxcombs as you must be prying into matters of State! I'd have you to know, sirrah, I am too loyal a subject to betray the King's secrets, and pray get ye gone, and don't interrupt me in my lawful occupation, lest

I stick my awl in your arse, and mark you for a fool that meddles with what you have nothing to do with." The cobbler being an old sturdy grizzle, the fellow was forced to bear both with this correction and reproof, and shrugging his shoulders was glad to sneak off about his business.'

'I, know,' said I, 'how to apply the moral of your story, and shall therefore be very careful how I trouble you in the future with any such questions that are either improper for me to ask or inconsistent with your safety to directly answer.'

By this time we were come to the door of the most eminent coffee-house at this end of the town, which my friend had before proposed to give me a sight of. Accordingly we blundered through a dark entry, where the blackguard of quality were playing their unlucky tricks and damning each other in their masters' dialect, armed with flambeaus against the approaching night, that the grandeur of the great and fortunate may not be hid in darkness, but shine in their proper sphere above lesser mortals, who bow their heads to my Lord's distinguishable lustre. At the end of the entry we ascended a pair of stairs which brought us into an old-fashioned room of a cathedral tenement, where a very gaudy crowd of odoriferous Tom-essences were walking backwards and forwards with their hats in their hands, not daring to convert 'em to their intended use, lest it should put the foretops of their wigs into some disorder. We squeezed through the fluttering assembly of snuffing peripatetics till we got to the end of the room, where, at a small table, we sat down, and observed that though there was abundance of guests, there was very little to do, for it was as great a rarity to hear anybody call for a dish of Politician's porridge, or any other liquor, as it is to hear a sponger in a company ask what's to pay, or a beau call for a pipe of tobacco. Their whole exercise was to charge and discharge their nostrils, and keep the curls of their periwigs in their proper order. The clashing of their snuff-box lids, in opening and shutting, made more noise than their tongues, and sounded as terrible in my ears as the melancholy ticks of so many death-watches.

Bows and cringes of the newest mode were here exchanged 'twixt friend and friend, with wonderful exactness; this being the finest academy in the whole universe for a painter to learn to draw the sign of salutation for a tavern. They made a humming like so many hornets in a country chimney, not with their talking, but with their whispering over their new minuets and borees, with their hands in their pockets, if freed from their snuff-boxes, by which you might understand they had most of them been travellers into the Seven Provinces. Amongst them were abundance of officers, or men who by their habit appeared to be such, but they looked as tender as if they carried their down beds with them into the camp, and did not dare to come out of their tents in a cold morning till they had eaten a mess of plum-panada for breakfast, to defend their stomachs from the wind. Yet, through a principle of undaunted courage, they must signalize their affections to their country in undergoing the fatigue of a Flanders campaign, to the great terror of their lady-mothers but to as much purpose, other ways, as if they had spent their time at Hippolyta's and the playhouse, or stayed at home to have been *gardes du corps* to the bellas, to protect them from being plundered of their virginities by the Town stallions, which ought to have been preserved as a recompense for those who truly deserved their favours by hazarding their lives in the nation's service. For as nothing more than the noble passion of love will animate a soldier with bravery, so, undoubtedly, is beauty the greatest reward of victory. At the ends of this principal room were other apartments where, I suppose, the beau-politicians retired upon extraordinary occasions to talk nonsense by themselves about state affairs, that they might not be laughed at.

Having sat all this while looking about us, like a couple of Minerva's birds among so many of Juno's peacocks, admiring their gaiety, we began to be thoughtful of a pipe of tobacco which we were not assured we could have the liberty of smoking lest we should offend those sweet-breathed gentlemen who were always running their noses into the arse of a civet-cat. But, however, we ventured to call for some instruments of evaporation, which were accordingly brought us, but with such a kind of unwillingness as if they would much rather to have been rid of our company, for their tables were so very neat and shined with rubbing, like the upperleathers of an alderman's shoes, and were of as nut-brown a colour as the top of a country housewife's cupboard. The floor was as clean swept as a Sir Courtly's dining-room, which made us to look round to see if there were no orders hung up to impose the forfeiture of so much mop-money upon any person that should spit out of the chimney-corner.

Notwithstanding we wanted an example to encourage us in our porterly rudeness, we ordered 'em to light the wax candle, by which we ignited our pipes, and blew about our whiffs with as little concern as if we had been in the company of so many carmen. At this, several Sir

Foplings that were near us drew their faces into as many peevish wrinkles, as the beaus at Bow Street coffee-house, near Covent Garden, did when the gentleman in masquerade came in amongst them with his oyster-barrel muff and turnip buttons to ridicule their foppery. But, however, regardless of their grimaces, by which they expressed their displeasure, we puffed on our unsavoury weed, till we had cleared one corner of the room and separated the beaus from the more sociable party, and made 'em fly to a great window next the street, where there was such sniffing and snuffing that the rest of the company could scarce keep their countenances.

Just in this interim, whilst the gaudy knot of effeminate philoginians were looking into the street, who should chance to come by on the other side of the way but the old dumb Father Redcap who, casting up his eyes and espying such a parcel of elegant figures standing at the window, made a full stop over against the coffee-house and began, according to his custom, to show his antic postures and buffoonery actions, dancing the soldier's dance and playing abundance of fool's antic pranks, to engage passengers to tarry and behold his apish gestures. And when he had collected a promiscuous multitude of tradesmen and soldiers, porters, chimney-sweepers and footmen round about him, he fronts his flaxen-wigged spectators at the coffee-house, who were stroking down their straggling hairs and sweetening the common shore of their insipid brains by their perfumed snuffs, and began to mimic the beaus, rendering himself immediately so intelligible to the rabble by his apt signs and ridiculous postures that the crowd set up a holler, and the eyes of the whole mob were directed to our squeamish tobacco-haters.

The poor deaf comedian, perceiving the mob well pleased, persisted in his whim and buffooned with excellent humours the strut, the toss of the wig, the carriage of the hat, the snuff-box, the fingering of the foretop, the hanging of the sword, and to each action formed so suitable a face that the most grave spectator could not forbear laughing. This put our orangery sparks to the blush, and made them retire from their casements, by which time our smoking had given encouragement to others to pluck out their boxes and betake themselves to the like liberty so that we smoked out the beaus, almost as bad as unlucky schoolboys used to do the cobbler, till they sneaked off one by one, and left behind 'em more agreeable company.

We could then discern there were some great men by the grandeur of their looks, the awfulness of their presence, and gracefulness of their deportment. There were several officers, with old English aspects, whose martial faces were adorned with weather-beaten wrinkles crossed with hacks and scars, those rugged beauty-spots of war, which they wore as true marks of their undaunted bravery. Having by this time ended our pipes, we wound up our diversion with a fashionable mess of Turkish sobriety, after which we scribbled down these following lines in a slate-book, and so departed.

> Here persons who for places wait,
>   Deceitful courtiers greet,
> And men of sense, made tools by fate,
>   Their crafty patrons meet.
>
> Here pensioned spies like saints appear,
>   Who do men's hearts inspect,
> And whisper in the statesman's ear
>   What they abroad collect.
>
> Here news by subtle tongues is spread,
>   To try the listening crowd;
> But what is truth's a secret made,
>   Whilst lies are talked aloud.
>
> Beau fools in clusters here resort
>   And are so saucy grown,
> They'll ask, 'My lord, what news from Court?'
>   Who smiles, and answers 'None'.
>
> To be informed few caring less,
>   But ask as 'tis the mode,
> No knowledge seek, but how to dress.
>   Their tailor is their god!
>
> Here flatterers meet their empty squires
>   And praise their shallow sense.
> The idiot in return admires
>   His fawning eloquence.

And that he further may enjoy
   A man of such desert,
He steps to Locket's, cross the way,
   And treats him with a quart.

The gamester does his bubble meet,
   And seems to be his friend.
Hence draws him to a tavern treat,
   Where he effects his end.

Both such who serve and plague the state
   Do hither make their way,
And crowds of human vultures wait
   To catch their silly prey.

Having now squeezed back through a long dark entry full of rapscallionly skipjacks into the open street, my friend bid me take notice of two great taverns on the other side the way. 'In those eating-houses,' says he, 'as many fools' estates have been squandered away, as ever were swallowed up by the Royal Oak lottery; for every fop who, with a small fortune, attempts to counterfeit quality and is fool enough to bestow twenty shillings' worth of sauce upon ten pennyworth of meat, resorts to one of these ordinaries, where a man that is as rich as Croesus may outlive Elagabalus, and spend more open money upon a dinner than a sergeant-at-law can get in a whole issuable term.'

As we were thus talking, a squadron of horse marched by in order to relieve the guard. My friend asked me my opinion of their appearance, and how I liked the sight of so many brave Englishmen on horseback, which, says he, had not been seen in these parts, till of late, these many years. 'Truly,' said I, 'I think they look more like soldiers and become their post much better in their old coats than the butterboxes did in all their finery; and indeed it's more natural for us to think they would do their own country greater service upon occasion, and would hazard their lives with more heartiness than it is reasonable to expect foreigners would do for us. Dutchmen, for aught I know, may fight in defence of Holland, or a Frenchman for the security of his own nation, but whenever the necessities of England shall force her upon either for assistance, she will find to her sorrow, she has but a broken reed to rely on.'

By this time they were passed by us, so we moved on till we came to the subterranean warehouse of an eminent dealer in old boots, shoes, slippers, spurs, spatterdashes and gambages. The front of his translating cavern being adorned with such sundry sorts of leather conveniences, I could not but think he was the only human farrier appointed to shoe all the inferior quality at this end of the town. My friend and I having proposed in a few days to ride down to Tonbridge, the well-finished palace of Cobblerius Caesar put us in mind of laying hold of this opportunity to fit ourselves with some accoutrements at best hand, of which we were destitute. Accordingly we descended into the cabin, by very steep gradations, with abundance of caution, as otherwise the hillocks of dirt upon the stairs, for want of the use of a paring-shovel, might have endangered our necks, as the jamb above us, without humbling our carcases, threatened us with a broken head. But with care and gentleness we got safe to the bottom where the grizzly crepidarian sat uniting of dissenting soles, who, by their stubborn disagreeableness, had broken the threads of unity and separated themselves, to their maker's dishonour, from their upperleathers. As soon as he saw us, he bid us welcome, dismounting his glass adjutants, who rid a-cock-horse on his nose, and laying by his work with as much cheerfulness as an old whore does the *Practice of Piety* upon the reception of a visitant, he asked us what we wanted. We told him boots, so he presently furnished us with all sorts and sizes amongst which parcel, after a little search, we pitched upon such that pleased us, and sat down upon a stool hewed out of the whole timber for duration's sake, in order to try 'em on.

In this interval a ragged Irishman (which in this town is said to be a wonder) came down and desired him, in his Irish accent, to show him a pair of shoes. Crispin being a little busy in giving us his attendance, believing us the better customers, happened, through carelessness, to hand him a couple of shoes which were not fellows. Teague drew on one and it fitted him very well, but when he tried the other he found it much too little and quite of another sort. 'By my shoul, Dear Joy,' says he, 'the man's futs that wore these brogues were not fellows. Prithee let me see another pair.' The cobbler, looking upon the shoes and finding his mistake, cast his eye upon the fellow's feet and discovered his stockings to be of different colours. 'I thought, master,' says he, 'you would have had your shoes as you have your stockings, one of one sort, and one of another, but however, if these won't do, I'll see further if I can fit you.' Accordingly he hands him another pair with the toe of one (as is usual) thrust into the other. The Irishman put on his old shoes again in a great passion, and took his leave in these words: 'By Chreest and Shaint Patrick, ye are a sheating kenave. De you tink E will buy a pair of brogues dat de little one ish big enough to hold de great one in ish bally? How, by my shoul, can you tink dey will fit my futs, dey are bott of a smallness.' And away he trips upstairs in his aged pumps, made sandals by much wearing so that they were forced to be laced on with packthread, and so marched off in a great fury, to relieve his pedestals at the next convenience, leaving us to chatter with our drolling mundungus-puffer, who fitted us with what we wanted at reasonable rates, like a man of conscience, without using half so many lies and canting reservations as a sober citizen in his shop, but gave us a hearty welcome into the bargain and so we parted.

When we had crawled up again into the street, like a couple of gentleman soldiers out of a twopenny ordinary, the first object with which our eyes were affected was the brazen statue of that pious prince, King Charles the First, on horseback, whose righteous life, unhappy reign, unjust sufferings and unparalleled martyrdom shall bury monuments, outlive Time, and stand up with Eternity. I could not without the highest concern, and deepest reflections on his great misfortunes, behold the image of that good man, in whose artful effigy may be seen the piety, majesty, mercy, patience and innocence of the matchless original, the causeless disturbances of whose reign, and the barbarous usage of whose person, will stick as thorns, I hope, in the sides of Faction, till they are crushed into that anarchy from whence they had their first beginning. Thus did we stand awhile ruminating upon the sad catastrophe of this unhappy prince, till at last his venerable statue inspired me with these following lines, which, I hope, the unprejudiced reader will receive with candour.

> Great were thy wrongs, thy patience still as great,
> When Faction ruled the Church, and knaves the State.
> Hard were thy people's hearts, but harder yet thy fate.
>
> Balm thou applied'st whilst they still vexed thee sore,
> The more their crimes, thy mercies grew the more.
> Thy godlike mind was rich, although thy treasure poor.

They sought thy ruin with rebellious spite,
And trod dark paths, whilst thou pursued'st the light.
As they increased their shame, thy glories shone more bright.

Had'st thou in rage thy victories pursued
And took delight in shedding rebels' blood,
Thou'd'st been secure, but wert, alas, too mild and good.

Contempt for all thy favours they returned,
Scoffed at thy power, and at thy person spurned,
Rejoiced o'er others' spoils, whilst all true subjects mourned.

The canting pulpiteers, by dreams made wise,
Turned gospel truths into audacious lies,
And taught the blood of kings a holy sacrifice.

Unlearned mechanics, full of zeal and noise,
Were turned, through grace, expounders of the laws,
And justified rebellion to be Heaven's cause.

When right, through want of due assistance, failed,
And wrong, through misled multitudes, prevailed,
The trait'rous torrent grew too strong to be repelled.

Thus the mad crowd, who could not ills foresee
Of just restraint endeavouring to be free,
Took off thy head, because themselves would headless be.

From Charing Cross, we turned up towards the Strand, at the entrance of which I observed an ancient stone fabric, in the front of which I beheld, with satisfaction, the handiwork of our forefathers, in whose sullied antiquity I could discern much more beauty than my genius can discover in any modern building. 'What a thousand pities,' said I, 'is it that so noble a palace, which appears so magnificent and venerable, should not have the old hospitality continued withinside, answerable to its outward grandeur.'

'Truly,' says my friend, 'it is a great scandal to the present age that quality should so degenerate from their ancestors, and instead of imitating the liberality of their grandsires in relieving the distresses of their neighbours, supplying the wants of poor friends and relations, and (to the honour of themselves and country) giving charitable entertainment to strangers and travellers, they now squander away their estates in whoring, gaming, and external foppery, to the disgrace of so flourishing a nation, the scandal of that dignity to which God has raised 'em, and to the ruin of themselves and families. For it may be observed that when great men, who are indeed no more than Heaven's stewards for the poor, discharged their duty to those unhappy wretches, who by the disabilities of nature or the contingent mutabilities of this life were reduced to necessity, they added to their own fortunes, by an improvement of their estates. And whilst they supported in their houses a commendable hospitality, they were always attended with such prosperity that their riches were preserved by Providence from any ruinous chance or fatal devastation. Whereas I could instance on the contrary (could it be done without reflection) many families now in being, who are brought to beggary from very plentiful estates, who neither signalised their loyalty to the Crown, their affection to their country, their kindness to their low relations, their charity to the poor, or good to the public, by any expensive act as ever was made manifest, but were wormed out of their patrimony by the fraud of gamesters, the subtlety of lewd women, the emulation of gaiety, and the treacherous delusions of hypocrites and flatterers.'

'Methinks,' said I, 'you have preached a very notable sermon, as this would rather have become the mouth of a clergyman than a man of your youth and airiness.' 'You must consider,' says he, 'we libertines have our sober intervals just as the grave Puritan in private has his comfortable refreshments. For the difference between us lies only in this particular: we seldom do what they often practise, and they practise seldom what we often do.'

We moved on along the Strand, as leisurely as a couple of *valets-de-chambres* out of places, in search of a dinner, meeting nothing remarkable till we came to the New Exchange, into which seraglio of fair ladies we made our entrance, to take a pleasing view of the cherubimical lasses, who, I suppose, had dressed themselves up for sale to the best advantage, as well as the fopperies and toys they dealt in. And indeed, many of them looked so very amiable, so enticing fair, that had I been happily furnished with some superfluous angels, I could willingly have dealt among the charming witches for some of their commodities; but as cursed cows have short horns, I could only walk by, and lick my lips at their handsome faces, as a hungry beggar when he stares into a cook's shop, and was forced so to content myself. The chiefest customers that I observed they had, were beaus, who, I imagined, were paying a double price for linen, gloves, or sword-knots, to the prettiest of the women, that they might go from thence and boast among their brother fops what singular favours and great encouragements they had received from the fair lady that sold 'em.

Finding nothing else amongst 'em worth observing, I digested a little of their shop language into a song, and so proceeded.

'Fine lace or linen, sir,
Good gloves or ribbons here —
   What is't you please to buy, sir?'
"Pray what d'ye ask for this?"
'Ten shilling is the price;
It cost me, sir, no less,
   I scorn to tell a lie, sir.

'Madam, what is't you want?
Rich fans of India paint?
   Fine hoods or scarves, my lady?
Silk stockings will you buy,
In grain or other dye?
Pray, madam, please your eye,
   I've good as e'er was made ye.

'My lady, feel the weight —
They're fine, and yet not slight,
   I'd with my mother trust 'em
For goodness and for wear.
Madam, I vow and swear
I showed you this same pair,
   In hopes to gain your custom.

"Pray, tell me in a word,
At what you can afford,
   With living gain to sell 'em?"
'The price is one pound five,
And, as I hope to live,

I do my profit give,
  Your Honour's very welcome.

'Knives, penknives, combs or scissors,
Tooth-pickers, sirs; or tweezers,
    Or walking canes to ease ye.
Ladies, d'ye want fine toys,
For misses, or for boys?
Of all sorts I have choice,
    And pretty things to please ye.

'I want a little baby,
As pretty a one as may be,
    With head-dress made of feather.
And now I think again,
I want a toy from Spain —
You know what 'tis I mean.
    Pray send 'em home together.'

Having taken a satisfactory survey of this jilts' academy, where girls are admitted at nine years old, and taught by eleven to out-chatter a magpie, outwit their parents, and by the improving instructions and example of their kind mistresses and neighbouring correspondents, are made as forward and as ripe in thought before they are out of their hanging-sleeves as a country wench is at five-and-twenty.

We then took our leaves of this cloister of kind damsels, so turned up by the Half-Moon Tavern, and proceeded towards Covent Garden, where we overtook abundance of religious lady-birds, armed against the assaults of Satan with Bible and Common Prayer Book, marching with all good speed to Covent Garden Church. 'Certainly,' said I, 'the people of this parish are better Christians than ordinary, for I never observed, upon a weekday, since I came to London, such a sanctified troop of females flocking to their devotions, as I see at this part of the town.' ' These,' says my friend, 'are a pious sort of creature that are much given to go to church, and may be seen there every day at prayers, as constantly as the bell rings; and if you were to walk the other way, you might meet as many young gentlemen from the Temple and Gray's Inn, going to join with them in their devotions. We'll take a turn into the sanctuary amongst the rest, and you shall see how they behave themselves.'

Accordingly, we stepped into the rank, amongst the lambs of grace, and entered the tabernacle with the rest of the saints, where we found a parcel of as very handsome, cleanly, well-dressed Christians as a man would desire to communicate with, of both sexes. They stood ogling one another with as much zeal and sincerity as if they worshipped the Creator in the creature, and whispering to their next neighbours, as if, according to the Liturgy, they were confessing their sins to one another. This, I afterwards understood by my friend, was only to make assignations, 'and the chief of their prayers,' says he, 'is that Providence will favour their intrigues.'

When the parson had made an end of what, with much earnestness, to little purpose, he had conned over to his amorous congregation, we made our exit from thence, and went through the Market, where a parcel of jolly red-faced dames, in blue aprons and straw hats, sat selling their garden-ware, but they stunk so of brandy, strong drink and tobacco, that the fumes they belched up from their overcharged stomachs o'ercame the fragrance that arose from their sweet herbs and flowers.

'This market,' says my friend, 'and that church hides more faults of kind wives and daughters among the neighbouring inhabitants than the pretended visits either to my cousin at t'other end of town, or some other distant acquaintance. For if the husband asks, "Where have you been, wife?" Or the parent, "Where have you been, daughter?" The answer, if it be after eleven in the forenoon, or between three and four in the afternoon, is "At prayers." But if early in the morning, then their excuse is, "I took a walk to Covent Garden Market, not being very well, to refresh myself with the scent of the herbs and flowers." Bringing a flower or a sprig of sweet-brier home in her hand confirms the matter.

'Now,' says my friend, 'we are so near, I'll carry you to see the Hummums, where I have an honest old acquaintance that is a cupper, and if you will pay your club towards eight shillings, we'll go in and sweat, and you shall feel the effects of this notable invention.' 'With all my heart,' said I, 'you know I am always conformable to whatever you propose.' So, accordingly, he conducted me to the house, through which we passed into a long gallery, where my friend's acquaintance received him with much gladness. I had not walked above once the length of the gallery, but I began to find myself as warm as a cricket at an oven's mouth. My friend telling him we designed to sweat, he from thence introduced us into a warmer climate. 'Pray, friend,' said I, 'what latitude do you think we are in now?' 'You must consider,' says he, 'we are making a short cut to the East Indies, and are now in about twenty-three degrees and a half, that's just under one of the tropics, but this heat is nothing to what you'll feel when you come under the equinoctial, where I can assure you we shall find ourselves in a very little time.'

We now began to unstrip, and put ourselves in a condition of enduring an hour's baking, and when we had reduced ourselves into the original state of mankind, having nothing before us to cover our nakedness but a clout no bigger than a fig-leaf, our guide led us to the end of our journey, the next apartment, which I am sure was as hot as a pastry-cook's oven for to bake a white-pot, so that I began immediately to melt like a piece of butter in a basting-ladle, and was afraid I should have run all to oil by the time I had been in six minutes. The bottom of the room was paved with freestone, to defend our feet from the excessive heat of which we had got on a pair of new-fashioned brogues, with wooden soles, after the French mode, cut out of an inch deal-board, or else, like the fellow in the Fair, we might as well have walked cross a hot iron bar as ventured here to have trod barefoot. As soon as the fire had tapped us all over, and we began to run at every pore like a conduit pipe, our rubber arms his right hand with a gauntlet of course hair camlet, and begins to curry us with as much labour as a Yorkshire groom does his master's best stone horse, till he made us as smooth as a fair lady's cheeks just washed with lemon posset, and greased over with pomatum.

At last, I grew so very faint with the expense of so much spirits, I begged as hard for a mouthful of fresh air as Dives did for a drop of water, which our attendant let in at a sash-window no broader than a Deptford cheesecake, but it let in a comfortable breeze that was very reviving. When I had fouled about as many calico napkins as a child does double-clouts in a week, our rubber draws a cistern full of hot water, that we might go in and boil out those gross humours that could not be emitted by a more gentle perspiration. Thus almost baked to a crust, we went into the hot bath to moisten our clay, where we lay soddening ourselves, like deer's umbles designed for mince pies, till we were almost parboiled. Talking by accident of a pain that sometimes affected my shoulder, occasioned by a fall from my horse, my friend by all means advised me to be cupped for it, telling me 'twas the best operation in the world for the removal of all such grievances. Being an utter stranger to this sort of phlebotomy, I was a little unwilling to undergo the experience of it, but by the persuasions of my friend, and my friend's friend, I at last consented. Upon this the operator fetched in his instruments, and fixed three glasses at my back, which, by drawing out the air, stuck to me as close as a cantharides plaster to the head of a lunatic, and sucked as hard as so many leeches at a wench's fundament, when troubled with the haemorrhoids, till I thought they would have crept into me and have come out on t'other side.

When, by virtue of this hocus-pocus stratagem, he had conjured all the ill blood out of my body under his glass juggling cups, he plucks out an ill-favoured instrument, at which I was as much frighted as an absconding debtor is at the sight of a Bill of Middlesex, takes off his glasses, which had made my shoulders as weary as a porter's back under a heavy burden, and begins to scarify my skin, as a cook does a loin of pork to be roasted, but with such ease and dexterity that I could have suffered him to have pinked me all over as full of eyelet-holes as the tailor did the shoemaker's cloak, had my malady required it, without flinching. When he had drawn away as much blood as he thought necessary for the removal of my pain, he covered the places he had carbonadoed with a new skin, provided for that purpose, and healed the scarifications he had made, in an instant. Then taking me up like a scalded swine, out of my greasy broth, after he had wiped o'er my wet buttocks with a dry clout, telling us we had sweat enough, he relieved us out of our purgatory, and carried us into our dressing-room. This gave us such refreshment after we had been stewing in our own gravy, that we thought ourselves as happy as a couple of English travellers, transported in an instant by a miracle, from the torrid zone into their own country.

Our expense of spirits had weakened nature and made us drowsy, so having the convenience of a bed, we lay down and were rubbed like a couple of racehorses after a course, till we were become as cool as the affections of a passionate lover after a night's enjoyment.

When we had refreshed our carcases by a plentiful dram of Doctor Stephen's Cordial, so full of gold that it looked as tempting as gilded gingerbread to the eyes of a froward infant, and had taken an hour's repose, to reconcile the fermented humours of our bodies to their orderly motion, we then got up, and began to cover our indecencies with those habiliments the tailor had contrived to hide our nakedness. To put these on to the best advantage, our rubber gave us his assistance, during which time he also entertained us with several delightful stories, which he told in such apt words, and with such agreeable humour, that he made my guts shake with laughing, like a trodden quagmire. And that the reader may be a partaker of our mirth, I have here made a recital of some of his short comedies, in which he himself was the principal actor.

'It happened,' says he, 'not long ago, that a very fine lady of the town came in to clean her skin and supple her industrious joints, as I suppose, to make her tender limbs the more pliable and fit for the exercise of love which she was, doubtless, that night to be engaged in. She was at the charge of a crown bath-extraordinary, enriched with essences and sweet herbs, to add such a fragrance to her body that might render her most putrescent parts as sweet as a calf's nostril. When she had put herself into this order, and made herself a suitable companion for the nicest bedfellow, she commanded her little mercury that attended her, to call a coach, and away she went.

'Immediately after came in a very topping beau from the tavern, pretty well loaded with wine, and used to sweating in the room which the lady had just quitted. Being very humoursome, he would not be persuaded to go into any other, so they were forced to show him the same apartment. One of the rubbers going into the hot room where the gentleman was to sweat, and turning one of the cocks, found that the stoker had been negligent, and that the hot water was all run off. As he had gone out a-fuddling, they knew not what shift to make to draw a fresh bath, and at last found they had no way left but to make the lady's bath to serve again. So they were forced to deceive the gentleman by telling him there was an extraordinary bath, preserved with sweet herbs for a person of quality who had sent to bespeak the room hot.

'The time being elapsed, they believed the lady would not come, and that it was great pity to let it run off without use, which if he pleased to accept on, he might have without paying any more than the common rates of the house. The gentleman, very well pleased with so kind a proffer, very gladly consented to make use of it and, after he had sweated a little, went into it. The rubber fishing for the herbs to scour the gentleman's skin, happened to feel something amongst 'em that felt very soft and pappy, and turning his head aside, and smelling to his fingers, found 'twas some unsavory lees which chanced to drop through the bung-hole of that mortal cask which had before been rinsed in the same water. The rubber, in a sad agony, began to be thoughtful of an excuse, in case the gentleman should discover it, fearing the affront might aggravate him to do him a mischief.

'At last the gentleman looking about him, saw the remains of her cleanly ladyship in his bath. "What a plague," says he, "is this nastiness that is swimming amongst the herbs!" "Sir," says the rubber, "it is nothing but Italian paste, which is accounted the most excellent thing to cleanse and make smooth the skin imaginable, and it is what my mistress cannot afford to use but in an extraordinary bath which is paid for above the common rates of the house." "Prithee, friend," says the gentleman, "if it be so good for the skin, rub me well with it, but egad," says he, "in my mind it looks as like a sir-reverence as ever I saw anything in my life." "Aye, sir," says the servant, "and so it does, but it is an incomparable thing to wash with, for all it looks so nastily, and is a compound of the richest gums and best castle-soap boiled up together, that can be bought for money." "Pray," says the beau, "take a little pains with me, and rub me all over with it very well. Who is it that makes it? I'll buy some for my hands." "It is made, sir," replies the rubber, "by a gentlewoman in this town, but where she lives I cannot tell. My mistress, were she within, could inform you, but she went into the City to dinner, and is not returned yet."

'Thus my comrade that attended him, by the good management of his tongue, brought off the mischance cleverly without discovery. The perfumes and sweet herbs in the bath so overpowered the scent, that the gentleman, though he nosed it, being amongst such a mixture of effluvia, it confounded his smelling, and rendered him incapable of distinguishing a fair lady's sir-reverence from the excrement of a civet-cat. So he rose out of his bath extremely pleased, and gave him that attended him half a crown for his extraordinary care and trouble. and so marched away with great satisfaction.'

Having thus concluded the foregoing story, he proceeded to the following: 'A gentleman of fortune, one day lying under a shrewd suspicion of debt, was dogged into our house by a bailiff, who came to the door whilst the gentleman was sweating, and asked for him. One of our rubbers, by chance opening the door, happened to know his calling, and comes in to the gentleman and tells him a fellow wanted to speak with him at the door, pretendingly from such a gentleman of his acquaintance, and that he knew him to be a bailiff. The gentleman thanked him kindly for his information, and put it into his head to get him in, and torment him a little in one of the hot rooms. Accordingly my fellow-servant went back to the Moabite and told him that the gentleman was within, and desired him to come to him. So he conducted the debtor-snapper, who was ready armed with his legal authority, into an ante-room of the next apartment to the gentleman, where he bid him wait a little, and the gentleman would come to him presently.

'In the meanwhile my fellow-servant came to me and the stoker, to consult after what manner we should punish him. I, like a good projector of unluckiness, told him my advice was for us to put on our calico gowns with the hoods over our heads, and disguise our faces with burnt cork as frightfully as we could, and arm ourselves with fire weapons out of the kitchen and so enter upon him all together, seize him, and carry him into the hot room, and there torment him as we should think fit.

'Accordingly we put ourselves in this order, rushed in upon him, and forced him into the hot room. The fellow, coming in the piazza way, was wholly ignorant what place it was, and took it by the front to be a gentleman's house; but feeling the excessive heat, and seeing himself in the hands of so ill-looked goblins, armed with a great beef spit, tongs and fire-fork, he began to roar out like a stuck bacon-hog, and fancied himself in Hell. Then, in a hoarse voice, said I to my brother-infernals, "First let us bake him, and then boil him." To which my comrade with the spit added, "And then I'll have him roasted." These terrible sentences so frighted the disturber of human quiet, in this new state of damnation, that he fell into a swoon, so that we were forced to put him into a cold bath to fetch him to life again.

'When he recovered, he looked as wild as a lunatic at full of the moon, and then cried out as much against the cold as he did before against the heat. Upon this we let run the cock of hot water, till we had almost parboiled him. Then he fell into a second fit, so that we thought it proper to take him out of the bath, and carry him into the ante-room for fear he should have died. There we shaved one side of his head and beard, and fixed on a couple of cupping-horns (which we sometimes use) upon his forehead; so carried him to the back door, and turned him adrift.

'He was so rejoiced that he found redemption from the Devil's clutches that away he ran as fast as a thief under a pursuit, and after him all the mob and boys in the street, crying out, "A mad cuckold! A mad cuckold!" And telling the gentleman what we had done, he returned us hearty thanks, and was mightily pleased at our unluckiness.'

X

HAVING NOW PURIFIED our scorbutic carcases in a resemblance of Purgatory, though in a Protestant country, and made our skins by sweating, bathing, rubbing and scrubbing, as smooth as an old drumhead that had been long beaten, we satisfied the demands of the house, gratified our groom for extraordinary pains in dressing our dirty hides, and then departed. We found our bodies so refreshed, and our spirits so enlivened, that we were weary of grovelling upon the surface of this gross world and began to fancy, like the flying Quaker, from the nimble motions of our spirits that we had got Icarus's wings, and were able, at one flight, to translate our sublime bodies into some loftier region, more suitable to our refined natures, being, as it were, renewed by this fiery trial and cleansed of all corruptions.

From thence we adjourned to the Wits' Coffee-house, in hopes that the powerful eloquence which drops from the silver tongues of the ingenious company that frequent this noted mansion, might inspire us with such a genius as would better fit the perfection of our renovated clay, now that it was purged of all impurities, and rendered a proper receptacle for the most discerning and poetic spirits. Accordingly, upstairs we went, and found much company, and but little talk; as if everyone remembered the old proverb, that a close mouth makes a wise head, and so endeavoured by his silence to be counted a man of judgement, rather than by speaking to stand the censure of so many critics, and run the hazard of losing that character which by holding of his tongue he might be in hopes of gaining.

We shuffled through this moving crowd of philosophical mutes to the other end of the room, where three or four wits of the upper classes were rendezvoused at a table, and were disturbing the ashes of the old poets by perverting their sense, and making strange allegories and allusions never dreamt or thought of by the authors. Thus, they excused some faults, which were really the slips or oversights of the poet, but made others so very gross, through prejudice and misconstruction, that none but critics of very little judgement, or very much ill-nature, could have wrested the sense of the words so much to the injury of him that writ 'em.

When they had showed their learning, as they thought, by arraigning and condemning many of the old Roman muses, they condescended so low as to call some of our modern poets to stand the test of their all-judging opinions, upon whom, in brief, they conferred these characters. One was a man of great judgement, learning, and fancy, but of no principle; another was one that had writ well, and could write well, but would not write; a third never writ but one good thing in his life, and that he recanted; a fourth had a poetical talent, but it was hid under a philosophical bushel; a fifth was a good Latin poet, but had sacrificed his muse to Bacchus, instead of dedicating her to Apollo; a sixth had got a great deal of credit by writing plays, but lost it all by defending the stage; a seventh had got some reputation by turning old ditties into new songs, but lost it all by turning a Spanish romance into an English stage play; an eighth had got honour by a dull poem, which his brother medico envied, and vowed he'd outdo him in verse, as he hoped also to be knighted.

Thus the carping Momuses proceeded according to the critics' custom, never to let anything, though well performed, escape their scrutiny, to the discovery of some colourable fault, nor any character pass their lips, though of the worthiest persons in the world, without being tagged with some calumny or other, on purpose to eclipse the brightness of those virtues for which they are chiefly eminent. And it may generally be observed of those who delight in criticism, that they are so curious in having the maidenhead of an error that if a better judgement finds a fault, which has had the good fortune to escape his censure, he will, if it be possible, find out a salve for that sore, and justify the author ever hereafter in that particular. And he will make it appear there is more sense lies hid in those words than in all the book besides, though he knows what he defends to be arrant nonsense. For he is usually so conceited in his own judgement, that rather than acknowledge he had overlooked an error, he will justify it not to be so. And of such a sort of critic, of which there are hundreds in this town, as well as some at the next table, I think it very proper in this place to give a character. Accordingly I dictated, and my friend writ.

A Modern Critic

Is a compound of some learning, little judgement, less wit, much conceit, and abundance of ill-nature. Wanting true merit, he aims to raise a reputation not by his own performances but by others' failings. These he takes more pleasure to expose than he does to mend, and reads an author as much in search of his faults as a wise man does for his knowledge. Whoever speaks Latin in his company must be as watchful of his words as a prince is of his actions, for if once he breaks Priscian's head he must be forced to break the critic's too, or else suffer himself to be baited as bad as the tiger at the cockpit. True spelling and pointing he admires as the chief ornaments of a poem, and always minds the sense much less than the orthography. Whenever he repeats any grave verse he has more turns in his voice and changes in his countenance than a young preacher in his sermon upon Death and Judgement. And when he reads a tragedy he out-mouths a player and corrects the stage with his extravagant gestures. Whoever talks of an author within his reading shall be sure to be attacked with those places that remain doubtful and obscure. These riddles he expounds and renders as plain (if you'll depend upon his judgement) as that the candle eats the cat, or the coach draws the horses. He would not give a farthing to understand anything but difficulties which have puzzled much wiser heads than his own to truly find the meaning of.

He's a man that seldom writes anything, but when he does, he is so very nice that it's carried as often to the corrector as a lady's stays, or a beau's coat to the tailor, before the typography and orthography are according to his judgement. His talk is usually like a maze or labyrinth, for none but himself has the clue to find the beginning and ending of his tedious comments with which, in all companies, he is very troublesome. Whenever he undertakes to reconcile an absurdity or expound a mystery, he usually does it with as much success as physicians when they labour to unfold the nature of such medicines to the patient which work by occult qualities, only tiring their ears with a few uncommon words which serve among fools as well as an intelligible explication.

He is one that is not wise but would very fain be thought so, and takes as much pains to sit astraddle upon other men's shoulders as would raise his reputation to twice the height, had he wisdom enough to apply the same industry to a better purpose. His head is a mere house of correction, his brains are the register of other men's faults, and his tongue the unmerciful scourge that punishes them. He is the storehouse of other men's infirmities, where seldom anything is laid up but what the authors are ashamed of. They are the mere wasps of the age, who are furnished with unlucky stings, but yield no honey.

Says my friend, 'You have deviated much from the character of a true critic, whose business in the Roman time was to judge the actions and works of men as delivered to the public by historians, poets, philosophers, and the like; to examine the probability and reasonableness of former transactions as they are handed down to us by our ancestors, to prevent their imposition on posterity; to enquire into the truth and usefulness of all sorts of learning, and report their opinions to the world accordingly; and to expound and give their best sense of all ambiguities and obscure passages which they find in any author. These were very commendable and serviceable tasks; but yours is such a coniwable of a critic, I know not what to make of him.'

'Why, then, I'll tell you,' said I. 'I give not this as the character of a real critic, but such a sort of a mongrel critic as he that you heard talk just now. He takes a pride in nothing but snapping and snarling at the little slips and unavoidable failings of authors, which are much beneath the notice of any judicious and good-natured reader, and would die were it not that these petty students in syntax, who handle men's faults in company as a juggler does his balls, till they have made as many as they please of 'em and think they cannot give greater demonstrations of their learning than in public to disparage such persons who have ten times the parts of themselves, foolishly believing that whatever they detract from others they add to their own reputation, and fancy every stain or blemish they can give to an ingenious man's character is a heightening of their own merit. These are the persons of whom I have given this rough sketch. They are only cavillers, or pretenders to criticism, and know nothing of the matter.'

'Nay,' says my friend, 'if it be those you aim at, you have said less than they deserve. I have observed, since I have sat here, that I have heard those gentlemen judge very severely of some modern authors who have not only merited but enjoy a general approbation and applause. And they have so rashly condemned some writings of an ancient worthy and honourable gentleman as if they had a commission to take away men's reputations without giving the least reason why, or an account wherein they have forfeited their credits.'

At another table were seated a parcel of young, raw, second-rate beaus and wits, who were conceited if they had but once the honour to dip a finger and thumb into Mr Dryden's snuff-box; it was enough to inspire 'em with a true genius of poetry, and make 'em write verse as fast as a tailor takes his stitches. These, too, were communicating one to another the newest labours of their brains, wherein were such wondrous flights, unaccountable thoughts, strange figures, hyperboles and similies, and upon such notable subjects, that to hear 'em read their works is at any time sufficient to cure the hypochondria, and turn the deepest melancholy into a fit of laughter. One plucks out a panegyric upon orange-flower water; another, a satire against dirty weather; a third produces a cleanly lampoon upon nasty tobacco smokers; a fourth a poem in praise of short puff-wigs, together with the excellence of paint, powder and patches.

What I heard of these, their most admirable flights, came too abruptly to my ears for me to make a fair recital of any part worth the reader's perusal, or else I would have gladly obliged the world with copies of some of the wild exuberances of their juvenile fancies. But, however, one of them was (as I guessed by his garb) a young officer who happened, in plucking out some other papers, to drop the following poem, which my friend believing to include no great matter of moment, imagined it would prove some such business as we found it to be, and so picked it up slyly without notice. Taking our leave of this Wits' Sessions-House, we brought it away with us. And finding something in it we thought might divert the reader, we have accordingly presented him with a copy, it being:

A Letter from a Lawyer in Town to a New-Married
Officer in the Country

Letters in prose, my friend, are common
As pride in priest, or lust in woman.
Our annual course of long vacation
To business giving a cessation
Affords me time to thus salute ye,
And pay in rhyme this friendly duty.
Not rightly knowing which is worse —
The lawyer's or the poet's curse —
Both silenced with an empty purse!
For now our pens, upon our words,
Are grown as useless as your swords,
We having but as little writing,
As, God be thanked, you have fighting.
You may draw sword, so we may pen,

To show our tools of war, and then
Like fools, e'en put them up again!

But what a pox is't I am doing?
Or where the devil am I going?
Now Pegasus I've once bestridden,
Methinks I gallop like a Dryden,
And pleased I'm in the vein, egad,
Blunder out verse like any mad.
Long as 'tis rhyme it's no great matter,
And bombast, whether praise or satire.
Mistake me not, and think I've writ
To show my parts, that is not it!
I'd not be envied for a wit.

For he that's rich in thought, is sure
To be in friends and pocket poor.
For wise men will not care to serve him
And fools would all be glad to starve him.
Wit carr's an edge, few can abide it —
And he that has it ought to hide it.
Such weapons in a man's possession,
Scare the unarmed from his conversation.
And is so far from being delightful,
It renders him that draws it, frightful!
For no man cares for the company
Of him that has more wit than he,
Nor can he with good will afford
The better genius one good word.
So dowdies will no praise allow
To her that has the lovely brow,
But will endeavour to confute ye,
She has more faults by half than beauty.
To wits 'tis fear that makes us civil,
Just as an Indian is to the Devil.

This ignis fatuus in my brains
That kindles up these rambling strains,
Makes my head light as any feather,

And leads me wand'ring God knows whither.
But poets when we make digression,
The fault we supple by confession
And so excuse the wild transgression.

I only meant to let you know
I'm well, and hope that you are so;
With all the merry knaves o' th' pack
Who love the fair, the brown, the black
And rather than submit to marry
Fly still at whore, as hawk at quarry.

Pray tell me how Lieutenant A_____
Maintains his vice with half his pay,
Who has, I hope, by good direction,
Repaired his rudder of affection,
And gained his natural complexion.
I fear it proved a scurvy job,
Bid him beware lest t'other rub
Should bring him to the powd'ring tub.

I want to know if Captain Blunder
Is still the country wenches' wonder,
And how he shifts for copulation,
T' oblige his lustful inclination.
I fear his tail's so much his master
'T has brought him under some disaster,
For bolus, pills, and sal-prunel'
(In which repenting sinners deal)
Were sent among ye by Jack Staily,
To quench those burning pains that ail ye,
Which have possessed, I plainly see,
Some label of mortality.

But hold, what is it I am doing?
I must not here appear too knowing,
Lest you, arch-wags, should turn the satire
And say I'm skilful in the matter.

But now, dear friend, I change my strain,
And grieve to think weak man so vain
That resolutions made of late,
Against a matrimonial state,
Should not defend you from the curse
Of fools, for better or for worse.
Prithee now tell what means this riddle,
That you should be so fond and idle,
T' eclipse the freedom of your life,
With that dull mournful clog, a wife?
What if she's youthful, rich and fair,
And virtuous too, she's still a care.
These are but chains to bind the faster,
And make man's plague the more his master.
Since married, I account thee one
Who the best threads of his life has spun,
And now his misery's just begun.

But use this caution through thy life,
Slave not thyself to please a wife
Lest through o'er fondness thou dost prove
A mere anatomy of love.

But since the earthen vessel, Man,
Whose life's comprised within a span,
Is by his nature weak and vain,
I must excuse your oversight
Committed 'gainst your reason's light.
And since you're catched in love's decoy,
I'll wish you, like the rest, much joy,
Hoping your choice has proved so good
That she's as chaste as you are lewd,
And then she could not be withstood.

You know, my friend, what can't be cured,
It's said of old, must be endured.
Since that's your case, I'll so befriend you,
As wish all happiness attend you.

May she prove just (I hope she's fair),
Calm, kind, and good as angels are,
And may her sweeter charms produce
(When sprinkled with your balmy juice)
A noble fruit of glorious use.

May your whole lives be harmony,
Mutual your loves, from troubles free,
And dutiful your progeny.

May she so live, that all her joys
May prove her merit, not her choice,
And to complete that happiness
I truly wish you to possess,
To your fair bride may you prove true,
And good to her, as she to you.

My friend, with gladness do I hear
You find your spirits much too clear
For fens, and their gross foggy air.

That you intend, within a while,
To bless your own dear native soil,
And leave that pois'nous croaking isle
To frogs, and toads, snakes, efts and ants,
Its native foul inhabitants.
But e'er you come, take care and see
You send me a retaining fee,
In cordial Nantes, or some such liquor,
To move my spirits round the quicker.

For man's but Heaven's water-mill,
In motion kept by the glass or gill,
And wanting liquor must stand still.
Don't, through oblivion, now neglect it,
For I assure you I expect it.

This being in rhyme my first essay,
I've jingled on a wondrous way.
Pray pardon my prolixity,
A common fault in poetry.

Excuse me, friend, in what I write t'ye,
And don't forget the aqua vitae
Is all I beg, and so goodbye t'ye.

Having thus diverted ourselves with the perusal of the foregoing
epistle, we steered our course into Brydges Street with intention to see
a play. But, when we came to the house, we found upon enquiry that all
the wiser part of the family of Tom-fools had translated themselves to
Bartholomew Fair. After struggling with a long see-saw between pride
and profit, and having prudently considered the weighty difference
between the honourable title of one of Her Majesty's servants and that
of a Bartholomew Fair player, a vagabond by the statute, they did at last,
with much difficulty, conclude that it was equally reputable to play the
fool in the Fair for fifteen or twenty shillings a day as 'twas to please
fools in the playhouse at so much per week. And, indeed, I think they
made a very commendable result, for I think there's no more distinction
between a Queen's House player and a country stroller, than there is
between a bulldog bred up in Clare Market and another educated in Her
Majesty's bear garden. And as he is the most valuable dog that runs
farthest and fairest, so is he the most reputable comedian that gets most
money by his fooling. For he that is a mountebank, it's no matter
whether he keeps his stage over against Whitehall Gate, or at Cow Cross,
for if the means to live be the same, it signifies little to his credit in what
place they are put in practice.

But, however, we were disappointed in what we proposed, and were
obliged to defer our intended measures till another opportunity. So,
considering it would be expected we should, according to the month, take
a survey of the Fair, we took coach to escape the dirt and the uneasiness
of a crowd, and adjourned thither. At the entrance, our ears were saluted
with Belphegor's concert, the rumbling of drums, mixed with the
intolerable squeakings of catcalls and penny trumpets, made still more
terrible with the shrill belches of lottery pickpockets, through instruments
of the same metal as their faces, so that had I not been foretold by my
friend of the astonishing confusions I must expect to meet with, I should

have been as much frighted at this unusual piece of disorder as Don
Quevedo in his *Visions*, when he saw Hell in an uproar.

We ordered the coachman to set us down at the Hospital gate, near
which we went into a convenient house to smoke a pipe and overlook the
follies of the innumerable throng, whose impatient desires of seeing
merry-andrew's grimaces had led them ankle deep into filth and
nastiness, crowded as close as a barrel of figs, or candles in a tallow-
chandler's basket, sweating and melting with the heat of their own
bodies. The unwholesome fumes of those uncleanly hides, mixed with
the odoriferous effluvia that arose from the singeing of pigs, and burnt
crackling of over-roasted pork, came so warm to our nostrils that had it
not been for the use of the fragrant weed, tobacco, we had been in
danger of being suffocated.

We drank small beer bittered with coloquintida, drawn by a lousy-
looked tapster, with the impudence of a gaol-bird in his face, a bunch of
rusty keys hanging on one side of his apron-strings, to keep him in equal
balance between a brush which was hugged under the contrary arm. He
plagued us as constantly with his impertinent 'Do you call, sirs?' every
two minutes, as surely as the clock strikes every hour, till at last he had
so affronted us with his over-diligence that we were forced to tell him we
would kick him downstairs if he came any more till we called him. By
this means we respited our uneasiness during our own pleasure.

The first objects, when we were seated at the window, that lay within
our observation were the quality of the Fair, strutting round their
balconies in their tinsel robes and golden leather buskins, expressing such
pride in their buffoonery stateliness that I could but reasonably believe
they were as much elevated with the thoughts of their fortnight's
pageantry as ever Alexander was with the glories of a new conquest;
looking with great contempt from their slit-deal thrones upon the
admiring mobility, who were gazing in the dirt at our ostentatious heroes
and their most supercilious doxies. They looked as awkward and
ungainly in their gorgeous accoutrements as an alderman's lady in her
stiffen-bodied gown upon a Lord Mayor's festival. When they had taken
a turn the length of their gallery, to show the gaping crowd how
majestically they could tread, each ascended to a seat agreeable to the
dignity of their dress, to show the multitude how imperiously they could
sit.

Then entered the conjurer of the whole company, merry-andrew, I
suppose as much admired by the rest for a wit as the finest dressed jilt

amongst 'em was by the mob for a beauty. As soon as he came to his stand, where he designed to give the spectators some testimonies of his ingenuity, the first thing that he undertook to give was a singular instance of his cleanliness, by blowing his nose upon the people, who were mightily pleased, and laughed heartily at the jest. Then, after he had picked out from the whole dramatic assembly a man of most admirable acquirements in the art of tittle-tattle, and fit to confabulate with the witty and intelligible Mr Andrew, he begins a tale of a tub which he illustrates with abundance of ugly faces and mimical actions, for in that lay the chief of the comedy, with which the gazers seemed most to be affected. Between these two, the clod-skulled audience were lugged by the ears for an hour; the apes blundering over such a parcel of insignificant nonsense that none but a true English unthinking mob could have laughed or taken pleasure at any of their empty drollery. The insipidness of this occasioned my friend to think that ever since the Andrew was whipped for singeing his pig with Exchequer notes, and roasting him with tallies, it has made St Bartholomew jesters afraid of being witty, for fear of disobliging the government. 'For,' says he, 'this is the dullest stuff that ever was spewed amongst the rabble since Heaven made 'em fools, or ever any such coxcomb in a blue doublet undertook to prove them so.'

The epilogue of merry-andrew's farce was, 'Walk in, gentlemen, and take your places whilst you may have 'em. The candles are all lighted and we are just a-going to begin.' Then, screwing his body into an ill-favoured posture, agreeable to his intellects, he struts along before the glittering train of imaginary heroes, and their Water Lane beauties, leading them to play the fool withinside, in answer to his performances without, whilst some that had money went in, and those that had none walked off equally satisfied.

The outside of the droll booths being all garnished with the like foolery, we found nothing further amongst 'em worth repeating; and being seated in a place where nothing was to be seen, we were forced to remove from our quarters, and hazard our carcases amongst the crowd, and our pockets amongst the nimble-fingered gentlemen of the diving mystery, or else we found we should see nothing worth the pains we'd taken. Accordingly we paid our reckoning, and buttoned up our pockets as securely as a citizen does his shop-windows when his family goes to church, and so launched ourselves into the tempestuous multitude, amongst whom we were hurried along, from the ground, by a stream of rabble, into the middle of the Fair, in as little time as a forward beau may make a fumbler a cuckold.

Thus we swam down with the tide, till we came to the rope-dancer's booth, before we could find any bottom. There (praised be our stars) we once more got safe footing upon terra firma, and stood a little to behold the agility of the tumblers, whose pranks, were they shown to a whimsical virtuoso, are enough to beget in him a new system of philosophy, and make him believe that to walk only upon our feet with our heads uppermost is nothing but a ridiculous habit we have contracted from our nurses, and that it is more natural for mankind to run races upon their hands with their heels upwards, if they would but practise it.

I was mightily pleased to see the women at this sport; for it made 'em seem to have a due sense of the ills done by their tongues, to degrade which, they turned 'em downwards, giving the pre-eminence to their more deserving parts, for which reason they practised to walk with their arses upwards. This, indeed, I think is but justice for that part to be most honoured that's most useful. And whether that be the head or the tail of a woman, I'll appeal to married men or whore-masters, who I must acknowledge to be better judges. 'Truly,' says my friend, 'I think you are much in the right on't, for a woman is a mere receptacle, and to see her standing on her legs is as unnatural a posture, in my mind, as to see a pipkin upon the fire with the mouth downwards.' 'Prithee,' said I, 'let's have done with this Jack-pudding's dialect, or people will think the Fair has inspired us with bombast.'

'Come,' says my friend, 'let us fling away sixpence apiece, and see what's to be done withinside. Methinks,' says he, 'there is something in this sort of activity that is both diverting and amusing.' I readily consented to his proposal, so in we went, where a parcel of country scrapers were sawing a tune, and a mixed multitude of longing spectators were waiting with impatience the beginning of the show, looking upon one another as simply as a company sat down at table that waits with an hungry appetite an hour for their dinner. At last they put up a little dumpling-arsed animal that looked as if it had not been six weeks out of a go-cart, and that began to creep along the rope, like a snail along a cabbage stalk, with a pole in its hand not much bigger than a large tobacco-stopper. This was succeeded by a couple of plump-buttock lasses, who, to show their affection to the breeches, wore 'em under their petticoats, which, for decency's sake they first danced in. But to show the spectators how forward a woman once warmed is to lay aside her modesty, they doffed their petticoats after a gentle breathing, and fell to capering and firking as if Old Nick had been in 'em.

These were followed by a Negro woman and an Irish woman. As soon as the Black had seated herself between the cross poles that supported one end of the rope, a country fellow sitting by me fell into such an ecstasy of laughing that he cackled again. 'Prithee, honest friend,' said I, 'what dost thou see to make thyself so wonderful merry at?' 'Maister,' says he, 'I have oftentimes heard of the devil upon two sticks, but never zee it bevore in my life. Bezide, maister, who can forbear laughing to see the devil going to daunce?'

When, with much art and agililty, she had exercised her well-proportioned limbs to the great satisfaction of the spectators, the Irish woman arose from her hempen seat to show the multitude her shapes. Her shoulders were of an Atlas-build, and her buttocks, as big as two bushel loaves, shaked as she danced like two quaking puddings handed to a table in one dish. Her thighs, as fleshy as a baron of beef, were so much too big for her body that they looked as gouty as the pillars in St Paul's. Her legs were as strong as a chairman's, her calves being as round and hard as a football, the swelling of the muscles stretching the skin as taut as the head of a new-braced drum. She waddled along the rope like a goose over a barn threshold, till at last, poor creature, willing to show the assembly the utmost of her excellencies, and putting nature upon a stress to cut a caper as high as a hog-trough, she happened to strain her twatling-strings, and let fly an unsavoury sound, as loud as a note of the double-curtal. 'Wounds, my lady,' says my neighbour the countryman, 'have a care you do no' fall, for, by the mass, you made the rope give a woundy crack.' The men laughed, and the women blushed. Madam Lump quitted the rope with a shameful expedition and, as it was thought, did her dancing trunks much damage by the unfortunate eruption.

This was succeeded by a pragmatical brother of the same quality, who mounted the ladder next, in order to ascend the rope. His looks foretold such an unhappy destiny that I was fearful of his falling, lest his hempen pedestal should have catched him by the neck. He commanded the rope to be altered according to his mind with such an affected lordliness that, presently, I perceived he was master of the apes by his imperious deportment. Looking stedfastly in his face, I remembered I had seen him in our town, where he had the impudence to profess himself an infallible physician. Upon this I asked my friend the meaning on't. 'Pooh,' says he, 'I am sorry you are so ignorant. Why, we have dancing physicians, tumbling physicians, and fools of physicians, as well as college physicians. Nay, and some of them too, if they will, can play much stranger tricks than you are aware of. But these fellows, you must know,' says he, 'are bred up between death and remedy, that is the rope and medicine, and as they grow up, if they happen to prove too heavy heeled for rope-dancers or tumblers, they are forced to learn first how to be fools, and once grown expert Jack-puddings, the next degree they commence is doctor, and so leave off a painted coat and put on a plush one.'

The person that danced against him was the 'German Maid' (as they style her in their bill) with a great belly, who does such wonderful pretty things upon the rope, having such proportion in her limbs and so much modesty in her countenance that I vow it was as much as ever I could do to forbear wishing myself in bed with her. She as much out-danced the rest as a greyhound will outrun a hedgehog, having something of a method in her steps, air in her carriage, moving with an observance of time, and playing with her feet as if assisted with the wings of Mercury. And this much further I must needs say on her behalf, that if she be but as nimble between the sheets as she is upon a rope, she must needs be one of the best bedfellows in England.

Then Doctor Cozen-Bumpkin mounts the slack-rope, and after he had lain down and swung himself a quarter of an hour in his hempen hammock, he comes down, believing he had done wonderful things; then he honours the mob with a gracious nod, and slips on his night-gown to prevent catching cold. Then up steps the Negress to the top of the booth, and began to play at swing-swang with a rope, as if the devil were in her, hanging sometimes by a hand, sometimes by a leg, and sometimes by her toes, so that I found, let her do what she would, Providence or Destiny would by no means suffer the rope to part with her.

This scene being ended, they proceeded to the conclusion of their entertainment, the tumbling, and indeed, it was very admirable to think that use should so strengthen the springs of motion, and give that flexibility and pliableness to the joints, nerves, sinews and muscles, as to make a man capable of exerting himself after so miraculous a manner. I could not but conceive it possible, from the strangeness of their tricks, to bring up a child, by practice to jump first off a brick, then two, so on to a storey, and at last from the top of the monument, without catching any more harm than a cat. When we had seen all, and the Master of the

Revels had bid us welcome, my friend asked me how I liked it. 'Truly,' said I, 'as for the tumbling, I am mightily pleased with it. But as for the dancing, I have seen that in the country performed by monkeys.'

The spectators being dispatched with a hearty welcome, we squeezed out of the door as close as a thimbleful of shot out of the barrel of a birding-piece. Instead of avoiding a crowd, we were got out of the frying-pan into the fire; and amongst the confused hummings nothing was distinguishably heard but the shrill cries of 'Nuts' and 'Damsons'.

Thinking it the prudentest way to take new sanctuary as soon as we could, we jostled into a booth, where was to be seen a dwarf comedy, surnamed a droll, which most commonly proves as wonderful a monster as any's to be seen in the Fair. It was under the title of that curse of a companion, *The Devil of a Wife*, which occasioned me to look round the audience to examine whether there was the same mixture of sexes as is customary at such sort of entertainments; but found, quite contrary to what may be usually observed, that there were ten men to one woman. The sex, as I suppose, being highly distasted at the title of the farce, they thought it greatly inconsistent with their ease and interest to encourage such a public dishonour done to the authority of termagants. These they account the only Amazons of spirit, who support and defend the reasonable privileges of their sex from the usurpation and encroachments of the husband, to the great abuse and violation of the wholesome laws of matrimony as these were long since settled by that reverend assembly of grave matrons, the Parliament of Women. The booth, notwithstanding, was pretty full, but of men chiefly, who had the plain-dealing looks of good sober citizens, and I believe happened most of them to be enslaved under petticoat government, and came hither to learn how to tame a shrew, and recover into their own hands the power and authority of their forefathers, which they had in vain surrendered to their wives upon the terms and conditions of peace and quietness.

By the time my friend and I had cracked a quart of filberts, and ate, each of us, two pennyworth of bergamot pears, to keep ourselves from idleness, the minstrels scratched over a concise piece of unintelligible discord called a Flourish, the curtain was drawn up, and the strutting representatives began their foolery. At their performances, I confess I was wonderfully pleased, for everything was done to such a perfection of uncouthness that had so many puppets made of sticks and clouts been but qualified with speech, we could not have laughed more heartily at their awkward and ridiculous imitations, everyone looking, notwithstanding his dress, like what he really was, and not like what he represented. So I fancied, all the while they were playing, I heard some of 'em crying 'Flag-brooms,' some 'Knives to grind,' and others 'Chimney-sweep,' whilst their ladies were making up the concert with 'Buy my cucumbers to pickle,' and 'Here's your rare holland socks, four pairs for a shilling', for I am certain they had accustomed their voices to some such cries, that had begot in their speech such unalterable tones that they are no more able to play a part, without giving a relish of their calling, than a fanatic parson is able to tell a story in his pulpit without hemming and hawing.

The whole entertainment was the strangest hodgepodge that ever was jumbled together, and an excellent farce to please an audience of such fools, who are apt to admire most that which they least understand; for I'll engage they find it a piece of puzzle that is harder to expound than one of Partridge's riddles, or Mother Shipton's prophecies. We were forced to make our patience as long as their play, being wedged in on both sides as close as a couple of City cuckolds in Guildhall at a Lord Mayor's election. At last they made an end as abruptly as they began foolishly, and let down the curtain which cut off the communication between our eyes and their actions. So, with the rest of the crowd, we from hence departed.

Having trespassed, like misers, too far upon nature and spent most part of the day without giving our bodies that refreshment which was requisite to enliven our spirits, and preserve health, after a short consultation we agreed to gratify our importunate appetites with a quarter of a pig, on purpose to be fools in fashion. In order to accomplish our design, with a great deal of elbow-labour and much sweating, we scrambled through the throng, who came pouring into the Fair from all adjacent streets, each stream of rabble contending to repel the force of its opposite current and striving, like tide and stream, to overcome each other. At last, with as much difficulty as a hunted buck gets through a wood with his horn on, by inch and inch we gained Pie Corner, where cooks stood dripping at their doors, like their roasted swines'-flesh at their fires, with painful industry each setting forth with an audible voice the choice and excellence of his pig and pork, which were running as merrily round upon the spit as if they were striving who should be first roasted. Some pigs were hanging upon tenters in the shop-windows, as big as large spaniels, half-baked by the sunbeams, and looked as red as the thighs of a country milk-wench in a frosty morning.

After we had gazed round us, to examine what cook was most likely to accommodate our stomachs with good entertainment, at last we agreed to step into a large shop where we had great expectancy of tolerable meat and cleanly usage. But no sooner had we entered the suffocating kitchen, than a swinging fat fellow, who was appointed overseer of the roast to keep the pigs from blistering, standing by the spit in his shirt, rubbed his ears, breast, neck and armpits with the same wet-cloth which he applied to his pigs. This brought such a qualm over my stomach that I had much ado to prevent the stuffing of my guts from tumbling into the dripping-pan, so scouring out again through an army of flies, encamped at the door in order to attack the pig-sauce, we deferred our eating till a cleanlier opportunity.

Note that this is but a small part of what's intended on the Fair, and whatever is deficient here, shall be supplied in the next.

XI

BEING QUITE SURFEITED with His Greasiness's cleanliness, our Jewish stomachs began to be as much aversed to Bartholomew Fair swines'-flesh as a Court lady is to onion sauce, or a young libertine to matrimony. The sight of a pig was as hateful to me for the fortnight as an Easter gammon of bacon to a Scotch pedlar, or Christmas porridge to an English Puritan.

The eagerness of our appetites being thus assuaged without the expense of eating, we faced about to the wooden Sodom and suffered ourselves to be carried back by an inundation of mobility into the body of the Fair. There, in compassion to one of the female gender who was labouring in the crowd like a fly in a cobweb, I laid my hands upon my friend's shoulders and, by keeping her between my arms, defended her from the rude squeezes and jostles of the careless multitude. In this interim she, to give me a remarkable instance of her gratitude, put her hand behind her and picked my pocket of a good handkerchief in return for my civility. When she had done her business, she shuffled into the crowd, and the next minute I discovered my loss, which, as it was but small, begot but a concern proportionable. I could not without some shame acquaint my friend with the matter, expecting he would laugh at me for my over-care of my lady and carelessness of myself. He accordingly ridiculed my small misfortune and told me, smiling, 'You must be as careful of women in Bartholomew Fair as country people are of stags in rutting-time. For their accustomary ways of rewarding kindnesses are either to take something from you, you would unwillingly part with, or to give you, on the contrary, that which you would be glad to be without.'

Having heard much of a comedian's fame, who had manfully run the hazard of losing that reputation in the Fair which he had got in the playhouse, and having never seen him in his proper element, we thought the time might not be very ill-spent if we took a sight of another 'Best Show in the Fair' (for so they all styled themselves) that we might judge of his performances. The number of kings, queens, heroes, harlots, buffoons, mimics, priests, profligates and devils in the balcony occasioned us to believe, with the crowd, that there were no less varieties to be seen within than there were signs of without, for indeed we might reasonably have thought, from their numerous appearance, that when they were all in the booth there would be but room for a slender audience.

To help make it up, we put our fools' pence into His Worship's pocket-apron, with which title the mob honoured the master of the booth, because, as they said, he had been a Justice of the Peace, and then entered the pit. There several of the top quality of the tickle-tale function sat cracking nuts like so many squirrels, and looking round 'em for admirers, hoping they might kindle such flames in some amorous spectator, with their studied looks and ogles, that nothing should be able to quench but the luscious embraces of the sweet lady that had raised his concupiscence. Their prevailing glances, I observed, soon took effect upon some juvenile gentlemen, whose youthful opinions of the pleasures to be found in love and beauty had rendered them, like gunpowder, as liable to be inflamed with every sparkling eye as the other is to be blown up by the casual touch of any fire it shall meet with. The baskets of plums, walnuts, pears and peaches, began now to be handed about from the City bubble to the suburbs jilt, and tittle-tattles of love were banded forwards and backwards, between the tongues and ears of those amorous frontiers of the impatient audience, who were forced to pacify themselves under their longing expectancies with nuts and damsons. Now and then they broke out into beargarden acclamations of 'Show, show, show, show!' At last, in answer to their loud-mouthed importunities, the curtain was drawn up to show a trunk-breeches king in a fool's cap, and a feather in it, attended by his cringing nobility, some Court jilts, and two or three flattering priests, which I suppose the poet thought to be as true a representation of an old English Court as possibly he could think on. After these had entertained the listening audience a little with their fustian confabulations, they made their exeunt, and the scene was shifted into a library where Friar Bacon, by his long study, had projected a brazen head, and was to wall the kingdom with the same metal, had not the Devil catched him napping and broke his most wonderful noddle into many pieces.

The priest, grown drowsy with much reading, rubbed his eyes, arose from his elbow-chair and, in my opinion, seemed both by his looks and actions much too ignorant as well as too young for such a notable undertaking. When he had raved and strutted about a little with his magician's wand, like a hero with his truncheon in a fit of jealousy, he began, like a true priest, to make large promises to the people of wonderful things which he very well knew would never come to pass.

Then after he had made a short oration in praise of his brazen head, the scene changed, and shut him up in his study to consult the Devil a little further on how to bring his admirable project to a reputable conclusion.

Then entered the miller and his son Ralph. The father seemed to be the same thing he imitated, and had a countenance so very pertinent to his profession that he looked as if (according to the miller's maxim) his conscience could dispense with taking five pecks out of a bushel. And as for his hopeful progeny, who was the only person we were desirous of seeing, I think he kept up so true a behaviour of an idiot that it was enough to persuade the audience that he really was in nature what he only artfully represented. I could not but conclude the part was particularly adapted to his genius, or he could never have expressed the humour with such agreeable simplicity. But, I fancy, if he was to play the part of a wise man it would be quite out of his way, and would puzzle him as much as it would a common whore to behave herself in company like a virtuous woman. There was nothing in the part itself but what was purely owing to his own gesture, for it was the comedian only, and not the poet, that rendered the character diverting. To be plain, they both acted and became their characters extremely well, for I cannot but acknowledge that I never saw anybody look more like a fool than the son, nor any miller look more like a cozening knave than the father.

The next part of the droll that was chiefly diverting, was the country justice, whose weakness and indiscretion, I suppose, were designed to let the people know what ignorant magistrates have sometimes the administration of justice, and how common a thing it is for a wise man to bow a learned head to an empty noddle in authority. These were the chief of their characters, jumbled confusedly together with a flying shoulder of mutton, dancing and singing of devils and suchlike pieces of conjuration by the diabolical Friar Bacon, with whose magical pranks the mob were wonderfully pleased, as well as greatly astonished. Having thus entertained us for about three-quarters of an hour, at last, with a most splendid appearance of all their lords and ladies, they concluded their droll. Then, from amongst this glittering assembly, one of the best-mouthed orators steps to the front of the stage and, with a cringing piece of formality, promises the audience to begin again in half and hour, as if they believed the people to be such fools to fling away their money so unprofitably twice in one day, when the seeing of them once is enough to tire any man of reasonable patience.

The show being thus ended, my friend asked me how I liked it. 'Truly,' said I, ''tis a very moral play, if the spectators have sense enough to make use of it.' At this saying, my friend burst into a fit of laughter. 'Prithee,' says he, 'wherein lies the morality of it?' 'Why, truly,' said I, 'it will serve to let us know how familiar a priest, notwithstanding his Holy Orders, may be with the Devil; how easily the clergy may impose upon the vulgar a belief of those things which never were or can be; what a blockhead may be a Justice of Peace; how a rich cunning knave may have a fool for his son; how old men love young bedfellows; how a woman will cheat her father to oblige her gallant; what stratagems lovers will project to accomplish their ends, and what Jack-puddings men will make of themselves to get a little money.' 'On my word,' says he, 'you have made a rare use of it, indeed! But I very much question whether anybody else will be half so much the better for it, for it may be observed that Bartholomew Fair drolls are like State fireworks; they rarely do anybody good but those who are concerned in the show.'

From thence, with much difficulty, we crossed over to the Hospital gate, being jumbled about in the crowd like a couple of Tories at a Whiggish election. Over against the gate stood a comical figure gaping and drumming, so that his beard wagged up and down like an alderman's chin at a Lord Mayor's feast, when chewing a goose's apron, and his eyes rolled about, like a libertine's at a christening when he stands godfather. This occasioned some of the ignorant spectators, that stood crowding beneath, to cry out, 'Lord! do but see how he stares at us, and gnashes his teeth as if he could eat us for looking at him.' On each side of him stood a wax baby which appeared very natural, insomuch that it induced us to walk in and take a sight of their whole works. We were much astonished upon our first entrance of the room at the liveliness of the figures, who sat in such easy postures, and their hands disposed with such a becoming freedom that life itself could not have appeared less stiff, or the whole frame more regular. The eyes were fixed with tenderness, which I apprehend as a great difficulty, so that the most experienced of our charming ladies could not, after an hour's practice in her glass, have looked more soft and languishing.

Whilst we were thus viewing the Temple of Diana, for under that title they had distinguished their show, up comes a country carter in his boots, armed with his weapon of correction, by which he governs and chastises his five four-legged subjects, belonging, as I suppose, to some hay-cart in the market. As soon as the hobbaddyboody was brought to the door of the room where the figures were seated, he peeps in, and seeing, as he thought, such a number of great persons steps back and doffs his hat. ''Ad's-bleed,' says he, 'I waant gooe in amang zo many vine voulk, not I; what, dost send mau up to be made a gam on? Pray gim mau my money agan, for I don't come here to be laughed at.' The mistress of the show, with all the arguments she could use, had much ado to prevail upon the fellow to go in, telling him wherein he was deceived, and that those fine people, as he thought 'em, were only waxwork, which was the sight that he was to see.

At last the bumpkin took courage and ventured into the show-room, but could not forbear making his country honours to the babies, till he was ready to claw the boards up with his hobnails. When he had looked round him and pretty well feasted his eyes, he turns about to the girl that shows 'em. Says he, 'They are woundy silent. I pray you, vorzooth, can they speak?' At which the young damsel fell a-laughing, saying, 'You must speak to 'em first, and then, perhaps, they'll answer you.' With that the foolish ignoramus did as he was bid, crying to one of the figures, 'How d'ye vorzooth? You in the black whood. E'vaith I'll give ye a pwot en you'n speak to mau.' At which the whole company burst into a laughter, which made the fellow so angry that in a passion he thus expressed himself. ''Adsheartlywounds, why what d'ye make a gam at a body vor? A plague bran ye for a pack of zempletons. Why, I zee zome little voulk but o'er the waiy, no higher than a flaggon; I beleeve they are the zons and daughters of these gentlevoulk here, and they could tauk as well as I can.' A notable pert gentlewoman standing by him, says she, 'Well, countryman, what would you think of that lady you spoke to for a bedfellow?' ''Ad's me loif,' says he, 'for all she looks so woundy gainly, now she's dressed, whon she comes to pluck off her paint and her patches, and doff her vine clouthes to come to bed, she, perhaps, may look as ugly as you do, vorzooth.' Which clownish repartee so dashed the lady out of countenance that her blushes showed she had a modest sense of her own failings and imperfections.

Having satisfied our curiosities with art's nicest imitation of human nature, we returned again into the multitude, considering what next folly we should commit, that would yield us any tolerable diversion. To see more drolls, we thought, would be as ridiculous as 'tis for a couple of sots to stagger from tavern to tavern all day long, where the entertainment is still the same, distinguishable by no difference but the name and sign. So we were quite tired with that sort of fooling, and upon further consideration of the matter in debate, we at last agreed to spend an hour in a music-booth.

In pursuance of our design, we pressed through the crowd till we crossed the Fair to the nor'-west side, where music-houses stood as thick one by another as bawdy-houses in Chick Lane. At every door there were two or three hanging-looked scaramouches who, rather than to encourage people to walk in, were, as I imagined, a means rather to affright 'em from entering, for fear of having their throats cut, or their pockets picked. But, however, hoping to fare as well as our neighbours, we ventured into one of their diabolical academies, where we supposed all sorts of wickedness were practiced for the good instruction of unwary youth, who are too apt to imbibe the poisonous draughts that flow from these pernicious fountains, to which we often owe the sorrows of our riper years. For we never clear our foul stomachs from those bitter remains which the venom, once we have once sucked it in from those unwholesome springs, will ever leave behind.

At our first entrance, the dancing in several disguises made it appear to me like a rendezvous of gipsies upon the election of a new king, or like so many strolling beggars making merry in a barn. As soon as ever the curtain was put up, and we approached the bar, a cracked bell was rung by a weather-beaten strumpet, dressed up in white, as if she had been going to beg some rogue of a gallant from the gallows. No sooner had the untuneable alarm reached the ears of the dispersed attendants, but a frizzle-pated suck-fosset, with a head bloated with much tippling, as round as a football, and an indigo muckender hanging down to his toes, according to the mode of a City beau-drawer, followed by half a dozen of his dancing scarecrows, some in masks as ugly as the faces that were without, bid us welcome in such hoarse fluxed voices that their speeches sounded to me more like the croaking of ravens, or the growling of the fourth string of a cracked bass, than like the organs of human utterance. Seeing us look a degree above common customers, I supposed they were in hopes we would prove the greater bubbles, and as a means to encourage us to the utmost extravagance, they conducted us to the further end of their fools' paradise, and placed us upon the hoistings, amongst cracks, rakes and bullies of the better quality. This separate apartment was exempt from the dishonour of inferior liquors, and nothing suffered to disgrace your table beneath a half-crown whore or a half-crown flask.

As soon as our wine came, and we had filled out a glass, the kettledrums and trumpets began to express their willingness to oblige us. This was performed with such harmonious excellence that no sow-gelder with his horn, or cooper with his adze and driver, could have gratified our ears with more delightful music. This was succeeded by a consort of fiddlers, with whose melodious diddle-diddle I was so affected that it made my teeth dance in my mouth, as if they had scraped me into a fit of a quartan ague. The next piece of harmony that laid seige to my ears was a most admirable new ballad, sung in two parts by seven voices. I called the drawer, and bid him ask them if they were not singing the cat-catch. He brought me word, No, and that it was a very fine playhouse song, set by the best composer in England. 'Why then,' said I, 'pray tell your songsters they deserve to be whipped at the cart's arse for attempting to sing it, and that I had rather hear a boy beat "Roundheaded Cuckolds Come Dig" upon his snappers, or an old barber ring "Whittington's Bells" upon a cittern, than hear all the music they can make.' Which message I suppose the fellow was afraid to tell 'em, lest they should crack his crown with their bass fiddle-sticks.

That we might have a taste of all their varieties, the next instruments they betook themselves to were hautboys, which are undoubtedly the best windpipes in the world, ill-played upon, to scare a man out of his wits, and I dare swear would raise the Devil, the father of all discord, much sooner than ever Friar Bacon or Cornelius Agrippa could by their diabolical invocations. For my part, I declare, their disproportioned notes and imperfect cadences had such an effect upon my ears that I thought their noise would have burst my head in as many pieces as gunpowder does a grenado-shell, and put my whole microcosm in such a disorderly trembling that had they tooted a little longer, I believe I should have been all disjointed, for such music is enough to make a man's bones dance out of their sockets, and put his whole body under a painful dislocation.

The harshness of their notes having, like a ring of bells, or a peal of cannon, boxed our ears into a deafness, they now began to treat our eyes with an entertainment and presented us with a dance in imitation of a footpad's robbery, and he that acted the thief, I protest, did it so much like a rogue, that had he not often committed the same thing in earnest, I am very apt to believe he could never have made such a jest on't; firing the pistol, stripping his victim, and searching his pockets, with so much natural humour, seeming satisfaction and dexterity, that he showed himself an absolute master of what he pretended to. And I cannot forbear having so little charity as to fancy that his last caper will be so far off the ground that he will quite lose his breath before he comes down again.

The next that presented herself to the view was a bouncing beldam, who had as much flesh on her bones as a Lincolnshire heifer, so that her hips, without the help of farthingales, looked as round as the stern of a Dutch fly-boat. Her buttocks trembled when she stirred, like a quaking pudding, and had she not been laced to the best advantage, her skin would have hung down in folds like the hide of a rhinoceros. The admirable qualifications of this lady were to dance with glasses full of liquor upon the backs of her hands, to which she gave variety of motions, without spilling, expressing in her exercise as much prodigality as if riches, fame and honour had been the rewards of her foolery, putting her greasy corps into a great sweat, and slaving as much at her paltry performance as a fat porter at ninepins in the Easter holidays, or a brawny milkwoman on a May Day. At last, having quite lost her spirits, she was forced to conclude her awkward steps and elephant capers, resting her unwieldy carcase on the nearest bench. There she panted like a racehorse that had won the plate, or a bear-dog after a let-go. The mob declared their approbation and applause by clapping their hands and knocking their heels, which was no little satisfaction to the wobbling squab, with whose unpolished salutation they were so highly delighted.

The next figure that appeared was a youthful damsel, who, to render her more charming, was dressed up in her holland smock and fringed petticoat, like a rope-dancer. Having disarmed most of the swordsmen in the room, she stepped into the centre of the booth, and there began to handle them as dexterously as a Welsh shepherdess does her knitting-needles, putting herself into a circular dance, wherein she turned as merrily round as the flier of a jack, or as nimbly as a gig under the scourge of a schoolboy, shifting her swords to all parts of her face and breast to the very great amazement of country fools, though very little danger to her own carcase. When, by her unalterable circumvolution, she had supplied the defects and weakness of the liquor and made most of the company drunk and giddy with observing the nimbleness of her tail, which, according to the knife-grinders' song, ran "Round, and around and around-a", she gave a stamp with her foot, like a doe rabbit after bucking, which served as a period to her dance. This, according to custom, was rewarded with a clap, being the true theatre and music-house method of expressing our thanks or approbation, which makes the ladies belonging to both places very apt to reward the love of their gallants after the same manner.

This was succeeded by abundance of insipid stuff so very sorrily designed and so wretchedly performed that, instead of either laughter or delight, it begot in me nothing but blushes and contempt; for I thought it an abuse to human shape for anything that bore the proportions of either sex to behave themselves so ostentatiously foolish, so odiously impudent, so intolerably dull and void of all humour, order, or design, there being more diversion in the accidental gestures of one ape than in all the studied performances of the whole company of pretending vagabonds. We therefore think it not worthwhile to trouble the reader with any further particulars of their ridiculous, poor pedantic fooleries, but shall leave 'em to a further shameful exposing of their own ignorance and proceed to a rough draught of the company who chiefly frequent these scandalous nurseries of all vice, vanity and villainy.

Some companies were so very oddly mixed that there was no manner of coherence between the figure of any one person and another. One, perhaps, would appear in a laced hat, red stockings, puff-wig and the like, as prim as if going to the dancing-school. The next a butcher, with his blue sleeves and woollen apron, as if just come from the slaughter-house. A third, a fellow in a Yorkshire cloth-coat, with a leg laid over his oaken cudgel, the head of which was a knob of the same stuff, as serviceable as a Protestant flail, and as big as a Hackney turnip. Another, in a soldier's habit, looked as peery as if he thought every fresh man that came in was a constable.

These mixed with women of as different appearances. One was in a straw hat and blue apron, with impudence enough in her face to dash a begging clergyman out of countenance, and he that can publicly ask for alms in a parson's gown, if he has a title to wear it, one would reasonably think, has impudence enough to face anybody. Another was dressed up in hood, scarf, and topknot, with her clothes hung on according to the Drury Lane mode, as if she could shake 'em off and leap into bed in the twinkling of a bedstaff. A third was in a white sarsenet hood, and had a posy in her bosom, as if she was come from the funeral of some good neighbour that died in childbed, and, amongst the rest, a girl of about a dozen years of age, whom, I suppose, they were early dragging up in the wicked ways of shame and misery, that her riper years might in no measure give her a sense of her unhappiness by checking her in her lewd practices, and render her but a dastard sinner.

These were at one table, and of one society, and though severally and singularly dressed, yet I could do no other than conjecture from their carriage and physiognomy that they were under one and the same influence, and that their unlucky stars had infused the like evil genius into every person among 'em; for the women looked like jilts; the men swore like pickpockets, and both were as drunk as swine and as merry as beggars.

Just beneath us, on the side of the hoistings, sat a couple of madams over a stone bottle of ale, who, by their want of stays, the airiness of their dress, the improvement of their complexion by paint, and the multitude of patches to add a genteel air to their servile countenances, we could guess no other than ladies of that wretched quality, whose pride, poverty, lechery and laziness, had reduced them under a necessity of exposing themselves to sale at a small purchase. For in came a fellow that I have heard cry "Brushes and Mousetraps" about Town, and a smith along with him, that I have seen hawk about iron candlesticks, and being almost drunk, their brains ran on coney-catching, and they must needs, after two or three awkward scrapes and compliments, beg the ladies' good company to drink a bottle of cider, which the willing damsels, without any manner of scruple, very readily complied with.

So they all removed to another table, which they thought was more commodious for their entertainment, where the old coxcombs' court to the ladies was so singular and comical that it made the whole company observators of their ridiculous behaviour. At last discovering, by the people's tittering, they were become a public jest, they agreed with their mistresses, as I suppose, to remove to some private place convenient for finishing their intrigue. But as they were leading their condescending madams out of the booth, with abundance of formal ceremony, the gallants, notwithstanding their holiday clothes, being known to some of the guests, were accosted as they made their exit with, 'Will you buy a mouse-trap, or a rat-trap? Will you buy a cloth-brush, a hat-brush, or a comb-brush?' They sneaked off with their doxies, as much ashamed as a perjured evidence out of Westminster Hall, or a Puritan out of a bawdy-house.

At another table sat a parcel of rural sots, who, with the gross spirits of common belch, were elevated to such a pitch of merriment that they began to talk bawdy, like old women at a gossiping, and swear 'adsheart-

lywounds as fast as a gamester curses the dice when he meets with ill-
fortune, showing as many ungainly postures over their liquor as a parcel
of swine made drunk with hog-wash. These, to make their ale run down
more cheerful, had got with them a female fiddler, who had charged her
tun-bellied carcase, like the rest, with more guzzle than her legs were
able to carry, and behaved herself, in sight of the whole company, with
such unparalleled impudence in singing bawdy songs with a hiccuping
voice, which she endeavoured to improve with intolerable scrapes upon
her cracked instrument, that I was afraid her nauseous behaviour, together
with her odious discord, would have raised in me such an aversion to
both women and music that I should never hereafter agree with the
common opinion; that is, esteem 'em as the choicest of blessings on this
side Heaven.

Then in came a couple of seamen in their canvas jackets, just stepped
from on board, to give themselves a taste of the Fair's relishable delights,
expressing in their looks such a wonderful satisfaction that a bailiff at a
prize, or a butcher at a bull-baiting, could not have showed more signs
of gladness. At last one of them ordered the music to play an old
Wapping jig, and plucked out of his pocket a clean white handkerchief,
which, I suppose, he borrowed of his landlady on purpose to dance with.
He was, as I imagined, no more able to cut a caper without that in his
hand, than a fellow is able to dance the morris without his bells, or a
beau court a lady without his snuff-box in his hand.

Thus equipped for the business, he stepped into the middle of the
booth, and after he had made his honours with as much grace as a cow
might make a curtsey, he began to caper and firk it round the room,
entertaining us with so many antic steps, merry-andrew postures, and
country cuts and shuffles with his feet, that no Jack Adams at Clerkenwell Feast, or a drunken ploughman upon my lady's birthday could have
been more diverting. His comrade cried out every now and then, 'Gad
ha' mercy, Robin! Now Kate of Dover's step! Cheer up, my lad! Ah,
bravely done, boy! Now for a sea-pie and a can of flip!' Thus he jigged
it about with his greasy hat in one hand and muckender in t'other till he
was quite out of breath, like a thrasher at a wake when he dances for a
favour, and where he that dances longest is always allowed to dance best.
Having thus put a period to his wild boree, his companion met him with
a quartern of brandy, but, after he had clapped him on the side for
encouragement, as a butcher does his bulldog, instead of spitting in his
mouth, he refreshed him with a cough and made him sit for the other let-

go. So sitting down with his arms akimbo he seemed as proud of what he had done as an admiral that had beaten the French fleet, or a mountebank that had drawn a tooth, with a touch, before a multitude of spectators.

What further lay within our observation were the sundry sorts of women who sat ready, upon small purchase, to gratify the lust of every drunken libertine. Some were very well dressed, and in masks, but notwithstanding their appearance, were as ready at your beck as a porter plying at a street corner; others were barefaced, and in mean garbs, whose poverty seemed equal with their impudence, and that so fulsome and preposterous that they are as great antidotes to expel the poison of lust as the modest and counterfeit behaviour of a cunning, pretty harlot is a means to enforce desire and beget a liking. A third sort of scoundrel strumpets were in blue aprons and straw hats, but by taking much mercury or the loud bawling of oysters about the streets, were as hoarse as a Jack-pudding at the latter end of the Fair. These were all good subjects to the Government, contributing more towards the maintenance of Her Majesty's Foot Guards than any people in the nation. For every one has a soldier or two at her tail, of whom she takes as much care as a bitch does of her puppies.

Having here taken notice of most of the particulars that lay within our view, by paying our reckoning we purchased our redemption from this epitome of hell. Being now almost dark, we took a turn round the outside of the Fair, on the back side of the booths, where we found several emblems of the world's giddiness. There were children locked up in flying-coaches, insensibly climbing upwards like meteorous State-tools who know not whither they are going but, being once elevated to a certain height, come down again, according to the circular motion of the sphere they move in, and decline from their meridian altitude to the low station from whence they first aspired, reflecting on their past pleasures with great dissatisfaction.

'These whirligigs,' says my friend, 'may be very properly applied to the common fate of great men, for when a man is once rising, it is not very difficult for him to rise to the top, but 'tis impossible for him, as you may see by these, to continue long at the same pitch. For the interest of him that governs the wheel and the politic motion of affairs for public safety require some to be rising and others falling. For this world is but Fortune's well, and mankind are the buckets thereof, which are cunningly hung so that the winding up of one must be the letting down of another.'

From thence we moved with the stream, and passed by a couple of puppet-shows where monkeys in the balconies were imitating men, and men making themselves monkeys, to engage some of the weaker part of the multitude, as women and children, to step in and please themselves with the wonderful agility of their wooden performers. These we passed by with as much contempt as an hungry tailor at Easter does a Fleet Ditch furmety-woman, or a prodigal debauchee an old mistress.

We squeezed on amongst the rest till we came again to the Hospital gate, which we entered with as little ease as a good Christian impatient of his dinner gets out of church when sermon is ended. At last we came into the cloisters where we met such a whispering and humming of 'God damnes, she's a bitch and t'other a whore,' and 'That's a fine woman, and t'other's a pretty creature,' that I thought the people were all mad and that this place was a Bedlam for lovers.

A gentleman with a red face who, my friend told me, was famed at all gaming ordinaries for a wonderful similizer, steps up to a very pert lady who, as I suppose, was not for his turn, and claps his bare hand on her neck. 'Dear madam,' says he, 'you are as cold as a cricket in an ice-house.' She turning short about, looked upon him, and replied, 'If you please to clap your fiery face to my backside, 'twill be the ready way to warm me.' At which smart return, all that heard it fell a-laughing. The gentleman, thinking it a little inconsistent with his honour to be thus put upon, had a great mind to redeem his credit by adding, 'Indeed, madam, I find your tongue's much nimbler than the rest of your members, for your body moves like a loaded wagon up a hill.' 'Dear sir,' says she, 'you look so like an honest gentleman, that I am bound, in gratitude, to return you at least an empty cart for your loaded wagon; and as for the hill, pray, sir, let it be Holborn, and I don't question but your good life in time may direct you to the use and application of both; so, sir, your humble servant.' And away she stepped into a raffling-shop, where some civil gentlemen followed her, and to reward her wit, loaded her, and her she-friend that was with her, with silver knick-knacks, and guarded her into a coach from the insolence of the Town cormorants, who had a wonderful mind to be snapping at so fair a bait.

This rendezvous of jilts, whores and sharpers began now to be very full, insomuch that the sour breaths of corrupt carcases, and the turpentine belches that were ever and anon thrown into our nostrils in the crowd, were so offensive that the pumping of a Derby ale-cellar, or the removal of an old close-stool pan, could not have surprised our smell with a more intolerable nosegay. This we were forced to endure or quit the place, which we were unwilling to do till we had made a more nice inspection into the pomps and vanities of this wicked world.

To further discover these we went into one of the shops that we saw most crowded, and, like poor spectators, with willing hearts and low pockets, stood in the rear peeping, as boretto-pensioners at the Groom-Porter's, over the shoulders of those that raffled. Among them, I observed this ridiculous vanity, that whatsoever the gentlemen won, they presented to the fair lady that stood next, though as great strangers, one to another, as Doctor Burgess and the whore of Babylon. 'You are insensible,' says my friend, 'of the cunning that's used by sharpers, to make this kind of diversion turn to good account. That pretty sort of a woman who receives so many presents, to my knowledge, is mistress to him who is now handling the box, who has no other business but to improve such a lucky minute to his maintenance; and he seems, as you see, to be an utter stranger to that lady he's so kind to, and only makes her mistress of his winnings, purely to draw the other gentlemen on to do the like, that what presents they foolishly bestow on her tonight, may serve to furnish his pockets for the hazard table on the morrow.'

Being tired with this pastime, we adjourned from thence, and crept up a pair of stairs, as narrow and as steep as the stone steps of a belfry, over which was written in golden capitals, in two or three places, THE GROOM-PORTER'S, designed, as I suppose, for fools to understand it was the honester place for his name being there, and that they might as fairly fling away their money here as in any place in Christendom. When, to the danger of our necks, we had climbed to the top, we stepped into a little room on the left hand, where lawyers' clerks and gentlemen's footmen were mixed higgledy-piggledy, like knaves and fools at an East India House auction, and were wrangling over their sixpences with as much eagerness as so many mumpers at a church door on a sacrament day about the true division of a good Christian's charity.

Being quickly surfeited with the boyish behaviour of these callow rakes, we moved from thence into the next room, where a parcel of old battered bullies, some with carbonadoed faces, and others with pimpgennet noses, were seated as close round a great table as country attorneys in a stage-coach at the conclusion of a term. Amongst 'em were a few declining tradesmen who, I suppose, were ready to start for some foreign plantation, and came hither to acquire the qualifications of a libertine that their portion in this world might be a merry life, and as short.

Curses amongst them were as profusely scattered as lies among travellers, and as many eyes lifted towards the heavens, in confusion of their stars, as there are on board a ship in a storm to implore safety. Money was tossed about as if a useless commodity, and several parts of the story of the Prodigal Son were acted here to a miracle. When four had the good fortune to come before seven, or ten before eight, the breeches of the losers were so nettled they were unable to be easy in their seats, and could no more keep the ends of their fingers out of their mouths than a porter, when he plucks off his hat, can forbear scratching of his head. The dice had far more influence upon 'em than the planets, for every man changed countenance according to the fortune of the cast, and some of them, I am sure, show all the passions, in half an hour, incident to human nature.

He that made the most observable figure amongst 'em was a butcher in his white frock, with a head as large as a Saracen's and cheeks as plump as a sow-gelder's when he proclaims his profession by his semicircular trumpet. His beard, though in carnival-time, was as well grown as a Hackney writer's in the middle of a long vacation, and looked as frowzy and irregular as the giant's whiskers in Guildhall, that seem so terrible to young apprentices. The hair of his head was as greasy as the fur of a cook's fly-flap, and shined with the pomatum of beef and mutton, like a satin cap upon the noddle of an independent teacher. I could not but take notice, whenever he made his stake, he cried, 'Go again,' which served me to understand he was a true Hockley-in-the-Hole sportsman, it being the same expression they use to their dogs, after the first let-go. I observed he was attended with great luck, enough to make us believe, according to the burlesque of Ovid's saying, that Fortune favours fat folks, or that her mope-eyed ladyship, like a true sow, was a great lover of blood, filth, and nastiness. Whenever he handled the dice he had so lucky a devil in the box, or at his elbow, that he very seldom threw out under three or four hands holding in, which occasioned his peevish antagonists to set him with such sour countenances that no lover that had lost his mistress, or a client that had lost his cause, could have contracted his face into a more fretful posture.

Length of time having made this diversion as dull as the rest, we left the losers to recover their losses, and the butcher to bring his hogs to a fair market; returning downstairs with as much care and caution of tumbling head foremost, as he that goes down Green Arbour Court steps in the middle of winter. When we were got safe to the bottom, being quite tired with the sundry follies we had seen, and the brain-breaking noises we had heard, my friend desired my company into Charterhouse Lane, where he was obliged to make a short visit to a patient, leaving me at an alehouse hard by to divert myself in his absence with a pipe of tobacco. This I did, accordingly, and refreshed myself with a pot of excellent English liquor, which was as comfortable to my palate, after our troublesome survey, as a down bed to the haunches of a weary traveller. By the time I had lit my pipe, in came a couple of old fellows who looked as if they were the superannuated servants of some great man, who to exempt himself from the charge of keeping 'em when past their labour, and to reward the faithful service of their youth, had got 'em into an hospital. They seated themselves down in the next box, and called for a pot of warm ale, over which, after they had accommodated their lantern jaws with a pipe of tobacco, they began to bemoan some great oppressions that were imposed upon 'em by the ruler of their society, whom they charged with these following accusations, beginning their complaint after this sorrowful manner:

'I remember,' says one, 'two old proverbs from my youth, which alas! I have found too true in my age: "New Lords, New Laws," and, "When the old one's gone, seldom comes a better." And i'faith, brother, as another old saying says, "We have found both too true to make a jest on," for our allowance, formerly, if any of us were sick and out of commons, was five shillings and elevenpence a week, but now our good master, Providence reward him for his kindness, has reduced us to four shillings and fivepence, which, let me tell you, brother, is a great abatement in so small a sum, and is a very great abuse of the pious design and charitable goodwill of the donor. We likewise, when we were sick, had a bushel of coals per week allowed us, to warm our old noses, under our infirmities, but now are stinted to just half the quantity, thanks to our good master for his Christian love and kindness to us.

'Sometime since, a brother pensioner was sick with a violent flux, from the middle of September to within ten days of Christmas, in which time his nurse went several times to the master, to obtain a grant of the five shillings and elevenpence per week, and a whole bushel of coals, declaring that his short allowance was not sufficent to support him in his low condition. But, notwithstanding all her reasonable pleas and importunate solicitations on her patient's behalf, the master would give no ear to her petitions, not taking into his consideration the coldness of the weather, or tediousness of his sickness.

'Besides, our diet is much abated of our ancient allowance, neither is the meat so good, and notwithstanding these great abuses and retrenchments of us the poor pensioners, he has procured his own salary to be advanced from fifty to two hundred pounds per annum; he now keeps his coach and lives as great as the governor of a town, instead of a master of an hospital. He gives this example of frugality, that he allows but half a crown a week to his trencher-scraper for his coachman's diet, for which he is obliged to afford him two meals a day. Therefore judge you what the poor fellow gets by his boarder.

'Some years since, upon the twelfth of December, which is held as an anniversary in commemoration of the founder, the reader, being absent upon some extraordinary occasions, was disappointed by one who promised to officiate for him, and the congregation was dismissed without prayers, notwithstanding the master was in holy orders, and at the same time present in the chapel.'

'Indeed,' replied the other, ''tis a sad thing we should be so served, but since we can't help it, we must content ourselves, I think, with the cold comfort of an old saying, viz., "What can't be cured must be endured"; for complaint without the prospect of redress is like a man venting his anger towards another by talking to himself.'

By this time my friend came in, to whom I communicated what I had overheard, who made light of it, as if they were such practical abuses as were scarce worth listening to, saying, 'You never knew any considerable hospital in your life, but the poor pensioners live like common seamen in an East India vessel, whose allowances are so short homeward bound that they are but just kept alive in a starving condition, whilst the officers grow fat at a plentiful table, and pinch estates in a little time, by abridging the just dues of their floating society.'

Thus heartily tired with our day's ramble, we paid our reckoning, and posted home to bed, with as good an appetite to rest as a new-married lover ever had to the embraces of his bride the first night, or a hungry ploughman to a plum-pudding on a Sunday when he had walked three miles from church.

Postscript

The wonderful eclipse which, according to the promises of astronomers, was to bring this wicked world within ambs-ace of the Day of Judgement, was invisible to us at London by reason of a stinking fog that arose from reeking dunghills, distillers' vats, and piping-hot close-stool pans, which, as the learned say, could neither be rarified nor dispersed till the eclipse was over, by reason that the beams of the sun were intercepted by the moon's body. Yet this truth is asserted by letters from many credible persons in several counties (who I hope are all well as I am at this present writing, praised be _____ for it), naming thousands, who beheld the prodigy as plain as the old woman who saw the needle in the barn door, who enquired (after she pretended to see the needle) whereabouts the barn stood. However, to confirm our infallible planet-peepers in their unerring judgements, it was seen upon the road by many travellers, especially by strolling tinkers and their budget-bearing trulls, Scotch pedlars, gipsies, vagabonds and cadators, who, if you cross but their hands with a piece of silver, or clear but their eyes with a cup of humming liquor, are able to see fairies dance, spirits walk, witches fly, prodigies in the clouds, blemishes in the sun, or worlds in the moon. And since our star-gazers, on their behalf, have such good evidence to prove the matter of fact, I think we had as good put the contest out of dispute, and agree with what they say, whose business it is to know most of the matter. But as further proof of the eclipse, which is still ridiculed amongst some obstinate unbelievers, these following persons do say, or think, they saw it as plain in the Town as ever 'twas seen in the country.

A vintner behind the 'Change, being very desirous of making a clear discovery of this dangerous interposition, got a piece of clay, and bestowed an hour's time in stopping up the bottom of his colander, all but the middle hole, through which he peeped from nine to eleven, and does think he saw the moon or a cloud between the sun and the colander, but cannot be positive which, and therefore his evidence is of little validity.

An upholsterer in Cornhill, being curious of being as wise as the rest of his neighbours, carried a looking-glass out of his shop into Stocks Market, and after he had earnestly looked for half an hour and had observed a small glimpse of the eclipse, a porter coming by with a heavy burden by accident stumbled and pitched the corner of his bundle between the upholsterer's neck and shoulders, knocking him down and breaking the looking-glass; and the porter, recovering himself, marched forward with his load. Up rises the fallen gazer from the ground, with nothing but the frame and back-board in his hand, and shaking his head at his misfortune, thus expressed himself to the people: 'Alas! Alas! I fear the terrible effects of this eclipse will be very fatal to poor England, for if just a glimpse of it will bring a man to this disaster, may Providence defend the whole kingdom from its malicious influence.'

Happening to be in company with a very famous astrologer, I was willing to enquire a little into what effects he thought this eclipse, that had made such a bustle, would have upon that part of the world to which 'twas visible, more especially England. 'Why,' says he, 'because you ask me the question modestly, I'll tell you, master. I do understand from the authentic censures of Albumazar and Ptolemy, concerning the circumvolution of celestial bodies, which procure perpetual mutability in this lower region, that this eclipse being at the new of the moon, when she first puts on her horns, does infallibly predict as many cuckolds to be at Horn Fair this year as have been seen there this seven years. Many litigious law-lovers this year will sell their coats to contend for the value of a button, and the lawyers prate the fools into compliance by bringing them to poverty. The poor will die this year faster than the rich, because there is an hundred of the one to one of the other. The fingers of envy will pick out the eyes of many a man's reputation, and the affections of women will be as easily gained and as hardly preserved as ever. To be plain, I believe we shall have much such another world on't as we had the last year, and so, I suppose, we shall not differ in opinion.'

XII

HAVING HEARD OF a famed coffee-house in Aldersgate Street, where doctors of the body, who study Machiavelli much more than Hippocrates, metamorphose themselves into State politicians, and the slippery tongues of thoughtless mechanics undertake to expound the mysteries of Scripture, by the power of grace without learning, we were willing to refresh our intellects with their improving discourses. In these, though we had but little expectancy of discovering much of the innocence of the dove, yet we had some hopes of inspecting a little further into the subtlety of the serpent.

Thither accordingly we steered our course, and entered the ancient fabric by antiquity made venerable, whose inside was lined with as great a number of Geneva Christians as if they were met to sign some canting address to cheat the government into a good opinion of their loyalty. Their zeal to the Good Old Cause was so legible in their looks as if they had contracted their faces into lines and shrivels by looking awry upon monarchy. Some were highly extolling the Dutch government, setting forth the freedom and prosperity of all such people who flourish under the happy constitution of a commonwealth. Others were commending the conduct of all affairs under the protectorship of Cromwell, and how far the felicity of the nation in those days exceeded the present happiness of the kingdom, so much boasted of by the blind lovers of kingly power and episcopacy.

At last up starts a bundle of verbosity, whom I had seen often at a coffee-house near the Court of Requests, scarce tall enough to be a complete man, nor short enough to be a monkey, having more mercury in his head than there is in a weather-glass. His tongue began to flutter about in his mouth like a wild bird trepanned into a cage, spitting as much venom against monarchy as ever was spewed up after a full stomach at a Calves' Head feast. His voice is as untuneable when he speaks as the screaking of a country sign in a high wind, so that were a blind man to hear him talk he might easily mistake the sound to be the whining of some puppy that wants the dug in his dam's absence. He has one rhetorical excellence which becomes him wonderfully: he will assert a falsity to be truth with as graceful an impudence as ever the Salamanca saviour of our lives and liberties, when he affirmed Don John of Austria to be a tall black man, who was quite opposite to this description. He is one who will never own himself to be in the wrong, and yet is never in the right; but takes as much pleasure in the justification of a lie as if he were cut out by nature to be a plot-evidence. What commonly he reports is as distinguishable from truth as copper is from gold, yet nothing does he bear with more impatience than contradiction. He has got *The Secret History of King Charles and King James*, also *Imago Regis*, and some other famed pieces of the Doctor's scurrility by heart, and has acquired from thence as rare a knack of railing against kings, justifying the martyrdom of King Charles and blackening the race of the Stuarts, as if he was at first a maggot bred in one of Shaftesbury's turds and afterwards became a wasp with a natural propensity to sting and wound the memory of so unfortunate a family.

I thought it so ungrateful to any charitable ear to hear a rattle-headed prattle-box set up to reform the Church, new-model the Government, and calumniate the best of princes, that I no longer could forbear giving him such a reproof as I thought so vain a babbler did in justice deserve. This he highly resented and grew as hot as a botcher's goose is to press down the nitty seams of an old doublet, so that I feared he would have burst out into such an ungovernable flame that nothing could have quenched it but a good cudgel.

My friend and I gave him no time to cool, but still fed his passion with a supply of sharp reflections on his past talk, till we had spurred him at last to such a pitch of madness that he boiled up into a ridiculous froth, which rendered him a laughing-stock to the whole company, boasting what interest he had in the Parliament House, and how many Ayes or Noes were ready to serve him upon all just occasions. We found ourselves obliged to prosecute our undertaking to the utmost, for we had reason to believe if we had lain down the scourge, he would have taken it up and have used it against us with much less modesty and more barbarity. So, being once engaged, we were forced, in our own defence, to pursue the battle to a complete victory, which, with much difficulty, we obtained, for he leaped up from his seat and ran away, branding us as he went out with the name of Papists. This was for no other cause but that we would not suffer him to rail without reason, talk nonsense without reproof, and tire the ears of the company with nothing but malicious invectives against the pious martyr and his sons, whose names are too sacred, being princes, for the utterance of so vile a tongue.

As soon as he was gone, I was desirous of knowing who this carcase full of spleen, ignorance and ill-nature could be; and to satisfy my curiousity, I enquired of a gentleman that sat next to me, who discovered by his talk he had some knowledge of him, and he told me the chief of his business was to sell pictures by auction. 'Nay,' says my friend, 'if he be an auctioneer, he's the more excusable, for cozening and lying are the two most necessary talents of his profession, and I'll warrant you he puts 'em both in practice as often as he has opportunity, because he would not willingly lose such profitable qualifications for want of using.

'Liars their odious talents often show,
That they by practice more expert may grow.
So knaves and needles in this point agree —
The more they're used, the sharper still they be.'

As my friend and I were reflecting between ourselves upon some of the insolent expressions of our shatter-brained renegado, a merry, pleasant-looked gentleman stepped into the coffee-house, sat down, and, whilst he was filling a pipe of tobacco, entertained the company with this following intelligence of a remarkable breakfast provided by a generous vintner on Tuesday, the 24th, in order to treat his guests on the following Thursday morning, upon which day all customers were to be free to feast their bellies, and 'You're welcome, gentlemen.' An account of this he gave us in a witty dialect, after a comical manner, which I will endeavour to imitate in hopes to divert the reader.

'Gentlemen,' says he, 'I have seen such a sight today as would make a Spaniard change his pace, and turn his stately steps into a dog-trot to run after it; nay, make a Dutchman in surprise pluck his hands out of his pockets and hold 'em up, like an Englishman going to be hanged, to praise the God of plenty for blessing his greedy eyes with so wonderful a feast; or put a Frenchman into as great an amazement as the snow did the Bantam ambassador.' 'Pray, sir,' says a grave gentleman that sat by, 'what, would it make an Englishman do nothing?' 'Yes, sir,' answered the other, 'it would make an Englishman whet his knife if it were dressed, and fall on without grace, and stuff his belly till it was as hard as a football, before he would rise from the table.' 'But, sir,' says the old gentleman, 'you'll forget, I am afraid, to tell us what it was; we want to know that, sir.' 'Why, sir,' says he, 'then I'll tell you. It was a piece of roasting beef, but of such an extraordinary size that ten men might ride upon't without incommoding themselves any other way than by greasing of their breeches, and but turn it on its back, and it will carry as many people withinside as a Gravesend wherry. It was the whole length of a huge, large, long, Lincolnshire ox, fed up from a calf upon all long grass, that he might grow the longer. There were no scales at the Custom House big enough to weigh it, so that they were forced to drive it down to Wapping in a cart and weigh it by an anchor-smith's steelyards, where they weigh their anchors, to discover the true weight. It proved, upon exact computation, to be four hundred and fifteen pounds, which magnificent piece of beef, notwithstanding its ponderosity, will certainly, on a day appointed, by some strong-jawed men of the law be taken up by the teeth, without the assistance of the Southwark Samson who breaks carmen's ribs with a hug, snaps cables like a twine-thread, and draws dray-horses upon their arses with as much ease as a Westphalia hog can crack a coconut.'

'But, pray, sir,' says Mr Inquisitive, 'how did they get it home to the tavern?' The gentleman replied, 'It was killed in Butcher Hall Lane and removed from thence by the assistance of as many butchers walking under it as there are porters under a pageant upon a Lord Mayor's day. Some of the bloody fraternity walked before, with their cleavers mounted on their shoulders, as so many maces, and thus they conveyed it home in as much triumph as if it had been a City magistrate going to persecute the bakers, and attended with as many mob as the victualler's corpse that lay in state and was carried to be buried with a drawn sword upon his coffin instead of a double chalk and a tap-tub.' 'Pray, sir,' said I, 'where is this leviathan of beef to be devoured, that a man may view this gluttonous prodigy before the cooks have mangled it out of all shape with their buck's-horn-handled scimitars?' 'Why, sir,' says he, 'at the King's Head Tavern at Chancery Lane End, where, at this time, the honestest vintner in London lives, where the best wine in England is to be drank, and the stateliest piece of beef in Christendom is to be roasted.'

Our pipes being out, though we imagined he might illustrate the story, Sir Harry Blunt-like, with some few advantages, yet we believed. in the main, there was something in it worth our inspection. So we determined to adjourn to the tavern where the gentleman reported this extravagant breakfast was to be eaten.

Accordingly we discharged our reckoning and made our exit, and being spurred on with the conceit of this amusing whim, as the gentleman had rendered it by his diverting account, we stumbled along o'er the pebble stones as fast as a Penny Postman, or a Temple student with a bill into the City to receive his quarterage, till we came to the door of this happy mansion, which, according to the report we heard, abounded in those delights that were in other taverns very difficult to be found. But we met with such crowds in opposition, some striving for entrance, and others for an exit, that we were forced to struggle as hard for our admittance as a couple of belated beaus do to squeeze into the pit when the girl is to sing a new bawdy song, or Doggett in *Love for Love* is to play son Benjamin. But at last, with no small striving, we shot the entry into a paved yard, where we waited as long for a sight of the carcase of the beast as a gentleman in adversity does for the sight of a great man, when his business is to beg a favour, or put him in mind of a promise he never intended to perform.

At last, in the interchange of comers and goers, we slipped into the kitchen, where there were about a dozen of the most eminent jack-winders in Fleet Street, some in their nightcaps and white aprons, like heathen priests going to kill the sacrifice, and others with their sweaty hair tied back in a black list-garter so that it might not hang in their light and hinder them in the performance of the difficult task they had undertaken, which was to spit this unwieldy monster with such mathematical judgement that it should run round by the help of a turnspit with as true a poise as the sail of a windmill in a fresh gale.

After they, in vain, had wounded the back of the beef in sundry places, either an aitchbone, a shinbone, a blade bone, or a rib standing in their way still denying entrance to their massy weapon, they puffed and blowed like so many Custom House porters lifting at a woolpack. At last, sitting down like a jury of an inquest over a dead corpse, they began to consult of some new measures to force this stubborn piece of man's meat into a submission of being roasted. At last one of the burgesses of the dripping-pan started up and wisely made this motion to the rest of the greasy brotherhood: 'My honest friends and neighbours, since we, the professors of, and well-wishers to the noble art of cookery, are assembled together in our proper element, the kitchen, upon this solemn occasion, let us not be baffled by the backbone of an ox, but let us stir up our brains with the fire-fork of understanding, and by the flame of right reason give fresh light to our judgements, that we may see to spit this pack-saddle of beef, or the reflections of the town will put us all upon the rack and every saucy Jack will tumble our reputation into the dripping-pan. I therefore declare my opinion is that we forthwith send for my neighbour Knockdowdy, the smith, and his man, Thump, and by the assistance of them and their sledges, we may complete our task in as little time as a man may boil an egg, or melt a pound of butter.'

Just as the whole society of lick-fingers had with great applause very highly approved of their brother skim-pot's advice, who should crowd into the cooks' territories but a carpenter, armed with a huge mallet, as if Providence had sent him purposely to their assistance, who undertook to do more work with his wooden weapon, at one blow, than all the choleric company of unthinking bunglers were able to do with their united strength without him. This speech gave 'em fresh courage, so that every epicurean minion started up as nimbly to his business as a master of anatomy at Surgeons' Hall to a dissection, instead of the spitting of a dead carcase. The underlings of the sweating tribe were appointed to sharpen broom-staves, the vintner having that day broke all the Kent Street merchants who came by the door, that the handles of their ware might be pointed into skewers for his beef, and the broom to be bound up into brushes, not to sell to his customers, but to kindle that mountainous Etna at which this more astonishing breakfast than ever was seen in Elagabalus's kitchen was to be roasted.

When, with the industry of all the culinarian crew, they had made a throughfare for the spit, from the right buttock of the beast to the left shoulder of the non-resisting morsel, such acclamations of joy were belched up by the greasy undertakers as would have dashed a mob out of countenance that were yelping out their huzzas at a gunpowder-treason bonfire. And he that was the chief leader of the knights of the frying-pan strutted about the kitchen with his arms akimbo, puffing and swelling like Drawcansir in the *Rehearsal* after, with his own single hand, he had slain a whole army, crying out with a majestical voice, ''Tis done, 'tis done! The mighty deed is done!'

These words were no sooner spoke but in comes Ragout-racy and, after him, a neighbouring brother sloven, chief president of the slab-dabs. Seeing the noble Duke of Carnis Bubalinae trussed up to his good behaviour on a spit (containing as much iron as by computation would have made a sheet-anchor for one of Julius Caesar's first-rates, when the whole fleet hid in Holborn ditch, upon his first landing in London), they fell into such a wonderful rage to think they should be so slighted, and not have timely summons to appear at so great a solemnity, and lose the reputation of having anything to do in so remarkable an adventure in their own proper business, that they both fell into a mighty passion with the master of the house. One vowed revenge to the vintner for his sake, and that he would put no more sack in his puddings for a twelvemonth. The other swore, for aught he knew, he would use no more claret in fish-sauce as long as he lived, but would make the knaves as humble to a cook as a tipstaff is to a Lord Chief Justice.

Every brother coquus was of his mind over the great indignity that had been put upon the profession by neglecting to invite not only two such neighbours and customers but men so eminent in their generation for conquering all difficulties in the noble art of cookery. He had spit so many shins, barons, sides and sirloins, that not to be at the spitting of His Grace the Duke, when they had so just a title to be present at the action, well, it was such an affront that if they had him but at home in either of their own kitchens, they would roast him. and toast him, and tumble him about in the dripping-pan till they had made him a greasy sop fit for the Devil's eating. Having thus vented their passions, they both looked bluff upon the bar, and turned out of the house in as splenetic a humour as if a saucepan of butter had run to oil, the venison pasty had been over-baked, or the fat fallen into the fire.

The chief operator and his assistants, who were so very joyful they at last had overcome the greatest of their difficulty, like prudent artificers began now to examine the truth of their work and try whether it was poised with that exactness as was necessary for the ease of the turnspit. But they found, like notable conjurers, that one side was too heavy by as many pounds as t'other was too light, which was no way to be remedied but by chipping and paring, till they had brought 'em to an equality, which, by the time they had cut off as many slivers as amounted to the weight of about six stone, was finished effectually with great gladness and applause.

Beefsteaks, we now observed, were as plenty about house as yolks of eggs in brewing-time; which encouraged us, notwithstanding the hurry, to sit down in the kitchen and take share of the superfluity, and also over our flask to take notice of the divers humours, and various sentiments, of the numerous spectators, who flocked in and out as fast to behold the novelty as if it had been the corpse of an old woman laid in state that had hanged herself for love of a young fellow of five and twenty.

Amongst the rest in came an old gentleman, who looked as grave as a modern philosopher in the laboratory of an alchemist that he might take a satisfactory survey of this uncommon eatable, which looked as frightful upon the spit as the flying dragon upon St George's spear when he rescued the damsel from the teeth and talons of the furious monster. After he had fumbled as long in his pockets as a hypocrite does to find a farthing for a beggar, he at last pulls out his artificial peepers which he mounted upon the handle of his face, that the wonderful object might be rendered the more conspicious. Round this he then walked with as much circumspection as ever a prying virtuoso did round a glass beehive to observe how the winged labourers work their honeycombs, telling the ribs, measuring the length with his crutch-headed cane, guessing at the weight, and turning up the rump as the monkey did the cat's tail when he ran the spigot into her fundament. Then, holding up his hands like a belly-saint craving a blessing upon his food, he broke out into this joyful rapture: 'Look ye, d'ye see, gentlemen, on t'other hand, it may be we are the happiest nation in the world. For let us but consider, d'ye hear me, what a blessing of Providence it is, as a man may say, that such a glorious sight as this, a glorious sight I say, is to be seen amongst us after so long a war. Let me tell you, had it continued till now, such a piece of beef as this, without great mercy, would have been a much more graceful sight than the fattest alderman in London.' Then he fell a-laughing at his jest till he brought himself into a fit of physic, which put a period to his learned oration.

The next spectator that was worth our notice was a kind of Captain Bluster, who was so brimful of oaths that he ran over like Southwark ditch at a spring-tide, and, I am apt to believe, were his bottom to be fathomed, he would prove to be as filthy. 'Why a pox,' says he to one of the drawers, 'was your master such a fool to have the head cut off, which would have been so great a grace to your pack-saddle monster that, I'll warrant you, there's never a cuckold in town but what would have had a peep at him?' 'The reason, sir,' says the drawer, 'that my master had it cut off, was because the range is not long enough to roast it.' 'Cats' nouns,' says the gentleman, 'your cooks are all blockheads, for they might have thrust it as short with the head on, as 'tis now without it.' 'How, sir?' says the master of the roast, with great indignation, 'I have been a student in the art of cookery above this twenty years, and I do affirm, sir, that what you say is impossible.' 'Then I do say,' replied the gentleman, 'that thou art a mere cod's head of a cook, and I can tell thee which way it may be done presently if the head had been on.' 'I'll hold you, sir,' says the cook, 'that price of the beef to a pound of kitchen stuff if the head had been on it, it must have required so much the longer fire to have roasted it.' 'No, no,' says the gentleman, 'it had been but jointing the neck, and you might have brought the head round, and have stuck one of the horns through the body, as you do the bill of a woodcock; what do you think of that, domine coquus?' 'I'faith, master,' says he, 'I did not think of that; now you have put it in my head, I don't question but I could have done it. But what should we have done with the horn that was next to the fire? For that,' says he, 'would have hung upon the range and stopped the going of the meat.' 'That,' says the gentleman, 'I should have designed for the cook's fees.' At this the company fell into a laughter, which kindled such a fire in the cook's countenance that his looks were almost sufficient to have scalded the company out of the kitchen.

By this time we had eaten a steak and drunk up our flask of wine, and being quite tired with the cook's clutter, the confusion of tongues, the hurry of the house and other inconveniences that always attend such public novelties, we adjourned to our own homes in order to dispatch some domestic business, which, together with reposing nature, took up our time till Thursday morning, upon which day this liberal entertainment was to be in a roasted readiness to oblige the guests.

When the morning came, my friend and I, having a great desire to discover what an attractive influence such a magnificent piece of beef had upon the stomachs of this town, resolved not to lose the opportunity of gratifying our palates, as well as feasting our eyes, and of coming in for our share of the benefit as well as the rest of the town's epicures. And we might also the better inform ourselves how the whim took amongst those tippling gudgeons for whom the alluring bait was in chief designed. When we came to the door we had more difficulty to get admittance than we had before, for as many people were crowding to see it at the fire, as there were to see the ox roasted upon the ice. When we had squeezed sideways through the entry, with as much pains as a fat man takes to shove his guts through a narrow turnstile, we got into the yard, where such a litter of drawers were scampering from cellar to bar, and from bar to company, it was difficult to believe the whole house could have entertained guests sufficient to have required such a number of attendants. As many bells were rattling at a time as o'er a greenbird's cage when the feathered animal (though it hates a cat) rings 'Whittington'. The servants were all puffing and blowing like greyhounds after a course, sweating like a couple of chairmen in the dog days who had just set down a bulky nobleman. The kitchen was now as hot as Guinea at noonday, yet we concluded there we should be best attended, being near the bar, and the least incommoded for want of room, could we but reconcile our bodies to the extraordinary heat, which we thought we could more easily endure than many other inconveniences we should have found elsewhere. Accordingly, we ventured into the kitchen, which, at first entrance, seemed hot enough to have baked a custard in the middle of it, but seating ourselves at a convenient distance from the fire, and where we drew in a little cool breath at a back door, we found ourselves well settled in a pretty moderate climate.

The poor carcase of the beast was by this time so lamentably mangled by the cuts and slashes of the broiling carvers, that had Sir Courtly Nice, or my Lady Squeamish, been to have taken a view of the roasting rarity, they would scarce have longed to have been partakers of the feast. The shoulders and the ribs were soon stripped as bare of their flesh, as if the Tower lions, or the tiger, had been just at breakfast on't, and the buttock and more fleshy parts were cut and digged so full of holes and furrows that it looked as disfigured as the carcase of a goose after a couple of tun-bellied churchwardens have had the picking of her. Yet the poor anatomy cocked its tail as it ran round upon the spit like Ralph's dobbin in a full gallop, and the turnspit was so discoloured with sweat, soot, smoke and ashes, that both he and his cookery looked as if one devil was roasting of another, letting fall so fast his greasy tears, as if it were an emulation between both who should afford the most dripping. The cook and his attendants were so very busy about the carcase of the beast that every round it took, it was at least two or three pound the lighter.

By this time a generous plateful of the good creature was brought as a present to my friend and I, with all the rest of the appurtenances at once, without the trouble of calling. This encouraged our appetites, and gave us a better liking to our treat; which in justice I must say, according to the old English way of praising beef, was as rich, fat, young, well-fed, delicious meat, as ever was taken into the mouth, masticated between the teeth, and swallowed into the belly of a true Englishman. By the time we had made an end of our plentiful commons, the bones of the whole carcase were pared as clean as the sharp-whetted weapons of the blunt dissectors could well pick 'em, insomuch that the vintner found himself under a necessity of sending for two barons more, or half his guests would have been disappointed of their breakfast. For the Templars, whose business called them to Westminster, had omitted their accustomary eating of roast beef in Hall, and came in roaring crowds with such devilish stomachs, which the exercise of their lungs in the Hall had made insatiate as their consciences, that their tongues, as fast as they came in, pleaded very hard in the behalf of their bellies, nothing being heard but 'Beef, beef, beef,' threatening to run all to the devil presently if the master did not retain 'em speedily by greasing their stomachs with a present of his fat opsonium. This he promised 'em to do with all imaginable expedition, and so pacified 'em with good words till the next was roasted.

Having now well freighted the hold of our vessels with excellent food and delicious wine at a small expense, we scribbled these following lines with chalk upon the wall, so took our departure from thence, and steered our course to a more temperate climate.

> To speak but the truth of my honest friend Ned,
> The best of all vintners that ever God made,
> He's free of his beef, and as free of his bread,
> And washes both down with a glass of rare red
> That tops all the town, and commands a good trade,
> Such wine as will cheer up the drooping King's Head,
> And brisk up the soul, though the body's half dead!
> He scorns to draw bad, as he hopes to be paid,
> And now his name's up he may e'en lie abed,
> For he'll get an estate, there's no more to be said.

Considering coffee to be a liquor that sits most easy upon wine, we thought it the best way to check the aspiring fumes of the most Christian juice by an antichristian dose of Muhammadan loblolly, and to hear what news the grizzly trumpeters of Fame's reports had raked up together from credulous noddles who hear without attention, believe without reason, and affirm without probability. Accordingly we went into a great coffee-house by the Temple Gate, where a parcel of grave men were thickening the air with the fumes of their nicotian weed. We sat ourselves down amongst the sage assembly, most of the company, we observed, being as choice of their words as a miser is of his treasure, each seeming as loath to open his mouth as the other his cabinet, which made me think they had either something extraordinary in 'em, that they locked up in their Pythagorean silence, or else that they were a parcel of cunning fools, who, having a sense of their infirmities, were unwilling by their talk to discover their ignorance. At last comes in an old newshound, who, in

hunting after intelligence was at a great loss, and so enquired of the rest
if any straggling news had come that way.

'News!' replied a jolly red-faced old toper, 'we have news enough, I
think, to comfort the hearts of the whole City in the days of affliction.
We may remember when the government of our metropolis was fallen
into the hands of the double-refined Christians, and the grandeur of the
mayoralty and the rest of of the ancient glories of London City were
reduced so low they were almost extinguished in the very socket of
dissension. But, since Providence has restored the Chair to the Church,
we see every succeeding Lord Mayor give us greater instances of a
general regard to the public welfare. Instead of the severe execution of
the laws upon poor wretches made already by their miseries the objects
of pity rather than of punishment, charity is extended to the releasement,
as well as relief, of prisoners. And succour is given to the distressed, the
fatherless, and widows, instead of uncharitable confinement and
unreasonable correction to these poor mendicants who have not above
ninepence or twelvepence a week from the parish, without begging, to
keep 'em from starving.

'Besides,' says he, 'authority we see rightly given into the hands of
those persons who have a just title to receive and execute the same by
being truly qualified, as the laws require, to prevent the ignorant from
dissenting from the Church and holding in contempt the true worship of
God, and the obedience due to their lawful sovereign. The common
people were too often drawn off from the true discharge of both these
duties by the ill examples of Dissenting magistrates. When the sword was
carried to the meeting-house how empty were the churches and numerous
the congregations of saints! But since the magistracy of the City is given
on the right side, the churches are everywhere as full as if true Christianity of late, by the industry of our clergy and care of our magistrates, had
been greatly advanced. And the assemblies of the over-righteous are
grown so very thin that, it is verily believed if things succeed as they
begin, the dancing-masters about this town may in little time have choice
of good schools at more reasonable rates than ever. And that, I think,
boys, is much better news than to see Paul's Church as empty as a
Saturday's 'Change, and the meeting-houses as full as Westminster Hall
in an issuable term.'

Most of the company agreeing rightly with the old gentleman's
sentiments, applauded him very highly for so heartily expressing his
affections to the Established Church. This serious speech of the old

cavalier's was a key to the hearts of all the rest, who began, after one had opened, like a pack of true beagles at full cry, to hunt down the Church's enemies with all imaginable speed. All expressed so venerable a character of the present Lord Mayor, that few magistrates have deserved, and scarce any enjoyed, and highly extolled him for his great charity towards the poor prisoners, and many other commendable acts of hospitality. These have deservedly raised him to so high an esteem among all good Christians, that if no mismanagement of his own, in the residue of his time, shall futurely sully his reputation, when he resigns his office he will leave behind him a worthy pattern of authority that will be a puzzling task for his successors, though brave men, to imitate.

> If any shall say want of manners or sense
>   Have made me this caution intrude,
> I justly may urge, to excuse the offence,
>   To be moral is not to be rude.

> Whoever to popular praises aspire,
>   Must do't by much trouble and cost.
> Though a very good name is so hard to acquire,
>   Yet nothing's so easily lost.

> The turns and changes of Fame and of Fate
>   Are to no mortal power foreknown.
> They may raise us today by good means to be great,
>   Yet tomorrow may tumble us down.

> May therefore your prudence and conduct be such
>   That the City may honour your name
> And give you such praise that no envy can touch
>   Or malice deservedly blame.

Having now wasted our time till about nine at night, we thought it a reasonable hour to take leave of the coffee-house and repair to our own lodgings, where my business engaged me to continue close till the triumphs of the City called me to make one of the innumerable multitude of gaping spectators.

When the morning came that my Lord Mayor and his attendants were to take their amphibious journey to Westminster Hall, where His

Lordship, according to the custom of his ancestors, was by a kiss of calves'-leather, to make a fair promise to Her Majesty, I equipped my carcase in order to bear with little damage the hustles and affronts of the unmannerly mobility, of whose wild pastimes and unlucky attacks I had no little apprehension. And when my friend and I had thus carefully sheltered ourselves under our ancient drabdeberries against their dirty assaults, we ventured to move towards Cheapside, where I thought the triumphs would be most visible, and the rabble most rude, looking upon the mad frolics and whimsies of the latter to be altogether as diverting (provided a man takes care of the danger) as the solemn grandeur and gravity of the former.

When I came to the end of Blow Bladder Street, I saw such a crowd before my eyes, that I could scarce forbear thinking the very stones of the street, by the harmony of their drums and trumpets, were metamorphosed into men, women and children. The balconies were hung with old tapestry and Turkey-work tablecloths, for the cleanly leaning out of the ladies, with whom they were chiefly filled, but the mob had soon pelted them into so dirty a condition with kennel ammunition that some of them looked as nasty as the cover-cloth of a led horse that had travelled from St Margaret's to London in the midst of winter. The ladies, at every volley, quitted their post and retreated into dining-rooms, as safer garrisons to defend themselves from the assaults of their mischievous enemies; some fretting at their daubed scarves, like a godly old woman that had dropped her bible in the dirt, singed the nap of her high-crowned hat, or broke her spectacles; others wiping their new commodes, which they had bought on purpose to honour His Lordship, each expressing as much anger in their looks as a disappointed bride, or a Dutch housewife when an Englishman has blowed his nose in her parlour. The windows of each house, from the top to the bottom, were stuffed with heads, piled one upon another like skulls in a charnel-house, all gazing at the lobcocks in their coney-skin pontificalibuses with as much attention as if an Indian prophetess had been riding through the city upon the back of a tiger.

Whilst my friend and I were thus staring at the spectators much more than the show, the pageants were advanced within our view, upon which such a tide of mob overflowed the place we stood in, that the women cried out for room, the children for breath, and every man, whether citizen or foreigner, strove very hard for his freedom. For my own part, I thought my entrails would have come out of my mouth, and I should have gone shitten home. I was so closely imprisoned between the bums and bellies of the multitude that I was almost squeezed as flat as a napkin in a press, or I heartily would have joined with the rabble to have cried, 'Liberty, liberty!'

In this pageant was a fellow riding a-cock-horse upon a lion, but without either boots or spurs, as if intended, by the projector, to show how the citizens ride to Epsom on a Saturday night to bear their wives company till Monday morning,

Or else to let the hen-pecked cuckolds know
A lion's tamed more easy than a shrew.

At the base of the pedestal were seated four figures representing, according to my most rational conjecture, the four principal vices of the City, viz., Fraud, Usury, Seeming-sanctity and Hypocrisy. As soon as this was past, the industrious rabble, who hate idleness, had procured a dead cat, whose reeking puddings hung dangling from her torn belly, covered all o'er with dirt, blood and nastiness. In this pickle she was handed about by the babes of grace, as an innocent diversion, every now and then being tossed into the face of some gaping booby or other, making him look of as delicate a complexion as if his cheeks had been painted by a Tom turd-man and a chimney-sweeper.

By the time this sport had gone a little about, they crying out, 'No squibs! No squibs!' another pageant approached us, wherein an old fellow sat in a blue gown, dressed up like a country schoolmaster, only he was armed with a scythe instead of a birch-rod, by which I understood this figure represented Time, which was designed, as I suppose, to put the City in mind how apt they are to abuse the Old Gentleman and not dispose of him to such good uses as the laws of God and the laws of man require, but trifle their time away in those three vanities which were represented by the three figures under the dome, viz., Falsehood, Pride and Incontinence, which are chiefly owing to the other four figures, the angels, representing, as I suppose, the City's Imprudence, Impatience, Intemperance and Inhumanity.

When this pageant was passed, the ingenious rabble had got a leather apron, which they tied full of sir-reverence, as hard as a football, and afterwards pricked it full of holes with a tailor's bodkin. Then they flung it from one to another. It spewed its excrements through the eyelet-holes upon everybody it met with, the mob crying out when it had hit anybody, 'All honey, all honey!'

By the time the plebeian gentry had diverted themselves about a quarter of an hour with this their odoriferous sweet-bag, a third pageant advanced forward, which appeared to the sight much richer than the rest. 'What think you,' says my friend, 'of these emblems?' 'I think,' said I, 'the chief figure in it represents, as I imagine, a lady of pleasure, being dressed in much costlier robes than the other female representatives, which may serve to let the City know that whores in this wicked age, to the great dishonour of virtue, wear richer apparel, at the expense of their keepers, than honest women. Those three maids that attend her as her servants signify the pride of a concubine, who will not be content without three servants when the lawful wife perhaps must be glad of one. And those four figures that are placed beneath the rest signify the sad calamities that attend the conversation of lewd women, viz., Pox, Poverty, Shame and the Gallows. This pageant is chiefly dedicated to the London apprentices, at the charge of the Society for Reformation.'

In every interval between pageant and pageant the mob had still a new project to put on foot. This time they had got a piece of cloth of a yard or more square, which they dipped in the kennel till they had made it fit for their purpose, then tossed it about. Expanding itself in the air, and falling on the heads of two or three at once, it made 'em look like so many bearers under a pall, every one lugging a several way to get it off his head, oftentimes falling together by the ears about plucking off their cover-slut. By the time forty or fifty of the heedless spectators were made as dirty as so many scavengers, the fourth pageant was come up, which was a most stately, rich and noble chariot, made of slit deal and pasteboard, and in it was sitting a woman representing, as I fancy, the Whore of Babylon, drawn by two goats, signifying her lust, and upon the backs of them two figures representing Jealousy and Revenge; her attendants importing the miseries that follow her, and the kettledrums and trumpets served to show that wheresoe'er she comes 'tis with terror and amazement.

The rabble having changed their sport to a new scene of unluckiness, had got a bullock's horn, which they filled with kennel water, and poured it down people's necks, and into their pockets, so that it ran down their legs into their shoes, and the ignorant sufferers, not readily discovering from whence the wet came, were apt to think they had bepissed themselves.

When they had exercised this new invention about a quarter of an hour the fifth pageant moved forward, wherein all sorts of trades were represented; a man working at a tobacco engine, as if he were cutting of tobacco, but often did not; a woman turning of a wheel, as if she spun, but did not; a boy as if he were a-dressing of an old woman's hat, but was not; which was designed, as I suppose, to reflect upon the frauds and failings of the City traders, and show that they often pretend to do what they do not, and to be what they are not, and will say what they think not, and will think what they say not, and that the world might see there are cheats in all trades.

The bully cits marched after in a throng,
Huzza'd by the mob, as drummed and piped along,
Whilst wise spectators did their pomp disdain,
And with contempt behold the draggling train.

XIII

THE TRIUMPHS OF the City being now passed by, they drew after them the mobility, to our safe deliverance, my friend and I clinging as fast to a post as a bear to a ragged staff, to avoid being carried away by the resistless torrent of the rabble; which, if we had quitted our hold, would have inevitably happened, to the further bruising of our ribs and the great penance of our toes. But on the contrary, finding ourselves as safe as a politic prince in the rear of an engagement, we began to consider in what new adventure we should spend the remainder of the day. And at last I remembered that I had oftentimes in the country heard wonderful tales and tidings from higglers, hawkers, carriers, drovers, and suchlike hobbaddyboodies, of several four-footed barbarian kings, with many of their ravenous subjects, who had for divers years been kept close prisoners in Her Majesty's palace and prison, the Tower of London, till their hair was grown so long it hung over their eyes, like the foretop of a parson's mare that goes six days to plough and the seventh to church; and till their nails were improved to such a terrible extensio, that the keepers, by relation, might as well venture to take a bear by the tooth as to come within the reach of 'em, lest they should be worse scratched than ever poor witch was by her languishing sufferer, to dissolve the charm.

The sundry reports of these amazing objects, together with many other enticing rarities, to be visited at a small expense within the ancient battlements of this renowned citadel (which I had received from the magnifying mouths of some boobily bumpkins who had stolen so much time from their wagons and hay-carts as to be spectators of these surprising curiosities) had begot in me such an earnest desire of beholding these foreign monsters, and domestic engines of destruction, with crowns, sceptres, and many other pompous knick-knacks worth any great man's coveting who prefers grandeur before ease, and riches before safety. So, having prevailed with my friend to concur with my proposal, we determined to steer our course towards this stately magazine, and to spend a little time in viewing the martial furniture of that famous garrison which statesmen dread and common people admire.

Having so lately escaped from the punishment of a crowd, we were very cautious how we relapsed into the same condition; for my Lord Mayor's Show being past, the mob began to divide their main body in distinct parties, a division attending each several company to their proper hall, gazing at the grave noddies, who being perplexed with either horns, corns, gout, stone or gravel, hobbled after their hautboys like the great old dons of the Law, when they dance the measures in an Inns of Court hall upon the first day of Christmas. Having hitherto very luckily avoided any dirty remembrances of the rabble's civility, notwithstanding we had carelessly been drawn into such a company as had been many a brave man's ruin, we (God be thanked) recovered our freedom from their unlucky hands without damage. But we were so fearful of falling a second time into their clutches that whenever we heard the waits, drums or trumpets behind us, we started forward with as much dread as a couple of church mice would do from the diapason of Paul's organ; for wherever we heard the bagpipes we were assured the bears were not far off.

We thought ourselves not free from the danger of some abuse till we got through Leadenhall Market into some of the back lanes, for the great streets were the channel of the mob, who were very careful, as they moved along, to improve every handful of dirt they could take up to the prejudice of somebody or other, crying 'All fair! No body! No body!' as they do in frosty weather when they break windows at football. The person injured would have nothing else to do, but to bear his wrong with much patience, for apprehension and reprehension would make 'em double the mischief.

We found little worth our observation as we passed along but many merchants' houses as stately as princes' palaces, and 'tis reported by such who have the opportunity of being judges of their inward hospitality, that their housekeeping within is answerable to their outward grandeur; which if it be, it's enough to make our nobility blush, to see themselves outdone in that commendable liberality wherein the honour and splendour of a great and rich man is most magnificently visible. Three or four of Quality's coaches were at one door, two or three chairs at another, as if the courtiers were come into the City to kiss the merchants' wives and borrow money of their husbands; an old game that has oft been played and will never be out of fashion whilst the City's richer than the Court.

When we came upon the Hill, the first object that more particularly affected us was that emblem of destruction, the scaffold, from whence greatness, when too late, has oft beheld the happiness and security of lower stations; reflecting with a deep concern on their sudden prosperity, and the restless ambition that had brought 'em to that fate which the contentment, under a moderate fortune and a private life, might have happily prevented. For he that sits too high in the favour of his prince is liable to be delivered up, upon public disorders, as a sacrifice to appease the fury of the people; and he that labours for a popular esteem is always looked upon by his prince to be a dangerous subject; so that, according to Phoebus's caution to his son Phaeton, 'tis safest to steer the course of our lives in a middle station.

At a little distance from this *memento mori* stood a very ragged indigent prophet, delivering, with a thin pair of jaws, a shock-doggish beard, and a devout countenance, the doctrine of Charity, with a much larger congregation round him than I have seen at church, giving as serious attention to their mendicant shepherd as if every listening member, according to his condition, designed to contribute something towards the relief of their distressed lecturer.

But before he had come to his use and application, a blind fellow, who had for many years been one of the Hill-pensioners, takes up his stand at a little distance, and out of a budget which had as many partitions as an old country cupbard, for his silver, farthings, short pipes, tobacco, and bread and cheese, &c., he pulls out a couple of little flutes, claps one to each corner of his mouth, and with his melodious roundelays drew off all the audience from Charity's poor chaplain, leaving the ubiquitarian apostle in a wonderful indignation, calling after 'em as they moved off in this manner: 'Beloved, pray, beloved, stay a little, I am just a-going to conclude. Alas! Alas! What a wicked age do we live in, when men shall forsake the word of the gospel to follow a hobbling guide, and prefer the tootings of a blind piper before the delightful music of salvation.' But away went all the people, notwithstanding his reproof, to tickle their ears with the harmony of their blind musician. The expectance of the paltry, instead of spiritual, pastor was quite baulked, the multitude being drawn off without showing him one example of their charity amongst 'em all. So he marched mumbling away, in a great fury with his flock, saying, just as he passed by us, they were a wicked congregation that deserved to be cursed, and he would pronounce an anathema against 'em. And looking over his shoulder towards the people, he breathed out this comical execration: 'I wish your ears were full of bird-lime, your eyes full of cat's piss, and your mouth full of sir-

reverence, that you might be all deaf, dumb and blind, every time you
stand to hear that blind hedge-bird whistle, when you may bless your
ears with a good sermon.' And having thus expressed himself, away he
rambled.

From thence we went into the first gate of the Tower, where a parcel
of lazy redcoats were loitering about like so many City bulldogs at the
Poultry Compter. We were no sooner past the first sentinel, but right
before us, against the front of a little house, hung a strange sort of a
picture. My friend asked me what I thought it represented, or whether I
had ever seen any creature that was like it. To me it seemed the picture
of some rugged-faced man's head; and after I had compared it in my
thoughts to everybody I could recollect, and all the ideas I could form,
I thought that by its flat nose and ill-favoured countenance it was the
likest the unborn-doctor, the seventh son of the seventh son in Moorfields, of anything that ever I saw in my life. My friend, smiling at the
oddness of my fancy, undeceived me by telling me 'twas a lion's head,
hung out as a means to inform strangers that come to see the Tower that
there is the royal palace, where the king of beasts keeps his Court, and
may every day, at a proper distance, be seen at dinner without danger.
But, like the Czar of Muscovy, if you stare at him too near he'll be apt
to do you a mischief. 'This,' says he, 'being the first sight, let us take it
in turn, and then you'll be better satisfied.'

Accordingly we went in, where the yard smelt as frowzily as a dove-
house or a dog-kennel. In their separate apartments were four of their
stern affrighting catships, one with a whelp presented to His late
Majesty, of which the dam was as fond as an old maid, when married,
is of her first child; one couchant, another dormant, a third passant
guardant, a fourth very fierce, was rampant, being a lioness, and as angry
when we spoke to her as a milkmaid when you cry 'Whow ball!' She put
out her paw to me, which was tipped with such ill-favoured sort of
pruning-hooks, that rather than she should have shaken me by the hand
I would have chosen to have taken Old Nick by his cloven foot, and
should have thought myself in less danger. One of the keeper's servants,
whilst he was showing us his unruly prisoners, entertained us with a
couple of remarkable stories, which, because the tragedy of the one will
render an escape in the other story the more providential, I shall proceed
to give 'em to the reader in their proper places.

A maid, some years since, being a servant to the keeper, and a bold
spirited wench, took pleasure, now and then, to help feed the lions, and

imprudently believing the gratitude of the beasts would not suffer them to hurt her, she would venture sometimes, though with extraordinary caution, to be a little more familiar with them than she ought to be. At last, either carelessly or presumptuously, she ventured too near their dens, and one of the lions catched hold of her arm, and tore it quite off at the shoulder, after a most lamentable manner, before anybody could come to her assistance, killing her with a grip, before he would loose her from his talons, till she was made a miserable object of her own folly, the lion's fury and the world's pity.

This story was succeeded by another, wherein was shown a miraculous preservation of himself, contrary to the cruelty the lion had before used to his unhappy fellow servant, which he delivered after this following manner: ''Tis our custom,' says he, 'when we clean the lions' dens, to drive 'em down overnight, through a trap-door, into a lower convenience, in order to rise early in the morning and refresh their day-apartments, by clearing away their filth and nastiness. Having through mistake, and not forgetfulness, left one of the trap-doors unbolted, which I thought I had carefully secured, I came down in the morning, before daylight, with my candle and lantern fastened before me to a button, with my implements in my hands to dispatch my business, as was usual; and going carelessly into one of the dens, a lion had returned through the trap-door, and lay couchant in a corner, with his head towards me. The sudden surprise of this terrible sight brought me under such dreadful apprehensions of the danger I was in that I stood fixed like a statue, without the power of motion, with my eyes steadfastly upon the lion, and his likewise upon me. I expected nothing but to be torn to pieces every moment, and was fearful to attempt one step back, lest my endeavour to shun him might have made him the more eager to have hastened my destruction.

At last he roused himself, as I thought, to have made a breakfast of me; yet, by the assistance of Providence, I had the presence of mind to keep steady in my posture, for the reasons aforementioned. He moved towards me without expressing in his countenance either greediness or anger, but on the contrary wagged his tail, signifying nothing but friendship in his fawning behaviour. And after he had stared me a little in the face, he raised himself upon his two hindmost feet and, laying his two fore-paws upon my shoulders without hurting me, fell to licking my face, as a further instance of his gratitude for my feeding him, as I afterwards conjectured, though then I expected every minute he would have stripped my skin over my ears, as a poulterer does a rabbit, and have cracked my head between his teeth as a monkey does a small nut. His tongue was so very rough that with the few favourite kisses he gave me, made my cheeks almost as raw as a pork griskin, which I was very glad to take in good part, without a bit of grumbling. And when he had thus saluted me, and given me his sort of welcome to his den, he returned to his place, and laid him down, doing me no further damage. This unexpected deliverance hitherto, occasioned me to take courage that I slunk back by degrees, till I recovered the trap-door, through which I jumped and plucked it after me; thus happily, through an especial providence, I escaped the fury of so dangerous a creature.'

The under-keeper having thus ended his stories, we proceeded to our further view of these Beelzebub's bloodhounds, or lap-dogs for a she-devil. Two of them were dead and their skins stuffed, one of them having been King Charles's lion, but had no more the fierceness in his looks that he had when he was living, than the effigy of his good master at Westminster has the presence of the original. The other that was stuffed was said to be Queen Mary's, but made such a drooping figure with his false entrails, that it brought into my mind an old proverb, with which I could not but agree, that a living dog is better than a dead lion.

The next ill-favoured creatures that were presented to our sight were a couple of pretty looking hell-cats, called a tiger, and a catamountain, whose fierce penetrating eyes pierced through my belly to the sad gripping of my guts, as if, basilisk-like, they could have killed at a distance with their very looks.

In another apartment or ward, for the convenience of drawing a penny more out of the pocket of a spectator, are placed these following animals: first a leopard, who is grown as cunning as a cross Bedlamite that loves not to be looked at. For as the madman will be apt to salute you with a bowl of chamber-lie, so will the leopard, if you come near him, stare in your face and piss upon you, his urine being as hot as aqua fortis, and stinks worse than a polecat's.

The next creatures that we observed were three hawk-nosed gentlemen called eagles, one black, and another in second mourning, a third with a bald pate, as if he had been pulling a crow with his two comrades, and like unmerciful enemies they had pecked all the feathers off his crown and left it as bare as a bird's arse. Next to these were a couple of outlandish owls, whose mouths lay under their beaks like an old citizen's under his nose, who has rotted out his teeth with eating custard at the

Lord Mayor's feasts. These owls, besides eyes as big as the glasses of a convex-lamp, had each of them long ears that grew like horns, under which they looked as venerably grave as two aged aldermen.

The next part of the show recommended to our notice were two preternatural objects, being a dog and a cat, pupped and kittened but with two legs each; the former having a bump upon his head, which, in derision to our high-crowned ladies, they are pleased to call a topknot. 'Prithee, friend,' said I to the man that showed 'em, 'what is it that you value these imperfect vermin for? There's but little satisfaction, I should think, in the sight of such ill-favoured monsters.' 'Sir,' says the fellow, 'whether you know it or not, these vermin, as you are pleased to call 'em, are as highly prized and as well looked after as any creature in the yard.' 'But pray, friend,' said I, 'for what reason are they so esteemed?' 'Why, sir,' says he, 'because they have but half their number of legs.' To this I answered, 'If that be all the reason, methinks they should take as much care to feed the poor human cripples, who were born with all their legs, and have lost one half in the nation's service, and are forced to seek their bread where they can find it; I believe I saw twenty begging upon the Hill as I came hither.' 'Ah, sir,' says the fellow, 'but they are no rarity. Were it as uncommon a thing to see a soldier or a sailor with but one leg, as 'tis to see a dog or a cat with no more than two, no question but they would live as well and be as much taken notice of as these are.'

From thence we were removed into another division, to see that alluring creature so much talked of by the old poets, called the hyena, which, as they report, has the voice of a man, and coming near a cottage would cry out like a traveller in some distress. By this means he decoys the shepherds out of their houses, and afterwards devours 'em; which story, whether it be truth or fiction, I could see nothing in the creature to determine.

Having thus paid homage to the kings of the quadrupeds, and the lofty monarch of the feathered kind whose ambition, when at liberty, makes him soar above all terrestrial beings, we moved forward to the second gate. Here a parcel of bulky warders in old-fashioned laced jackets, and in velvet flat-caps hung round with divers coloured ribbons, like a fool's hat upon a holiday, looked as fierce as a file of Artillery ale-drapers in buff, when they are going to besiege a dunghill in Bunhill Fields and play at soldiers one against another to please the rabble. We had no sooner made a nimbler step than ordinary beyond the portcullis, as cautious citizens do by the Monument, for fear it should tumble upon their heads, but one of these brawny beef-and-pudding-eating janizaries demanded, like a busy constable at midnight, whither we were going. Thought I, we are no sooner come from Her Majesty's lions but we are fallen into the clutches of some of her bears, but did not dare to tell 'em so, for fear the bloody-coloured animals would have fallen into a passion with me, and have spoiled our sight. So instead of that, I informed 'em, like an honest tell-truth, our real business. They told us we could not be admitted to gratify our desires without we took a warder with us; which we found we were forced to consent to, or return back without the satisfaction we proposed. Upon this we ordered him to attend us, and had the honour of walking up and down the Tower, as great as a factious lord committed for suspicion of high treason.

The first thing we observed, when we were past the gate, was a great brass gun painted over of a copper colour. Sure, thought I, this was not done in a jest, to let folks who come in here see that guns, like bells, are as great turncoats as those that command 'em, meaning parsons and officers. For the one will roar, the other ring, the third preach, and the fourth fight, for any power that's uppermost; and 'tis verily believed by all people who have any regard for that prevailing principle, Interest, that they are all in the right on't.

The next place that fell in its turn within our notice was the Traitors' Gate, where the fall of the moat-waters, or the cataracts on each side, made so terrible a noise that it's enough to fright a prisoner that lodges within the hearing on't out of the world before his time of execution. The passage was fortified by a parcel of iron guns, which to me, that understood 'em not, seemed as old and as rusty as the hinges of the gates of Babylon; but were, no doubt on't, in a good condition of giving a sufficient repulse to any enemy that should attempt a violent entrance.

We were from thence conducted through another gate, upon an ascent as steep as Holborn Hill, though not so often dangerous, on the right hand of which stood a stately square stone fabric, distinguished by the name of Julius Caesar's Tower. This must needs be as dark withinside as a country beehive, having but one door and never a window that I could see, only a little slit or two no bigger than the mouth of a Christmas-box in proportion to its vast body. It was made so very close, as I conceive, to keep fire and gunpowder at their proper distance, lest, by an unhappy conjunction of both, it should send more stones into the City than the shopkeepers' wives, notwithstanding their present want, would know how to make good use of.

The next remarkable place that we came to was the church, whose rugged outside appeared with such antiquity that I dare engage the external wall was far more reverenced by the true-blue Protestant Foot Guards than all that could be heard or seen withinside.

A little beyond this holy closet of a church stood the famous armoury, now placed under a new and modish name, The Arsenal, of which I had heard such a general applause that I was particularly desirous of obliging my curiosity with this martial entertainment. Accordingly we ordered our burly guide to conduct us thither, who, pursuant to our request, ushered us up a stately staircase, where, at the corner of every lobby and turning of the stairs, stood a wooden grenadier as sentinel, painted in his proper colours, cut out with as much exactness upon board as the picture of a housewife with her broom, very usually set up in great families as good examples to servant wenches, to make 'em mindful of their cleanliness. But though there were several figures, the painter, through the narrowness of his fancy, had made their postures and their faces so exactly alike that it would be as hard for a Moorfields doctor who judges distempers by urine, to tell mares' piss from maids' water, as it would be to distinguish one from the other, were they not differently posted.

When we came to the top of the stairs we were saluted, as I suppose, with two or three of the armourers' substitutes; one amongst the rest, who I imagine was esteemed as their principal orator, advanced before us, cap in hand, with as much ceremony as a dancing-master ushers the parents of his pupils into the school upon a ball-day; beginning to tell us at our entrance, with an audible voice, the signification of those figures which were first presented to our view; having everything as ready at his finger-ends as the fellow that shows the tombs at Westminster, or as a Savoy vagabond has the explanation of his raree-show.

The first figure, at our coming in, that most affected the eye, by reason of its bigness, was a long range of muskets and carbines, that runs the length of the armoury, which was distinguished by a wilderness of arms, whose locks and barrels were kept in such admirable order that they shone as bright as a good housewife's spits and pewter in the Christmas holidays. On each side of these were pistols, baggonets, scimitars, hangers, cutlasses, and the like, configurated into shields, triumphal arches, gates, pilasters, scallop-shells, mullets, fans, snakes, serpents, sunbeams, a gorgon's-head, the waves of the ocean, stars and garters, and, in the middle of all, pillars of pikes, and turned pillars of pistols; and at the end of the wilderness, firearms placed in the order of a great organ.

'This,' says my friend, 'is an allegorical emblem of a wolf in sheep's clothing. For these engines of destruction are never played on to any purpose but in wars, whose harsh and threatening sounds proclaim nothing but wounds, death, discord and desolation. To have such mischievous implements disguised under the form and figure of a musical instrument, which breathes forth nothing but peace, innocence, delight and harmony, is putting the Devil into a canonical robe, or, as I said before, a wolf into sheep's clothing.'

The next thing that our expositor recommended to our particular notice were Sir William Perkins' arms, taken under ground at his country house, as our voucher told us, pointing more especially to Sir William's own carbine and pistols, of which he made such a terrible story that it would have frighted a country fellow from looking at 'em; telling us they were screwed barrels, heptagonically bored. 'Why, friend,' said I, 'thou talkest as if thou understandest Greek; prithee, what is the meaning of that word heptagonically?' 'Oh, sir,' says he, 'it means a barrel that will mould a bullet into a slug I don't know how many times square, and will kill as many men again, and go six times as far as an ordinary barrel of the same bigness.' We could not forbear smiling at our interpreter's ignorance, who we expected would have told us the barrel consisted of seven sides, and answering him according to his folly, we seemed to be well satisfied with the account he gave us.

Over the top of this range of treasonable implements was placed a little brass blunderbuss upon which he fixed his eyes, turning up the whites like a good Christian at prayers, and shaking his head about half a dozen times, like a sorrowful father about to reprove his graceless progeny. Then plucking one of his hands out of his Dutch gloves, he pointed to it with a trembling finger and began to open upon the subject after this manner: 'That blunderbuss,' says he, 'was designed by the bloody assassinators to have killed the king, which God of His great goodness hath most happily prevented, bringing the bloody conspirators to condign punishment, and their traitorous weapons into the power of that glorious prince whose life they so basely sought. They are here, blessed be Providence, hung up in his armoury, as the perpetual memorandum of His Majesty's escape from the hands of his Popish enemies, to God's great glory, King William's safety, and England's happiness.'

Our little holder-forth having done his blundering lecture upon the king-killing blunderbuss, we removed from thence to another stand, where he showed us a parcel of Dutch firelocks with which the King landed at his first coming to England. These were carried, I suppose, by the monsters of men in bearskins with Saracens' heads, long beards and terrible countenances, the report of which so frightened the citizens of London and their wives that they were in as great a consternation as at the midnight cry of the coming of the cut-throat Irish.

Having thus taken a short view of the most renowned armoury in Christendom, according to the report of those who are far better judges than myself, we returned downstairs with our warder, who waited at the door to save his legs whilst we feasted our eyes with that glittering sight which was to him no novelty. When we had descended the grades, at the bottom door a bulky frizzle-pate (who, we might guess by his fatness, could write himself no less than servant to Her Majesty) stood in a readiness to receive the accustomary purchase money for that sight which had given our eyes such an extraordinary satisfaction.

Being now left to a further consideration of what we should see next, we took a little turn to deliberate upon the matter, but were forced quickly to make a result; for the Tower rooks began to flutter about us like so many salesmen about a country fellow in Long Lane; only as the one asks whether ye want coat, waistcoat, or breeches, will you buy any clothes; so the other, after the same manner, and in much the same dialect, whether you will see the Crown, the whole Regalia, or the King's marching train of Artillery.

My friend and I considering the marching train of Artillery consisted only in great guns, enough of which might be seen about the Tower without paying for't, made us think it scarce worthwhile to spend our money to take a sight of these threatening pot-guns. All as could be said of 'em, if we had seen 'em, was that they cost the nation a great deal of money, were able to beat down walls, would give a devilish bounce, and knock a man on the head at a great distance. So we agreed to pass by these, and adjourn to the Horse Armoury whither we ordered our guide to conduct us accordingly.

When we were come to the door there stood ready to receive us two or three smug-faced Vulcans, who were as amiable in complexion as if, to make themselves infernal beaus, they had powdered their frizzled locks with lampblack and beautified their physiognomies with kennel water; the lines of their faces being so pounced with dirt that from the

shoulders upwards they looked like so many antics' heads in an
alehouse-box, drawn upon the wall in charcoal by a drunken painter.

After our guide, who looked in his warder's robes as if he had been
cut out of a tapestry-hanging, had given a caution to the smutty
interpreter of this raree-show to tell us with deliberation the names of his
glittering troop of superficial heroes, the spokesman introduced us among
the monumental shells of our deceased princes, which only by the
industry of common hands shined bright in memory of those that wore
'em. As we gently moved along and viewed the princely scarecrows, he
told us to whom each suit of armour did belong originally, adding some
short memorandums out of history to every empty iron-side; some true,
some false, supplying that with invention which he wanted in memory.
He now and then endeavoured to break a jest to divert his customers, but
did it so like an Irishman that I had much ado to forbear telling the
fellow what a fool he was in endeavouring to be witty.

In our circular progress round these men of metal mounted on wooden
horses, we came to the armour of John of Gaunt, so famous for his
strength and stature, and, indeed, if his coat of defence was fit for his
body, I believe he was as big as any of the poetical giants that waged
war against Heaven. For, on my conscience, a man may speak without
lying, that is, I mean standing, that his armour is near as big about as the
Trojan Horse, as you may guess by his very codpiece, which was almost
as big as a poop-lantern, and better worth a lewd lady's admiration than
any piece of antiquity in the Tower.

As we were thus amongst the relics of our ancient kings and generals,
I could not forbear reflecting on some appearances before me, till I
fancied myself sunk into Death's subterranean territories where the just
and wicked, by the impartial Skeleton, are equally respected. Nor could
I, without concern, behold tyrants and martyrs, conquerors and cowards,
lawful princes and usurpers, shine equally bright, by the skill of an
armourer, in the eyes of the common people. For if the spots of injured
blood were to stain the warlike ornaments of some who have long since
spilt it, their arms, which now look bright, would appear of a sanguine
dye and record to posterity those cruelties which ought never to be
forgotten.

Whilst I was thus making myself uneasy with these melancholy
thoughts, we were advanced to the armour of Will Sommers, the jester,
to which they had added an ill-favoured face, with horns upon his head,
and upon his nose a pair of spectacles, on which our jocular commentator

was pleased thus merrily to discant. 'This figure,' says he, 'represents that drolling gentleman, Will Sommers, who was jester to King Henry the Eighth. He had the misfortune, poor gentleman, to be in the condition of many an honest gentleman, even at this day, that is, to have a very handsome wife who loved her neighbours much better than her husband. To this, like an honest, well-meaning, contented man, he would never give credit, though he had been often informed of her failings. And because he was so blind, like many a poor cuckold in this age, that he could not see his horns, which were conspicuous to everybody else, he was presented, by a nobleman who had kissed his wife, with a pair of spectacles to help his sight, by which he discerned his cuckoldom. It is therefore ordered he shall still wear them to put old men that have handsome young wives in mind that they may easily see they are cuckolds by the help of their own spectacles.'

The next subject he began to enlarge upon was King Henry the Eighth's codpiece, which was lined with red and hung gaping like a maidenhead at full stretch, just consenting to be ravished. 'This,' says he, 'is the codpiece of that great prince who never spared woman in his lust, nor man in his anger. And in it, to this day, remains this virtue, that if any married woman, though she has for many years been barren, but sticks a pin in the member-case, the next time she uses proper means, let her but think of her Tower pincushion and she needs not fear conception.'

From thence we passed by several princes' armour, of which was nothing delivered but a bare name, till we had completed our round and came again to the door, where hung upon a post the armour of King Somebody, made in the fashion of a petticoat. In this, as our dirty orator reported, he sometimes went a-masquerading, and when he had got a pretty lady that he liked in a corner, he used to whip it up by thrusting the skirts all up in folds above the belly. And under it there appeared a most princely sceptre, with which he ruled the women, and made them do homage upon their backs whenever he required it.

This being the conclusion of this warlike opera, we paid our money and made our exit, our stuttering perambulator turning his head over his shoulder, like a fox that had stole a goose, to ask us whether we would see the crowns, or no. 'Marry,' said I, 'not I. Crowns are mighty things and ought to be reverenced at a distance. I have heard many a wise man say there's danger in coming too near 'em. Besides, if a body should not make a leg handsomely and worship 'em as one should do, which a country clown, you know, can perform but awkwardly, they may think a body stiff-necked, and take one for a disaffected person to the government.' 'Prithee,' says my friend, 'I thought you had more wit than to be afraid of a fine thing; why, prithee, a king's crown is no living creature; it cannot bite thee.' 'I know well enough,' said I, 'it is not a living creature. No more is a king's writ, yet I have known it grip many a man to his ruin; therefore, I tell you, I care as little to come near the one as I do the other should come near me. Besides, I'll warrant you, our conductor can inform us as well as if, at our expense, we had gone ourselves to see 'em.'

Upon this my friend asked old bluff-jacket what part of the Regalia, as he called it, was to be seen. He told us, there was the royal crown, and a new one made for the coronation of the late Queen Mary, and three other crowns worn by Her Majesty, with distinct robes upon several occasions. Also the salt-spoons, forks and cups used at the coronation. This account we thought as satisfactory from the mouth of our guide as if our own eyes were witnesses of the matter, and so cozened the keeper of our eighteenpence apiece, which we thought would serve much better to exhilarate our souls and feast our appetites than to please our eyes and satisfy our curiosity.

Having thus taken a remarkable view of most of the Tower rarities, in respect to the Governor, we gave his house the right hand as we came out, and rewarded the warder with one of Her Majesty's pictures in silver, to his thorough satisfaction, and so departed.

We now walked down from the Wharf, where, at the entrance, stood such a parcel of Greenwich water-dogs that I thought they would have tore us in pieces before we could have elbowed our way through 'em. At last, with much difficulty, sour looks, and negative answers, we happily cleared ourselves of these freshwater sharks and took a pleasant walk by the river-side, where great guns lay drawn into their proper order, ready to declare the will and pleasure of that great monarch who alone commands their voices, and gives their sound interpretation to the common people. For though the loud-mouthed disputants have but the utterance of one monosyllable, called bounce, yet does their univerbal language carry along with it such a dint of argument that neither logic, rhetoric, or philosophy, are able to withstand the force on't.

About the middle of the Wharf was a stone arch over the passage to Traitors' Gate, where stood a sentinel who, I observed, was very careful nobody should lean upon it, or touch it, lest their elbows or their fingers should wear away Her Majesty's freestone. And to piss against it was a crime that deserved capping at least, except (like swearing at Priscian's Club) for every such offence you would forfeit sixpence. So I found it was held much better by the Guards, that a good subject burst himself than they lose the advantage of a ridiculous and shameful custom, which oftentimes frights fools out of their money and serves wise men to blush at.

We walked round the Tower, and came again upon the Hill, where mumpers, soldiers and ballad-singers were as busy at chuck-farthing and hustle-cap as so many rooks at a gaming ordinary, wrangling and squabbling about the foulness of their play, like so many knavish pettifoggers in the King's Bench Walks about the unfairness of their practice.

From thence we rambled into a remote part of the town, which my friend told me was as much incognito to many thousands in London as it was to me before ever I came into't. There were as many turnings and windings in and out of every street as, I believe, could be contained in Fair Rosamond's bower; and that which made me the more astonished was, we could walk by forty or fifty houses and not see an alehouse, which was a greater sign of a sober neighbourhood than I had observed before, since I came to London.

As we were thus wandering carelessly about, on the other side of the way we saw a door very finely painted, which allured us to cross the kennel and give our eyes the satisfaction of taking a view of what Mr Painter, as we thought, had put up at his door to stand the censure of the public. But when we came over, we found, according to our apprehension, such a parcel of strange hieroglyphics as would have puzzled an Egyptian magi to have told the meaning of 'em. There was a goat and a scorpion, a fish and a centaur, a ram and a crab, and many other suchlike whims, at which we could not forbear laughing. At last, reflecting more seriously upon the whim, we found it to be a representation of the Twelve Signs; from whence we presently concluded no less than an eminent conjurer, or some strange foretelling star-peeper, could be Lord of the House whose door was so gloriously set off with such a number of constellations.

As we were thus spending our conjectures upon that inhabitant's profession, out comes a figure at the door with such a malignant aspect that a great-bellied beggar-woman, as she asked him for a farthing, turned her head, I observed, another way, for fear her looking in his face might cause the child to be like him; one eye looked upwards, and the other downwards, as if he was star-gazing with one eye and minding his way with the other. What he was, we knew not; but the house looked as if a conjurer lived in't, and the man looked as if he was bewitched. I asked my friend the name of that place, and he told me 'twas Prescot Street.

'Pray,' says my friend, 'take notice of yonder tavern, at the sign of the Green Monster. That tavern,' says he, 'has ruined almost as many vintners as Sir Base-ill Fiery-face. I have known three or four break on't, whether for want of trade, the knavery of the merchant, or mismanagement, I know not. The first, indeed, had a very handsome wife, but very jiltish, who was supposed to be very kind to the person that set her up. But when she had once gratified his lust at a great expense, he, vexing at his folly when he had cooled his courage, resolved, like a true lecher, to turn his lust that could not last into a revenge that should. Accordingly he brought ruin upon the whole family; the husband running away into Ireland and leaving the poor woman to shift for herself with nothing but what God sent her. This she has since trusted into the hands of a draper, but what use he makes of it you may easily judge.' 'Truly,' said I, 'I commend the woman for trusting what her husband left her with in the hands of such a trader, who, when he is never so much tired with her, cannot at last, without great dishonour to the linen-draper's trade, leave her without a smock to her back. For this is very commonly the fate of women who unhappily enter into such illegal contracts.'

From thence, like roving pirates who coveted no harbour, we sailed about, we cared not whither, till mere accident and our own motion, without shaping any course, brought us into a street which both my friend and myself were equally strangers to, in which we espied a sumptuous tabernacle, which being built so distinguishably from the House of the Lord, and contrary to the form of Solomon's Temple, we were very desirous of knowing which of the buzzing sectaries made use of it for a hive wherein to work (with fear and trembling) the honeycombs of their devotion, which I very much feared yielded more wax than honey. And meeting in our way with a downright, honest sort of a fellow, I asked him what he called that street. He told me Penitent Street. I asked him further if he knew any peculiar reason why it was so christened. He answered me very roughly, 'Because it was built,' he supposed, 'for a parcel of deep sinners to live in, and they called it by that name, to put 'em in mind of repentance.' 'Who does this meeting belong to?' said I. 'A wicked congregation,' says the fellow. 'Prithee,' said I, 'who is their teacher?' 'The Devil, sir,' says he. 'I mean,' said I, 'who is it that preaches, or holds forth here?' 'Oh, oh,' said my respondent, 'now I overstand ye; why they call him Ca-sa-sa-ca-la-man-ca Doctor, I think,' says he, 'or by such a kind of a hard name, which I can't remember, though I have seen him and heard him often. But as for my part, he does so whine when he speaks, I had as lief hear a capon crow, as hear him preach. And as for his face, on my conscience, I think he has a chin to't as long as the handle of my pickaxe.' 'Honest friend,' said I, 'I thank ye, we'll trouble you no further, for I know the man well enough by your description; goodbye to you.' 'Nay,' said I to my companion, 'since my old acquaintance, the Doctor, has fallen luckily into my way, according to my old custom I must give him a taste of my kindness:

'God's people sure are once again run mad,
    To choose so vile a soul to be their teacher;
No nation such a saviour ever had,
    Or Christian congregation such a preacher.

'His doctrine sure can be no more than farce;
    What fools can follow such a vile instructor?
A perjured vicar who adores an ass;
    Which, since he does, mine arse upon the Doctor.'

XIV

THE MERRY CHRISTMAS carnival was now come on, when the good housewife makes her husband eat his dinner upon a trencher to preserve her new-scoured plates in their shining beauty, and pinches the guts of her servants for the preceding week, that her windows might be splendidly adorned with superstitious greens, and that her minced-pies and plum-porridge might be richer than her neighbour's.

We rambled from the reverend Doctor's boarded theatre, who being lately disgusted at the ingratitude of his audience, had divested 'em of the cushion and pulpit-cloth which he before had presented them with, and left 'em as lost sheep, to run headlong to destruction without a guide.

Being now quite out of our knowledge, we wandered about like a couple of runaway apprentices, having confined ourselves to no particular port, uncertainty being our course and mere accident our pilot. Every street we passed through smelled as strong of roast beef and rosemary as Pie Corner does of pig and pork in the wicked season of St Bartholomew. Journeymen and apprentices we met everywhere, as thick as fools in Cheapside flocking to S_____m's lottery; the former to collect their Christmas-box money and the latter to see themselves cozened out of their foolish expectancies. Every alehouse we came to was serenaded with a drum to thunder their rattle-headed customers into a good humour of spending their pence like asses, which they got like horses. Every now and then we came to a common vaulting-school, where, peeping in, we saw drunken tarpaulins and their tawdry trulls dancing to a Scotch bagpiper or a blind fiddler. According to the prophecy, there were seven women to one man, and at least seventeen strumpets to one that had modesty enough in her looks to be thought otherwise.

Sometimes we met in the street with a boat's crew, just come on shore in search of those land debaucheries which the sea denies 'em; looking like such wild, staring, gamesome, uncouth animals, that a litter of squab rhinoceroses, dressed up in human apparel, could not have made, to me, a more ungainly appearance. They were so mercurial in their actions, and rude in their behaviour, that a woman could not pass by 'em but they fell to sucking her lips, like so many horseleeches. They were ready to ride her in the open street, as if they were absolute strangers to Christian civility, and could have committed a rape in public, without a sense of shame, or fear of danger. They quarrelled with one another who should have the first kiss, like so many wanton puppies after her proud ladyship, snarling and contending who shall be next happy in her beastly favours. Every post they came near was in danger of having its head broke, for every one, as he passed by, would give the senseless block a bang with his cudgel, as if he wished every post he met to be either the purser or the boatswain. The very dogs in the street, I observed, shunned 'em with as much fear as a loitering vagrant would a gang of press-masters. Having been cautioned against ill-usage by the stripes they have formerly received, as soon as ever they see a seaman, the poor curs run away with their tails between their legs to avoid the danger of the approaching evil.

I could not forbear reflecting on the prudence of those persons who send their unlucky children to sea to tame and reform 'em, which, I am well satisfied, is like sending a knave into Scotland to learn honesty; a fool into Ireland to learn wit; or a clown into Holland to learn breeding. By any of these measures, they that send 'em may be sure that instead of mending the ill-habits they have contracted, the first will return more wild, the second more knavish, the third more foolish, and the fourth a greater booby.

By the time we had made these observations and reflections on those maritime kind of monsters, who had little more to show they were men than that they walked upright, we had straggled into Wapping; and, being pretty well tired with our walk, we went into a public house to refresh ourselves with a sneaker of punch, which was most likely to prove the best liquor that end of the town could afford us.

The first figure that accosted us at our entrance was a female Wappineer, whose crimson countenance and double chin, contained within the borders of a white calico hood, made her fiery face, in my fancy, look like a round red-hot iron glowing in a silver chafing-dish. The rest of her body, being in proportion to her head, bore so corpulent a grace that had a bag of cotton, or wool-pack, been laced into a pair of stays, adorned with petticoats, and put upon stilts, it would have made a figure of such similitude to her person that the best wax-worker or carver in Christendom could not have represented her, in either of their arts, with truer dimensions or greater likeness. My friend having a sword on, I observed that to him she was most respectful in asking him, in a voice as hoarse as a boatswain, 'What will you please to drink, noble Captain?' For she believed she could distinguish a commander from an inferior tar as well by his sword as she could a monkey from a jackanapes by his tail. After we had answered her question, she soon prepared us a little bowl of spiritual diapente, which, for want of better, we were forced to dispense with.

Up in the chimney-corner sat a great hulking fellow smoking a short pipe of stinking tobacco, looking as melancholy upon the fire as a female wretch does upon a Smithfield pile when she is brought to be burnt for high treason. By and by in comes my landlady, and, like a true lover of industry, begins to read him a lecture against laziness, tormenting the ears of the poor dejected water-rat with a severe reprehension, after the following manner:

'Why, how do you think, John, in your conscience, I am able to maintain you in this lazy life you lead? Thou knowest I have no money, God help me, but what I work as hard for as any woman in the parish. Therefore, John, it behoves thee to consider I am not able to let thee lie upon me in this condition.' 'Why, what a rope ails you, mother?' replied the fellow. 'Why, would you have the conscience to turn me adrift, now I have spent all my money aboard you, before I have got me another voyage? You are as hasty with a body to turn out, as a boatswain in a storm.' 'Why, but, John,' replied the landlady, 'dost think to get a voyage by smoking in the chimney-corner?' 'No,' says John, 'but how do you think a man can look out without a penny of money in his breeches? I swear by the purser's honesty, I had as lief step up to furl the mainsail in a gust of wind without a knife in my pocket.' To which replied the old beldam, 'Why, I would not have thee think what I speak is out of any ill will to thee, for I hope thou think'st I am willing to do anything for thee, as far as I am able. Here, there is sixpence for thee, and prithee, John, go and look out, and don't fling it away idly. For, consider these hard times, 'tis a great deal of money.' He takes the sixpence, thanks her, and she thus continues: 'There are several ships going out bound to the West Indies, that want men, and I know thou art as able a seaman as ever walked between stem and stern of a ship, that any commander will be glad to enter thee.' 'As to that, mother,' says he, 'I can speak a proud word for myself; there is ne'er a part of a seaman, from the splicing of a cable to the cooking of the kettle, but what I know as well as the boatswain. Well, mother, wish me good luck. I'll try what

I can do, as the gunner said to the cook's daughter.' She wished he might prosper in his endeavours, and away he went.

I could not but reflect on the unhappy lives of these salt-water kind of vagabonds, who are never at home but when they're at sea, and always are wandering when they're at home, and never contented but when they're on shore. They're never at ease till they've received their pay, and then never satisfied till they have spent it; and when their pockets are empty they are just as much respected by their landladies (who cheat them of one half, if they spend the other) as a father, who has beggared himself to give him a good portion with his daughter, is by his son-in-law.

Whilst we were thus busying our brains with thoughts relating to the condition of a seaman, in steps another of the tarpaulin fraternity, with his hat under his arm, half full of money, which he hugged as close as a schoolboy does a bird's nest. As soon as he came into the entry, he set up his throat like a country bridegroom half drunk, so overjoyed at his prize as if he was as little able to contain himself under the blessing of so much money, as a bumpkin is under a foresight of the pleasures he expects to find in the embraces of his new-married hug-booby. ''Ounds, mother,' says our marine Croesus, 'where are you?' She hearing his tongue, thought by his lively expressing himself he had brought good news and came running with all speed to meet him, crying, 'Here I am, son Bartholomew. You're welcome ashore. I hope your captain and ship's crew are all well.' 'By fire and gunpowder, I don't care if they be all sick. Why, we are paid off in the Downs, and I am just come up in a hoy. I hope I can have a lodging with you, mother.' 'Ah, ah, child! Dost think I won't find a lodging for one of my best children?' In answer to which he innocently returns this compliment, 'Sure never any seafaring son of a whore had ever such a good mother upon shore as I have. 'Ounds, mother, let me have a bucket full of punch, that we may swim and toss in an ocean of good liquor, like a couple of little pinks in the Bay of Biscay.' 'I always said,' said she, 'thou wert my best boy. Well, I'll go prepare thee such a bowl that every cup thou drink'st on't shall make thee wish for a loving sweetheart.' 'Now you talk of that, mother, how does sister Betty?' 'She's very well,' says old suck-pocket. 'Poor girl, she'll be home presently. I expect her every minute. I believe she has asked for you above a thousand times since you have been on board. I dare swear she would be as glad to see you as if you were her husband.'

In this interim, whilst she was mixing up a sea cordial for her adopted sea-calf, John happens to return from his enquiry after a voyage. 'Lackaday, John,' says his landlady, with a seeming sorrowful countenance, 'here's the saddest accident fallen out since you went abroad, that has put me to such a puzzle I know not how to order my affairs, unless you will let me beg one kindness of you.' 'What a pox,' says John, 'I'll warrant you now 'tis to lie upon that lousy flock-bed that lies upon the boards in the garret.' 'Why, truly, John, I must needs tell thee I have one of the best friends I have in the world just come on shore; and if you don't oblige me, I shall be put to a sad nonplus. Here, John,' says the old wheedling hypocrite, 'here's to thee; come drink, 'tis a cup of the best brandy, I'll assure you. Here, John, fill a long pipe of tobacco; well, son John, you say you'll let your mother's friend have your room, child, won't you?' 'I don't care, not I,' says the foolish lubber, 'he may ha't and he wool; I think I han't long to stay with you; I know, now I have spent my fifty pound with you, you want to be rid of me.'

By the time the bowl was just begun between mother and son, who should step in, in the lucky minute, but sister Betty, and there was such a wonderful mess of slip-slop licked up between brother Bat and sister Bet that no two friends, met by accident in a foreign plantation, could have expressed more joy in their greeting. But as soon as ever the Whitechapel salutation was over, Mrs Betty, I found, began to exact some further arguments of his kindness than just barely kissing, and asked him, what — had he brought his sister Betty no present from sea with him? 'Yes, yes,' says he, 'I have sure. I can as soon forget the points of my compass as forget my sister Betty, as good a girl as ever was kissed in a cabin or lost her maidenhead in a hammock. I told thee if ever I came home again I would present you with a ring, and there's money to buy it.' 'How now, hussy!' crys the mother. 'How dare you put your brother to this charge, you forward baggage, you? Pray give it him again, you'd best, or I'll ring you, marry will I, minx!' The daughter, well acquainted with her mother's hypocrisy, replied, 'I did not ask him for't, that I did not. I won't give it him, that I won't! As long as he gave it me I will keep it, that I will. Why shouldn't I?'

By this time our punch was exhausted, and remembering we had heard of a famous amphibious house of entertainment, compounded of one half tavern and t'other music-house, it made us willing to dedicate half an hour to what diversion we might there meet with. Accordingly we left the old subtle beldam and her young jilting fricatrice to empty the fool's cap of his nine months' earnings, and send his hat and his pockets to sea again as empty as his noddle.

As soon as we came to the sign of the spiritual helmet, such as the high priests used to wear when they bid defiance to the Devil, we no sooner entered the house but we heard fiddlers and hautboys, together with a humdrum organ, make such incomparable music that had the harmonious grunting of a hog been added as a bass to a ravishing concert of caterwauling performers in the height of their ecstasy, the unusualness of the sound could not have rendered it, to a nice ear, more engaging. Having heard of the beauty and contrivance of the public music-room, as well as other parts of the house, very highly commended, we agreed first to take a view of that which was likely to be most remarkable. In order to do this, we ascended the grades and were ushered into a most stately apartment, dedicated purely to the lovers of music, painting, dancing, and t'other thing too. No gilding, carving, colouring, or good contrivance, was here wanting to illustrate the beauty of this most noble academy, where a good genius may learn with safety to abominate vice, and a bad genius as (with as much danger) to practise it. The room, by its complete order and costly improvements, looks so far above the use it's now converted to that the seats are more like pews than boxes; and the upper end, being divided by a rail, looks more like a chancel than a music box. I could not but imagine it was built for a fanatic meeting-house, but they have forever destroyed the sanctity of the place by putting an organ in it, round which hung a great many pretty whimsical pictures. Particularly one wherein was described the solemnity formerly used at Horn Fair, which at first I took (till I was undeceived) for an assembly of grave citizens going to deliver a petition to a Court of Common Council to desire them to make a by-act, or an act by the by, that is, to prevent cuckold-making.

There were but few companies in the room; the most remarkable person was a drunken commander, who, plucking out a handful of money to give the music sixpence, dropped a shilling, and was so very generous that he gave an officious drawer, standing by, half a crown for stooping to take it up again.

The master, finding we were much pleased with the order and beauty of his room of state, was so civil as to ask us to see his house, which kind offer we very readily embraced, following him into several cleanly and delightful rooms, furnished for the entertainment of the best of company. To render 'em the more diverting, they had so many whimsical figures painted upon the panels that you could look no way but you must see an antic, whose posture would provoke laughter as much as the dumb man in the red cap when his brains are agitated with a cup of porter's comfort.

When he had showed us the most costly part of his tippling convenience, he brought us into the kitchen, which was railed in with as much pomp as if nothing was to be dressed in it but a dinner for a prince. Overhead hung an harmonious choir of canary birds singing, and under them a parcel of seagulls drinking. They made such ordinary figures in so fine a room, that they looked as homely as a Bantam ambassador in one of the King's coaches. From thence he ushered us downstairs into a subterranean sanctuary, where his Sunday friends may be protected from the insolence of the churchwardens, who every Sunday, like good Christians, break the Sabbath themselves, to have the lechery of punishing others for the same fault.

Round this sots' retiring-room were painted as many maggots as ever crawled out of an old Cheshire cheese; in one panel was a parcel of drunken women tormenting the Devil, some plucking him by the nose like St Dunstan, some spewing upon His Worship, others endeavouring to piss his eyes out, and many other suchlike whimsies. But the most remarkable of all was the banana tree, which bears an evil fruit of which women are most wonderful lovers. Beneath its umbrage are a great number of the kind sex contending for the windfalls, and some are so unreasonable that, notwithstanding they have gathered up more than they are able to stick in their girdles, yet exert the utmost of their strength in endeavouring to shake the tree. Some measured what they had picked up by their spans to try whether the size was standard, and others quarrelled for those of the largest growth, like so many sows for a great apple. In this condition we left 'em to dispute the matter, and returned upstairs, where we drank a quart of good red, thanked the master for his civility, and so departed the house, which may very justly be styled, by such who love good wine and a pleasant room to sit in, the 'Paradise of Wapping'.

Proposing but little more diversion at this end of the Town, we thought it our best way to be returning homewards. Accordingly we faced about and, to make our walk the more pleasing, we chose a different path to what we had before travelled, which brought us, after a little rambling, to the Danes' Church. It seemed, by the outside, to be a very regular and commodious building. This put me to enquire of my friend whether he had ever seen the inside. He told me, yes, and that it was a neat and well compact tabernacle, but the congregation to whom it appertained were such a parcel of wainscot-faced Christians they were enough to scare an English parson out of the pulpit, were he to ascend amongst 'em, and it stunk so of pitch and tar that as soon as ever he had clapped his nose into the church he thought himself between-decks. Their uncombed locks, tobacco breaths, and seafaring apparel, adding such further fragrancy to the former that no rats that had taken sanctuary in a Cheshire cheese could have smelt more frowzily. 'And further,' says my friend, 'it is as vainly as ridiculously reported that the church is covered with one entire leaf of copper, without joint or solder, which was cast in Denmark; but how they stowed it on shipboard to bring it over, and how they brought it from the waterside to the church, and how at once they raised it to the roof, neither the inhabitants of the Square, nor anybody that reports it, could ever yet inform me. For granting it were true, the dimensions must be so large, and the ponderosity so great, that it would require in the casting, as well as in the disposal, such wonderful art and industry that would be worth discovery.'

From thence we rambled on, like a couple of sweeteners in search of a country gudgeon (who through greedinesss of gain, would bite at his share in a dropped half-crown, a gilded ring, or rug and leather), till we came to a heathenish part of the Town, distinguished, as we found by enquiry, with the applicable title of Knock Verges, adjoining to a savoury place which in ridicule of fragrant fumes that arise from the musty rotten rags and burnt old shoes, is called by the sweet name of Rosemary Lane. Here such a numberless congregation of ill-favoured malkins were gathered together with their hand-baskets that we thought a fleet of French Protestants had just arrived, and were newly come on shore with bag and baggage to implore the charity of English well-disposed Christians to shelter them from the terrible persecution of rags, lice and poverty. But upon a true inquisition into the meaning of this tattered multitude, being assembled in this surprising manner, we were informed by a little draggle-tail flat-cap, it was Rag Fair, held every day from between two and three of the clock in the afternoon till night, where all the rag-pickers in Town, and such as swap earthenware for old apparel, also the criers of old satin, taffeta or velvet, have recourse to sell their commodities to Cow Cross merchants, Long Lane sharpers, and other brokers. These were as busy in raking into their dunghills of old shreds and patches, and examining their wardrobes of decayed coats, breeches, gowns and petticoats, as so many cocks upon a pile of horse dung, scraping about the filth to find out an oat worth picking, or as a parson's hog on a Monday morning, rooting about a churchyard to find a sir-reverence worth snapping at.

The adjacent magistrates, we were informed, had used the utmost of their endeavours to suppress the meeting, but to no purpose, for their numbers bid defiance to all molestation, and their impudence and poverty are such that they fear neither jail nor punishment. You may here see the very scum of the kingdom in a body, consisting of more ragged regiments than ever, I believe, was mustered together at any other rendezvous since the world's creation.

It's a rare place for a miser to lay his lechery at a small expense, for twopence will go as far here in woman's flesh as half a crown at Madam Quarles's, and with much less danger of repenting his bargain. It's a very healthful part of the town to cure lazy people of the yellow jaundice, for body-lice are so plenty that I dare engage they may have them without buying. It's a good market for country farmers to buy their scarecrows at, for let them but bargain with the rag-women to dress 'em up some malkins in imitation of themselves, and they need not fear but fright the birds out of their corn, and hogs out of their pea field; for, I observed, every dog that came by scoured through 'em with as much expedition as an offending soldier that runs the gauntlet through a regiment. Some of them who, by many years' industry, had conquered the difficulties of this world and raised themselves to the prodigal pitch of twenty shillings beforehand, were crept into little huts and holes, about as big as a dog kennel, and lorded it over the poor street-sitting vagabonds like a country Justice of Peace over his poor neighbours.

The women that cry 'Pancakes,' and the girls that cry 'Diddle, diddle, dumplings ho,' were wonderful busy amongst 'em, and several little alehouses are already crept in amongst 'em to ease 'em of their pence as fast as they can raise 'em by the sale of their commodities.

The flesh of the inhabitants, as well as the market-people, looked of such a dingy complexion as if Dame Nature had mixed kennel dirt with her clay, as bricklayers do with their mortar to make it bind the faster, or else, as if fresh water was as scarce in their neighbourhood as 'tis in Antigua. All strangers that came by looked about 'em as if frighted, and, like us, till they were better satisfied, thought they'd fallen into a congregation of vipers, who looked as if the good and bad angels were sharing their interest in this world, and in order to separate the righteous from the ungodly, the Devil had drove his parcel to this end of the town.

Here he had drawn 'em together in order to embark for his infernal territories, for it would amaze anybody, at first sight, to think what such a number of poor wretches could do together, unless, like seamen in a long calm, they were going to draw cuts about devouring one another.

The chief of their customers were mumpers and people as ragged as themselves, who came to barter scraps for patches. I observed it was a very current swap to change food for raiment, that is, such needful repairs as a beggar's breeches may want between the legs, or his coat at armpits or elbows. Some rags, I observed, were parcelled out for better purposes, and would not be exposed to any but ready-money customers. Many of their stocks were so very small that I found twopence or threepence was accounted amongst some of them considerable takings. Yet this observation I made, that amongst all that I beheld, as I passed through 'em, I saw not one melancholy or dejected countenance amongst 'em, but all showing in their looks more content and cheerfulness than you shall find in an assembly of great and rich men on a public festival. From this we may conjecture that poverty is commonly attended with a careless indifference that frees the mind from reflecting on its miseries. For, undoubtedly, were these despicable paupers but to let the unhappiness of their circumstances once affect their thoughts and become the object of their consideration, it would have such a melancholy effect upon their spirits as would be soon legible in their looks, and discernible even in their actions, which would want that vigour and vivacity necessary to perform whatever they undertake.

As we were thus descanting upon the ragged sons and daughters of necessity, a formal figure passed by us in an ancient plate-buttoned suit, with an old-fashioned silver-hilted sword tucked up to the waistband of his breeches, and in a long wig buckled up in small rings, as if, like an old cavalier's whiskers, every hair had been turned up with gum-water, the curls hanging all as stiff as a pig's tail, and as regular as the worm of a bottle-screw. His hat was as dusty as the top of a slut's cupboard, and his hands and face looked as rusty as an old neglected picture that had lain seven years in a garret full of rubbish. As he waddled by us in great haste, he gave my friend the civility of his hat which was by us returned, but, looking after him, I observed he had left the print of his fingers where he had handled the brim, as plain as a chimney-sweeper could have done if he had clapped a mealman upon the shoulders. But, taking notice of his complaisance, I asked my friend if he had any acquaintance with him. He told me, he had seen him sometimes at the

Green Dragon Tavern, but had little knowledge of him any other than that he had heard several odd stories of him from some who used the house and were better acquainted with him. He is very famous among those that know him for three slovenly neglects, viz., he very seldom washes his hands or face, very rarely brushes his hat, and never combs his wig but when he goes to church, which is not above once in a twelvemonth. He is a man of no extraordinary principles, but one who has run through a great many cunning professions without success, as merchant, brewer, lawyer, etc., and, failing in all, is at last, through a natural propensity to exert his wits, turned sharper.

By this time we were got into Goodman's Fields, where, passing by the Little Devil Coffee-house, my friend gave me such large encomiums both of the people and their punch, that I, like himself, was unwilling to let slip so good an opportunity of refreshing my intellects with a little of that most edifying liquor, which, if compounded of good ingredients, and prepared with true judgement, exceeds all the simple, potable products in the universe.

At our first entrance of the public room, we found a jolly company blessing one another over a plentiful bowl of this corroborating creature, whose excellencies were visible in the very looks of its lovers, the worldly air of their countenances being changed into a heavenly cheerfulness. This pleasing sight gave me great encouragement to walk upstairs, where, in a room neat enough to entertain Venus and the Graces, we were in a minute's expedition supplied with an Indian goblet of their infallible cordial, which, in half an hour, had carried off the dregs of our phlegmatic stomachs, and had so sublimed our thoughts that we found ourselves elevated above the common pitch of human conversation. Having the company of our landlord, and a friend or two of his, as jolly as himself, the cup passed round in a circle as an emblem of eternity, till at last I was so highly inspired by the noble virtues of our nectar, that I had much ado to forbear thinking I was in a state of immortality. And that which added much more to our felicity and crowned the pleasures of our liquor, were these following advantages: my landlord was good company, my landlady good-humoured, her daughters charmingly pretty, and the maid tolerably handsome. She can laugh, cry, say her prayers, sing a song, all in a breath, and can turn in a minute to all sublunary points of a female compass; yet this much I must say in her behalf, that she's obedient to her mistress and obliging to company, and I dare swear, as far as a man may guess by outward appearance, she'll prove an excellent bedfellow to him that has the luck to marry her, and a kind companion to an honest friend that loves kissing in a corner.

After we had thoroughly awakened our drowsy brains with a sufficient quantity of this unparalleled punch, my friend writ the following verses:

In Praise of Punch

Immortal drink whose compound is of five,
More praise dost thou deserve than man can give;
A cordial that supports the troubled heart,
And dost infuse new life in ev'ry part:
Thou clear'st our reason, and inform'st the soul,
And makes us demigods when o'er a bowl.
Inspir'd by thee we're raised to such a pitch
That things beyond mortality we reach,
Such as without thy power no Stagirite e'er could teach.
Had our forefathers but thy virtues known,
Their foggy ale to lubbers they'd have thrown,
And stuck to thee who gives the soul a sight
Of things that study ne'er could bring to light.
Which, if they had, I may with reason say,
Our great-great-grandsires might have seen this day;
Had they the effects of this di'pente seen,
Five would have, sure, the golden number been.
Let music judge thy harmony alone,
A fifth's a concord, but a seventh's none.
Therefore thou surely dost excel in heaven,
And justly take the upper hand of seven.
Thou friendship knit'st, and does the same preserve;
They who neglect thee do not live but starve.
Slight those great benefits they might possess,
Which wine can't equalize, or words express.
Thou clear'st all doubts, and driv'st away all care,
And makest mankind show truly what they are.
When to thy power we cheerfully submit,
And round the bowl, thy flowing confines, sit,
We paradise regain, and re-enjoy
A happy state which nothing can annoy.

The sober muckworms who thy name abuse
And with contempt the jolly cups refuse,
Are plodding knaves who're fearful to betray
Some base designs they are about to play,
And therefore, without danger, cannot trust
Evils with thee, that art divinely just.
Thou art the key to human heads and hearts:
O'er thee the learned and witty show their parts.
Thou put'st new vigour into life's old springs.
The poet rhymes, and the musician sings,
The artist does his rules and means disclose,
The lawyer, feeless, tells you what he knows.
The parson quits divinity and drinks
At all our little slips and failing wings,
Nor tells you what he's read, but what he thinks.
The virgin all her coyness lays aside
And hears a love petition without pride,
Showing those faults before by art she hid.
The wife will by her true behaviour show
Whether she's horned the good man's head or no.
The subtle widow will her love set forth,
And frankly tell you what she's really worth.
    In thee one virtue more I must commend;
Of liquors thou'rt the only woman's friend:
'Twill make the youth his utmost power exert,
And the old fumbler play the young man's part.
To thee, my only mistress, could I raise
An everlasting monument of praise.
For thus much may I justly say in fine,
Thou hast an excellence surpassing wine
And art the only cordial that's divine.
Therefore to know this mighty truth I want;
If a saint first made punch, or punch first made a saint.

We now turned back again to our buzzing metropolis, the City, where modesty and plain dealing were laid aside to pursue the wonderful expectancies so many thousands had from a mixture of projectors' knavery and their own folly. The *Gazette* and *Post* papers lay by, neglected, and nothing was pored over in the coffee-houses but the

Ticket catalogues. No talking of the Jubilee, the want of current trade
with France, or the Scotch settlement at Darien; nothing buzzed about by
the purblind trumpeters of State news, but Blank and Benefit. 'My son
had five pounds in such a lottery but got nothing' 'My daughter,' says
another, 'had but five shillings, and got the twenty-pound prize.' People
were running up and down the streets in crowds and numbers, as if one
end of the town was on fire, and the other were running to help 'em off
with their goods. One stream of coachmen, footmen. apprentice boys and
servant wenches flowing one way, with wonderful hopes of getting an
estate for threepence; knights, esquires, gentlemen and traders, married
ladies, virgin madams, jilts, concubines and strumpets, moving on foot,
in sedans, chariots and coaches, another way, with a pleasing expectance
of getting six hundred a year for a crown.

Thus were all the fools in Town so busily employed in running up
and down from one lottery or another, that it was as much as London
could do to conjure together such numbers of knaves as might cheat 'em
fast enough of their money. The unfortunate cried out, 'A cheat, a cheat,
a confounded cheat; nothing of fairness in't.' The fortunate, in opposition
to the other, crying, ''Tis all fair, all fair; the fairest adventure that ever
was drawn.' And thus everybody, according to their success, expressed
variously their sentiments, though the losers, who may be said to be in
the wrong of it to venture their money, were most right in their
conjectures of the project; and the gainers, who were in the right of it to
hazard their money, because they won, were most wrong in their opinion
of the matter. For I have much ado to forbear believing that luck in a bag
is almost as honest as fortune in a wheel, or any other of the like
projects.

'Truly,' says my friend, 'I confess I cannot conceive any extraordinary opinion of the fairness of any lottery, for I am apt to believe that
whenever such a number of fools fall into a knave's hand he will make
the most of 'em, and I think the Parliament could not have given the
nation greater assurances of their especial regard to the welfare of the
public than by suppressing all lotteries, which only serve to buoy up the
mistaken multitude with dreams of golden showers to the expense of that
little money which with hard labour they have earned, and often to the
neglect of their business, which doubles the inconvenience. The gentry,
indeed, might make it their diversion, but the common people make it a
great part of their care and business, hoping thereby to relieve a
necessitous life, instead of which they plunge themselves further into an

ocean of difficulties. What if one man in ten thousand gets five hundred pounds? What benefit is that to the rest, who have struggled hard for fools' pence to make up that sum, which perhaps falls to one who stood not in need of Fortune's favours?

'Prithee,' says my friend, 'let's go to Mercers' Chapel and see how the crowd behave themselves there. Ten to one, we shall see something or other that may be diverting to ourselves, and worth rendering to the public.' Accordingly we directed ourselves thither, to which rendezvous of adventurers, as well as ourselves, abundance of fools from all parts of the town were flocking, none showing a despairing countenance, but all expressing as much hopes in their looks as if every one had an assurance from a Moorfields conjurer of having the great prize. Some were thoughtful how to improve it, should it so happen; some how happily they'd enjoy it; women, what fine clothes they'd wear; maids, what handsome husbands they'd have; beaus, what fine wigs they'd wear; and sots, what rare wine they'd drink; the religious, what charitable works they'd do; and young libertines, what fine whores they'd keep.

In the porch, or entry of the hall, was a bookseller's shop, where the printed benefits were sold, for which the people were so impatient that there could not be more clawing amongst mumpers at a nobleman's gate (when he goes out of town) at the distribution of his charity. With much ado we crowded into the hall, where young and old, rich and poor, gentle and simple, were mixed higgledy-piggledy, all gaping for a benefit, like so many Fortune's minions waiting for a windfall from her blind lady's Golden Pippin tree, whilst the projector and the honourable trustees sat, laughing in their sleeves, to see fair play dealt out to the attentive assembly, whose avaricious hearts went pit-a-pat at the drawing of every ticket.

Every now and then, when a benefit arose, some impatient novice or other crying out, 'That's mine,' bustled up to the trustees, producing his ticket to prevent that fraud which, though he had ventured his money, he was fearful might be practised amongst 'em. It sometimes proved the adventurer had mistaken his number or the number that was drawn to the benefit, which proved such a disappointment to 'em that their silly looks would render 'em a laughing-stock to the whole congregation of Fortune's courtiers, every one equally big with the hopes of being the only favourite.

My friend and I, having no pretence or title to be ranked, by any accident, in the number of the fortunate, having ventured nothing in their plausible piece of uncertainty, thought it not worth our while to spend any further time amongst 'em, but concluded to march about our business, and leave the numerous sons and daughters of Fortune to flatter themselves with the vain hopes of their mother's kindness. So we came out to go to a neighbouring coffee-house, where we smoked a pipe and consulted of some new measures to take in our next *Spy*. This being done, we retired home, where I scribbled the following lines upon lotteries, with which I shall conclude:

What sundry projects the ingenious find
    T' allure and cozen avaricious fools;
And draw the common people, who are blind
    In all their stratagems to be their tools.

The hope of sudden wealth does most deceive
    When 'tis from labour and from danger free;
Let but the hopes be plausible you give,
    And most men will with your designs agree.

For all men love prosperity and ease,
    And when its prospect they with safety have,
Though at a vast long distance, yet 'twill please
    The silly wretch whom want does most enslave.

This made the lott'ries with the crowd prevail;
    The odds, though great, they never mind to scan
As long as each among the num'rous all
    Has equal hopes to be the happy man.

The vast deduction for the pains and charge
    Of ten per cent, in reason, is too great;
And where the gain in justice is too large,
    The very profit is alone a cheat.

Thousands, 'tis plain, would soon have been undone
    Had the late Act much longer been delayed.
Where many suffer to enrich but one,
    All such designs are in their nature bad.

All loose vain projects ought to be debarred
    Which are of evil to the public known,
Wherein projectors have a large reward
    For doing what had better ne'er been done.

This is enough to prove they hurtful are,
    Since among all the adventurers you meet,
To one who's reason to believe 'em fair
    A thousand shall cry out, 'A cheat, a cheat'.

He that projects or models the design,
Like the box-keeper, certain is to win:
In lott'ries 'tis the same as 'tis in play:
The knaves are vultures and the fools their prey.

XV

AS A FAIR Town Miss, of a twelvemonths' standing, when she has surfeited the appetites of those debauchees who are always ranging after novelty, and rendered herself contemptible by being too common, puts on a dark foretop, blacks her eyebrows, changes the mode of her dressing, her lodging, and her name, and sets up for a new creature, so we, for fear of falling under the same fate, have thought fit to vary a little from our former method, in hopes to preserve the same liking to our design which we believe the world has hitherto had, from the encouragement it has given us to continue our undertaking.

Our chief alteration will be to treat more upon men and manners, opening the frauds and deceits practicable in many trades, also of the sundry sorts of conversation, with moral reflections on the same, characters of trades, and those that follow 'em; and remarks upon all occurrences worth notice. In pursuance to which method I shall begin with Victuallers, showing their usual rise and means of success, and also shall lay open their pride, sauciness and ingratitude, which either most men have, may, or will find, by their own experience.

Of Victuallers

In times of sobriety, when alehouses were as scarce as churches, not above one in a parish, when any tradesman was undone by the levity of his wife, the disobedience of his children, by fire in either house or codpiece, or any other losses and crosses incident to a man in this world, upon his humble application to the magistrates of the ward or precinct wherein he lived, they would grant, or procure him to be granted, a licence to sell ale, that he might be doing something to defend himself and his family from being burdensome to the parish. And being unhappily fallen into a peevish temper by reflecting on his misfortunes, he was usually distinguished in his new employment with some of the following nicknames and titles, as Alderman Snarl, Captain Rusty, Sir John Tun-belly, Esquire Gruff, Doctor Grunt, or the like, being looked upon no other than an old cracked fiddle fit for every merry prattle-box to play upon. Neither could the good woman (whose business it was to draw the tipple, and who kept her shoulders warm with a piece of an old blanket instead of a night-rail) avoid being new-christened by some drunken godfather or other by the name of Mother Huff, Mother Damnable, the Witch of Endor, Dame Saucy, Goody Blowze, Gammer Tattle, or the like.

But now the world, like a man advanced from poverty to prosperity, is so strangely altered that as soon as a tradesman has got a little money by the business he was bred to, observing the fluency of fools' pence, the lordliness of the victuallers, the laziness of their lives, the plenitude of their purses, and welfare of their families, he is resolved to thrive upon his own small stock at the same rate, and pursue the hopes and prospect of growing rich with the same expedition. Accordingly he takes a house well situated for his purpose, where in a few years' time, behaving himself at first very humble, he breaks half his acquaintance of his former trade in coming to see him; advancing himself, in a little time, to some petty office of the parish with which he begins to swell and look as stiff and as prodigal as an alderman after knighthood.

From thence, in a little time, dignified with the office and title of Mr Churchwarden, by the very conceit of this he is so puffed up that during the possession of the poor-box he reckons himself as great as the Pope, and measures a foot more in the waist upon his first entrance into this parochial authority than he did in seven years before he was chosen to't. His wife must now be called Madam, his sons, young masters, and his daughters, misses, and he that salutes the old lick-spigot with any other title than that of Mr Churchwarden, runs the hazard of paying double taxes, besides the forfeiture of his good looks, friendship, and conversation for as long as he lives afterwards, without Providence, by some casuality, brings him back to his first humility, which is to be done no other way than poverty. He now begins to leave off his colours and to get the print of his apron-strings out of his coat, so that, as he walks along the street, it would be a hard matter to guess at his profession, were it not for the many rings on his fingers, and the stiffness of his gait.

His own house now is not big enough to hold him. Besides, he begins to have such an aversion to the liquor he sells that he hates malt-drink as bad as a grocer does plums, or an apothecary physic. Wine is the only cordial that will go down with him, which he purchases with the pence of those poor sots who are guzzling belch at his own alehouse to maintain him at the tavern. He expects great reverence from all his little neighbours, and will loll against the door-case and swing his bunch of little keys half a dozen times round his finger, before he will answer a poor neighbour a civil question.

Those who were the first instruments in procuring him a trade are as much out of his memory as a woman's first husband when she's in bed with a second. And if they tick sixpence with him, he puts on as pleasing an aspect as the Devil when he looked over Lincoln. If he that has spent fifty pounds in his house asks to borrow a crown of him, his wife made him swear not above three days ago that he would never lend one sixpence again as long as he lived, or else he would have done it with all his heart. If any person, though a good customer, owes him anything and happens, by extraordinary business, to be retarded from coming to his house as usual, there is a verbal hue and cry published after him presently among all his acquaintance that are customers, as thus: 'Pray, how does Mr Such-a-one do? We have not seen him this age. I remember the time when he used to think mine the best beer in the parish; but now, I suppose, he has found out some that he likes better. Indeed, I take it very unkind of him. I never gave him any occasion to leave my house, as I know on. I am sure he had always good drink for his money, or if he came without I never refused to trust him, as my bar-board can testify. And my measure is as large as anybody sells. I wonder we should lose his company thus.' Yet other heavy-headed dunces can sit and hear this and not conceive he would say as much by them, were they under the like circumstances. They sit and guzzle down six times more than does 'em good, to the injury of their bodies and impoverishment of their pockets, to make a parcel of peremptory, ungrateful scoundrels their masters, who, with conduct and good husbandry, they might keep at staff's end and force 'em to use that modesty and civility as becomes their servile station.

Some few indeed there are who, having the advantage of an education above the employment they have taken upon 'em, know how to treat everybody with such a proportion of respect as is due to their quality or appearance; being of another mould, generous and obliging, and quite opposite to that mercenary, brutish temper with which most of 'em are possessed, either by nature or acquirement. Those who have no more manners than to use the hog-grubbers' saying, that they know no difference between a porter's twopence and a gentleman's, ought, I think, to have none but porterly customers. And he that knows how to bid a porter give place to his betters, deserves a good trade from gentlemen.

There are three sorts of victuallers, all differing very much from each other, according to the several parts of the Town wherein they are situated. At Wapping and that way, they lord it over the people like a boatswain over a ship's company, and look as bluff upon their tarpaulin guests as a mate when first made commander, or a White Friars printer over a gang of ballad-singers. In the City he is hail-fellow-well-met with any of his customers on this side a Common Council man, but to all above he is forced to pay a deference, and bow as low to the deputy of a ward as a country innkeeper does to the sheriff of a county. But at Charing Cross you may find 'em so very humble and obliging for every twopence they take that a gentleman foot-soldier, or a lord's footman, shall have as many bows and cringes from the master and his family over the drinking of a pot, as a French dancing-master shall give the mistress of a boarding-school when she gives him half a piece for his day's teaching. Whether it be poverty, living amongst courtiers, or being bred gentlemens' servants and so kicked and cuffed into good manners by their masters, I'll leave the reader to determine.

There are scarce any of these sundry sorts of malt-pensioners (excepting some few such aforementioned) but what, if you use their houses constantly, shall think you an entailed customer and shall use you worse, and respect you less, than they shall the penurious niggard that spends a penny once in a week and begs a bit of toast into the bargain. Therefore the best method the reader can use to avoid the insolence and ingratitude of these mongrel sort of Christians is to act pursuant to the advice of an experienced toper. This is, never to use any one house long, but observe this maxim, 'When you find the dog begin to wag his tail upon you, 'tis time for you to seek a new tippling-office, or it's ten to one, if you have been a customer long enough for the spaniel to be acquainted with you, you will find the master grow slighting and the servants impudent.' And since the viciousness of the age has occasioned every parish to abound with such great numbers of these morose, mercenary, foul, fat-feeding, unneighbourly cormorants, I will proceed to give you a further character on one of the worst sort, in verse, which I desire the reader to accept on, as follows:

The Character of a Common Victualler

The monster that progressively is bred
To raise his fortunes by the tippling-trade

(As oft they do), must be of spurious race,
Begot by chance without the bounds of grace,
Born of some lustful wench who could not stay
Till fortune flung a husband in her way,
First dropped and then preserved at parish pay.
Or else, brought up on pack-horse from the North,
Born there of parents who were nothing worth,
Sent up to Town, as thousands were before,
To nick and froth, and learn the double score,
The northern sharpness in his rural face
Soon recommends the stripling to a place
Whereby some thriving countryman he's taught
To cheat the guests in ev'ry quart, a draught.

Thus when for seven years he has obeyed
And learned each knavish myst'ry of his trade,
Some labouring drudge with twenty pounds he meets,
Who longs to dance the shaking of the sheets.
With her he couples, and improves his pence
With his own hoarded fools' benevolence;
Who, great as kings when drunk do often grant
Those boons to tapsters which themselves most want,
Then takes a house, hangs up a Yorkshire sign,
New paints the door-case, makes the lattice fine.

Thus entered, such sharp measures does he take
By which he thrives whilst twenty tradesmen break;
At first, industrious as an Indian slave,
Close as a miser, cunning as a knave,
Humble and fawning as a pedlar's cur,
And to each cobbler answers, 'Coming, sir.'
His bread and cheese he frankly does impart,
And ev'rything is done with all his heart.
Porters are welcome near the fire to sit
And may command, the varlet can submit.
Without offence red herrings they may broil,
And tattle o'er their pot a wondrous while.
Himself will on a neighb'ring errand run;
What e'er you speak for, in a trice is done.

If guests desire to keep 'em up till late,
Both without grumbling will their leisure wait;
No frowning from the tyke, or maund'ring from his mate.

Thus are they careful to oblige at first,
But as they thrive, like curs, they grow more cursed.
Full cellars and full pockets change the scene
And make the lout a prince, his drab a queen.
The cobbler then must at a distance keep,
And porters with their hats in hand must creep.
No frape must hover o'er the kitchen fire,
They no such paultry company do desire.
'Sit up, you fellow. Move your seat, you clown,
And let my master such-a-one sit down.
Pray troop, I keep a public house 'tis true,
But do not light my fires for such as you.'

In comes a neighb'ring servant for some ale,
'Pray dash it with a little drop of stale.'
'I've brought no money, you must set it down,'
The maid thus answered by the surly clown:
'Pray tell your master I shall draw no more
Until he comes or sends to clear his score.
I'd rather in my cellar keep my beer
Than send it out on trust I know not where.'

Perhaps, some neighb'ring tradesman next appear:
'Where shall we be to drink a pot of beer?
Can't we go up?' 'No marry,' says the quean,
'None has been upstairs since the room was clean.
Here, boy, the bell, or else the kitchen show.
Good gentlemen, I'm sure, have sat below.'
'Nay, if we can't go up, we will not stay.
I'll warrant we'll find houses where we may.'
'We do not want your custom, you mistake.
Pray troop, one swallow won't a summer make.'

Thus is the baseness of their nature shown,
No sooner prosperous, but imperious grown.

By wealth made saucy, by misfortune cowed;
When poor, too humble, and when rich, too proud.

Of Astrologers and Wise-Women

No common errors, frauds or fallacies in the world have so far subdued the weaker (and consequently the greater) part of mankind as the juggles and deceits practised by a parcel of pretended astrologers, who undertake to resolve all manner of lawful questions by jumbling together those distant bodies, in whose nature or influence they have just as much knowledge as an old country woman has of witchcraft, or a German juggler of necromancy. In the first place, I have had an opportunity of examining several nativities calculated by those who have had the reputation of being the best artists of this age, wherein I have observed sickness, length of days and all other fortunate and unfortunate contingencies assigned to the natives, have been as directly opposite to what has happened through the whole course of their lives, as if the fumbling star-groper had rather, through an aversion to truth, studied the rule of contraries, that he might always be found in the wrong on't.

In the next place, their method in deceiving people who come to enquire after stolen goods, is such a barefaced ridiculous piece of banter that I wonder any creature that bears human shape can be so stupidly ignorant as not to plainly discern the impositions that are put upon them by their canting Albumazar. In the first place, he enquires about what time, and after what manner, the things were lost, and what strangers they had then in the house. From this he reasonably infers, whether the spoon, cup, tankard, or whatsoever it be, was taken away by the common thief, or stolen by a servant or person that uses the house, or whether concealed by the master or mistress on purpose to make the servants more diligent.

If his conjecture be that it was taken by a common thief, he describes a swarthy black ill-looking fellow with a down-look, or the like, most wisely considering that such sort of rogues are seldom without a gallows in their countenance; telling, withal, that the goods are pawned, and will scarcely be recoverable without they take the thief speedily, in order to effect which he will give them his best directions. This, the credulous ignoramus desires in writing for fear he should forget; which the sour-looked conjurer gives him accordingly, after the following manner: 'Go a quarter of a mile north from your own dwelling, and then turn easterly and walk forward till you come unto the sign of a large four-footed beast, and search within three or four doors of that sign. You will go near to take him, if you go soon enough, or hear of him. He is of a middle stature, and in poor habit.' Away goes the fool, as well satisfied with the note as if he had the rogue by the elbow, and if by any accident they do hear of the thief, all is ascribed to the wonderful cunning of their wizard.

But if, on the contrary, he believes it to be taken by a servant or anybody that uses the house, he bids 'em, hab nab at a venture, to go home satisfied, for they shall certainly find the spoon, etc., in three or four days' time, hid in a private hole in such a part of the kitchen, or he'll make the devil to do with those that have it, and force them to bring it in open shame and disgrace at dinner-time, and lay it down upon the table in the sight of the whole family. Away goes the person well satisfied with what this Ptolemaist has told 'em, and declares to everyone in the house how the thief was threatened, and after what manner the spoon should be found within the time appointed, or else woe be to them that have it. This frightful story coming to the ears of the guilty, brings 'em under such dreadful apprehensions of the conjurer's indignation, if they do not lay what they've taken within the time, according to the direction, that the first opportunity they have, they will place it to the utmost exactness in whatever hole or corner he has appointed for the finding it. And this is the very reason why, in such sort of cases, people so oft recover things that have been missing in their houses, according to the doctor's direction, which the ignorant look upon to be all devilism and conjuration.

Or if the master or mistress has concealed anything from their servants to make 'em more careful, they are also ready to observe the dictates of the cunning-man, that the servants might believe what was missing was really stolen, that they might be more watchful of things in their trust, to prevent the like mischances for the future.

So in this particular part of the profession there may be something said, from the consequence of it, in behalf of their wizardly sort of policy, it being a means oftentimes of bringing those petty thefts to light which would otherwise lie undiscovered, to the prejudice of the loser. But as to their pretended knowledge in matters beyond the view of common reason, it is all a cheat, and I am sorry this present age should give such evidence of its weakness as to encourage such a parcel of illiterate and scandalous deceivers of the common people to flourish and live publicly great, by such base and unjustifiable means as casting figures, telling fortunes, selling charms or sigils, or the like.

Their further frauds and practices I shall more plainly detect in these following stories, some of which I can warrant as truths from persons of my own acquaintance.

There is now living a famous wise-woman in Whitechapel, who is a great pretendress to the gipsies' art of fortune-telling, and has acquired such wonderful credit and reputation among servant wenches and poor ignorant people, that she has forty or fifty sixpenny fools every morning to attend her. Most are women, some to know when they shall be married, some big with child, who have lain with so many they wanted to be resolved which was the right father; some married women whose husbands are at sea, or in foreign plantations, who come to know whether she could give 'em any glad tidings of their deaths or no; some to know whether they should be prosperous in their marriage, voyage, or business in hand, or not; others about stolen goods, and the like.

An ingenious married gentlewoman, having heard much of Mother Telltruth's fame, and giving but little credit to common reports, finding it hard to believe that Providence had made any of her sex so much wiser than they should be, resolved to let her own experience determine whether the woman was a witch, or if her followers were all fools. Accordingly she had recourse to her abode, where she thrust herself in amongst the querists who were thronging in, like so many spectators to see a devout old woman that had hanged herself for religion. Everyone took their turn to be resolved, like customers at a chandler's, first come, first served, or like smiths and cobblers in a twopenny barber's waiting for the chair.

At last it came to the gentlewoman's turn to apply herself to the oracle, and approaching near the elbow-chair of infallibility she gave a low curtsey as a type of her ignorance, as well as submission, and told her the chief of her business was to be satisfied when Providence would bless her with a husband. The most knowing prophetess, after she had ogled and examined her physiognomy with a very penetrating circumspection (the lady keeping her countenance) she told her the man was yet unknown to her whom she should certainly marry within a few weeks, by whom she should have three children, and then bury him and marry a second time, soon after, very much to her advantage as well as satisfaction, and should live very comfortably with him, to so great an age that she should be forced to walk with a stick.

'Sure, forsooth,' says the gentlewoman, 'you must deal with the Devil, or how should you know all this?' 'Indeed, child,' replied the sorceress, 'thou art mistaken, what I tell thee is purely from my art.' 'No, no,' says the querist, 'it must be certainly from the Devil, for he's the only father of lies, and I'll swear you han't told me a word of truth yet, for I have had a husband this nine years, and have had seven children by him, all living at this present, therefore your art, forsooth, has wonderfully failed you.'

'Pray,' says the old gipsy, 'let me see your hand once more.' Upon a review of which, says she, 'I find I was mistaken, for I find now thou hast a husband, but he's such a very little one, that 'tis as much as ever I can do to discern his signification in thy palm.' In particular she happened to guess right, for her husband was a very little man, which put the lady into an extravagant fit of laughter. Being well pleased with the cunning of the old baggage, she went away well confirmed in her opinion that there was nothing in her pretended skill, but mere guess and subtlety.

A country gentleman, not long since being in Town, happened to be strangely infatuated with an opinion of astrology, and resolving to venture some money at the Royal Oak lottery had recourse to a famous old planet-juggler, giving him a guinea to assign him a lucky hour for his purpose aforementioned. According to their customary way of cozening people, he erected a scheme, and after he had made himself half purblind by poring upon his gimcrack, and jumbling together a parcel of figures to amaze the querist, he positively prefixed a certain time wherein he should be fortunate. The gentleman, pursuant to the star-groper's directions, put twenty guineas into his pocket and away he went to attack the Devil's treasury, where, according to his oracle's prediction, he met with such great success that he brought off a hundred pound of the Oak's money. He returned to his conjurer with a full assurance of breaking the lottery in a little time, presented the old fox with ten guineas, and desired he would consider of another time wherein he might again be fortunate.

The old shark very greedily swallowed the golden bait and made him large promises what the stars should do for him, bidding him call about two or three days hence, and he should have time to be more exact in his calculation. The gentleman goes home wonderfully pleased, and returns to his prophet Bubble-Blockhead according to appointment, who prefixes another night wherein he should be surely prosperous.

Away goes the gentleman a second time, flushed with an assurance of the golden fleece; but had not been long at play, but his stars (by their retrogradation) brought him under a necessity of sending his man home for more money, which he was forced to repeat two or three times before the Oak shut, so that for the hundred pound he had won, he had lost two, and began to be as angry with the heavens and the stars as a young poet that had lost his mistress. Going back to his deceitful Ptolemy in a wonderful rage, he told him he and his stars were a couple of lying confederates, and forever after became as great an enemy to astrology as a schoolboy is to a birch-rod after a sound flogging.

The third story I shall entertain you with, though it be something staler than the former, yet, being applicable to my purpose, I think it may be admitted without exception. On Southwark-side there lived a famous student in those two fraternal sciences, physic and astrology, who, to deceive people with more facility and assurance, had several bells placed in his study above stairs, the ropes of which hung down the wall of a dark staircase. One signified lost sheep, another clothes stole off the hedge, another strayed or stolen horses, which were the chief things people had recourse to him about, so that a man who attended the door used first to sift 'em and discover what they came about, and then ring for the doctor and dispatch intelligence at the same instant.

It happened once that a butcher, having lost some sheep out of the neighbouring marshes, came to request a cast of the doctor's office, believing he could put him in a way of recovering his strayed wethers. Accordingly he goes to the house, where, at his first entrance, the servant asked him his business. Without mistrust, he told the fellow his mischance, who bid him not be dismayed, for the doctor, without doubt, would do him service in the matter. 'He's a little busy,' says he, 'in his study, but however I'll venture to ring for him.' Then he tingles the sheep bell, upon which down comes the doctor, having put on his fur cap and conjuring countenance, that half frighted the poor sheep-biter.

At his first appearance, 'How now, friend,' says he, 'I'll warrant you have lost some sheep, and you want me to give you tidings of 'em?' 'Yes, noble doctor,' says the fellow. 'Come,' says the doctor, 'walk into my parlour, and I'll endeavour to give you satisfaction.' The butcher followed the doctor, and happened to have a bulldog who crept under one of the chairs before anybody minded him.

The servant, according to custom in such matters, had recourse to his wardrobe of shapes, and dressed himself up in a bull's hide, waiting for his master's conjuring homily to summons him to appear. The doctor, after he had talked a little with the butcher about the business in hand, bid him be sure to sit still and not be frighted at anything he saw, for nothing should hurt him; and after he had made a large circle, and mumbled over a little unintelligible jargon, he gives the devil his cue to make his terrible entrance. The butcher's dog, being of a true beargarden breed, seeing the appearance of a bull, makes a fair run, seizes the doctor's familiar, and makes him roar like what he represented. The conjurer rising in a great passion, ''Ounds, what d'ye mean? Take off your dog, you rogue; take off your dog!' The butcher smoking the cheat, 'Not I, by my troth, doctor, I know he's as good as ever run, let 'em fight fair, doctor. If you'll venture your devil, I'll venture my dog.'

Never was poor devil so mauled by a hell-hound in this world before; the doctor being glad to pay the fellow for his sheep, and to lock up his tongue from dispersing the detection.

Pursuant to the method I propose, I shall conclude this and every distinct trade or profession with a short character in verse.

Of a Cunning-Man

> Poor tailors, weavers, shoemakers, and such
> Illit'rate fools who think they know too much,
> Are the chief senseless bigots that advance
> A foolish whim to further ignorance.
> Buoyed up by chance-success would things foreknow,
> Aim to be wise, and still more foolish grow,
> Peep twenty years at stars, at sun and moon,
> And prove themselves but idiots when they've done.
> Then finding by experience they are lost
> In that true knowledge which they fain would boast,
> They draw in fools to pay for th' time their study cost.
> All their whole art consists in barren words,
> Mere sound, but no true argument affords.
> On a faint shadow do they all rely,
> What few believe, and none can justify.
> Mars by heroic actions got a name,
> Venus for beauty and her whoredom, shame,
> Mercury for speed was famous, and for theft,
> And now most had, when by himself he's left;

Good, if well mixed, like hair amongst the loom,
If not, he's fatal to the native's doom:
So to the rest such influence they ascribe
As we, they say by nature's course, imbibe.
'Tis true, the persons whence the name's derived,
Were whores, and thieves, and heroes whilst they lived.
But these bright planets which surround the earth,
Had the same force and power before their birth:
E're they were christened they were still the same,
At first a part o'th'universal frame,
And do no influence borrow from an empty name.
Mars can no hero by his aspect make,
Nor Venus force a virgin to forsake
Her virtue, nor can Mercury prevail
On happy unstained innocence to steal.
No, no, 'tis education makes us fit
To virtuous live, or to base means submit.
All their pretended impulse is a quacking cheat,
Only upheld by knaves, believed by fools;
The first their workmen, and the last their tools.
All their pretences are but empty show,
Wise would they seem, but still they nothing know.
Instead of reason, which all art defines,
Their brains are filled with planets, orbs, and signs;
Their knowledge little, their grey hairs but green,
Their learning less, and their profession mean,
Their conversation dull, each senseless word
Is humbly paid to some ascendant lord.
A globe's their sign. In alleys do they dwell
And though fools think they've conference with Hell,
Do all things know, yet little truth can tell.

A Modern Reformer of Vice, Or a Reforming Constable

He is a man most commonly of a very scandalous necessity who has
no way left, but, pimp-like, to live upon other people's debaucheries.
Every night he goes to bed, he prays heartily that the world may grow
more wicked, for one and the same interest serves him and the Devil. He
always walks armed with a staff of authority, sealed with the royal arms,

and all wise people think the fellow that carries it a great blot on the scutcheon.

He searches a bawdy-house as a churchwarden does an alehouse, not to punish vice but to get money. He squeezes whores as a thief-catcher does highwaymen, and takes from them the fruits of their iniquities, making them twice as wicked as they would be, by putting them upon fresh villainies to keep themselves from starving. He brings no woman to punishment for her ill-courses but for want of money, and she (if poor) that whores for pleasure more than profit is sure oftenest to be whipped for't. Constables are a sort of unlucky bird-catchers, and every naughty house their net, the whores their decoy-birds that allure others into their trap, and are freed themselves from that danger they have brought the innocent into. They are only encouragers of what they pretend to suppress, protecting those people for bribes which they should punish, well knowing each bawdy-house they break is a weekly stipend out of their own pockets.

Meet 'em when you will, you will never find one in their custody above a flap-cap or a cinder-wench, who, because their rags won't pawn for a dozen of drink, must be made an example of. She that has the prudence to whore with half a crown in her pocket may sin on without danger, whilst the poor needy wagtail must be cautious how she kisses at ill hours, in ill houses, or in ill company, lest she be carried to Bridewell, where, instead of being reclaimed, she is hardened by her indelible shame, in her miserable state of wickedness. The only good they've done, is to put a sort of socket-money upon whoring, and themselves are the collectors of the tax. For this reason the price of venery is advanced; which makes it the more practised, for the cheapness of a commodity always throws it out of fashion, and things easily purchased are very seldom minded.

Of all people I know, I think their employment is most like the dog-whippers of a church, whose business it is to watch the tails of every proud bitch and lascivious puppy from committing an indecency. They are the wicked servants to a pious society, who have undertaken to ensure the nation from vice, and their business is to run up and down town to quench people's lust, as the steel-cap salamanders do to extinguish fire.

The suppressing of vice and reforming manners is, in the society, a most commendable undertaking. But except they take care to regulate their officers and prevent the daily abuses they commit, which are everywhere complained of, I fear the ill-management of their mercenary people employed will be an injury to their project, and bring a very good design under a great disreputation, and hinder many persons from giving encouragement to that noble work, which they would otherwise think worthy of their assistance, But whilst a parcel of loose fellows and self-serving profligates are employed to search after and detect those who are scarce worse than themselves, it is reasonable to believe the innocent will be often injured, and the wicked practices of vicious persons concealed from the magistrates who have a will they should be brought to light and a power to punish 'em, if bribery to inferior officers did not protect 'em in their lewdness.

They make it their business not so much to suppress base women, and those sanctuaries they now daily act their vices in with security, as they do to go snacks with those infamous beldams who make it their livelihood to encourage and shelter mercenary strumpets in their wickedness, and preserve 'em from the lash of the laws which they would otherwise more commonly fall under. There are many employed that are of scandalous fortunes and desperate characters; who are very conversant with, and protect, the very libertines they should bring to punishment. These undertake their office through no good principle, but only for a mercenary end of twelve shillings a week salary, and their consciences are so corrupt that for twelve shillings more they would, upon occasion, swear they heard the dumb man in the red cap swear fifty oaths, and that they saw the sober gentleman that drinks nothing but water-gruel as drunk as ever they saw a foot-soldier in a bawdy-house, or a porter in a brandy-shop.

I cannot forbear taking notice of a poor fellow's saying as I was passing along the street. 'I'll warrant,' says he, 'they thought they had much reformed my manners when they made me pay a shilling for an oath when I had never another in the world. But, ifeck, I was pretty even with them, for going home and telling my wife what had happened, we set foot to foot and cursed the constable for two hours by the clock, and that was our satisfaction for going to bed supperless.'

Vice, 'tis true, is grown to a great and lamentable pitch in this wicked age we live in; but whilst a parcel of mercenary fellows are continued in office, who are as wicked and profane themselves as the profligate wretches they look after, there will appear, I doubt, but slender signs of a reformation. Of such sort of constables or informers as these, there

being many employed about this town, I shall proceed to give you a
further character.

Informing Constables and other Informers

Do most through interest, and but few through zeal,
Betwixt the laws and the offender deal.
Poor sinners may their persecution fear
As cozening bakers do a strict Lord Mayor.
But the gay courtesan who trades for gold
That can but grease a palm when she's in hold,
No Justice need she dread, or Bridewell fear,
But, without danger, sin from year to year.
Nor need the moneyed libertine e'er see
The awful brows of stern authority;
But drink and swear till weary of his vice,
Would he sin on, at an informer's price.
They chose their pious office for its gain,
To dwell upon the sins of other men:
Not with a good intent to vice reclaim,
Or bring offenders unto open shame.
Few do we see that are examples made,
But the poor strumpet, or the starving blade,
Who, wanting money, do the scourge endure,
Not punished for their vice, but for being poor.
   Vice deserves public punishment, 'tis true;
But those that live upon the ills I do,
And on my failings for their bread rely,
Do what good mortals cannot justify.
If the poor harlot shall her soul betray
For money, which informers take away
To let her go, it is the world's belief
Th' receiver's full as guilty as the thief.
   If I by chance am drunk, or should I swear,
The man that does against me witness bear,
Purely to share the money in my purse,
I'm bad, 'tis true, but such a knave is worse.
If what he does is with a true intent
Of bringing vice to shame and punishment,

And well considers if himself be free
From all those failings he condemns in me,
If not, 'tis not true zeal but impudence
For him t' accuse the offender of offence;
The hangman more may say in his defence.
Those vermin, who for interest do engage
To dabble in the vices of the age,
By subtle means draw silly creatures in,
And, Devil-like, first tempt 'em to the sin,
Then, when they've gained the wanton dame's consent,
They drag the wretch away to punishment,
Lest she has money; or, if none, agrees
To pawn her clothes to bribe such rogues as these,
Who are the scum that do the town infect
Much worse than those they're hired to detect.
Poor loose shabroons, in bawdy-houses bred,
By others' vices, like their own, are fed.
A scoundrel crew that o'er the city swarm,
Can by false accusations do more harm
To guiltless persons, fearful to dispute,
Than good by all the jilts they persecute.
If heedless youth in an ill-house they find
(Dropped in as strangers, and no ill designed),
Then, with a painted staff, and awful threat
Of hauling them before some magistrate,
The tim'rous youngsters, lest their friends should know,
Bribe the reforming wolves to let them go,
What is it less, in those that take the fee,
Than picking pockets by authority?
What moral zealot justly can afford
To mercenary shammocks one good word,
Who live by filthy means, like flies upon a turd?

Comical Accidents and Occurrences

A West Country grazier's son, coming up with some of his father's cattle, and being a stranger in the Town, happened to straggle cross Smithfield from his inn, to drink a cup of ale at a townsman's house. He sat so long and so late that he made himself pot-valiant with his countryman's liquor, and instead of crossing the Rounds to his lodging, for want of a guide, he staggered down Hosier Lane and, unhappily, followed his nose down Snow Hill till he came to the Ditch-side. There, feeling the rails, he thought, in the dark, that he had been at the Rounds in Smithfield, and spending some time in groping for a place to go through, at last he broke out in a passion, ''Adsheartilywounds, I think the Devil's run away with the turnpike! I believe I mun be forced to skip over at last.' Accordingly he laid his hand on the rails, and jumped over into the Ditch. By good fortune, he fell into a lighter of coals where, getting but little harm, according to the old proverb, he got upon his legs and began to rave like a Bedlamite. 'A pox take ye for a pack of Lonjon rauges. D'ye leave apen your trap-doors to catch country vaulk in your cellars?' Then, flinging about the coals, he cried, ''Ads-heart, either let me out of your coal-hole or I'll break all thy windows, and thump and feeze thee, and make thee vart again vor a vilthy voul verson thou.'

The weavers have received such encouragement from the great hopes they have of the Bills being passed, for the prohibition of all wrought silks and calicoes from India, that, for this week past, they have solemnly protested (notwithstanding it is Lent) against the eating of stale sprats, rotten red herrings, and the cuttings of salt-fish, and are already advanced to the buying of bullocks' pettitoes, nappers' nulls, grunters' muns, and the like. Nay, further, it was observed last market-day that an eminent master of the shuttle in Spitalfields (who has not above twelve in his family) bought, in Norton Folgate, a stone and a half of good cow-beef, to the great wonder and amazement of the butcher. So it is generally believed on all hands, if the East India Company puts not a spoke in their cart, they will, in a little time, shift off the poverty which they have long groaned under and, to the whole nation's happiness, be seen in a flourishing condition.

XVI

MY COMPANION HAVING given me the common civility of a London inhabitant to a country friend or acquaintance, i.e., showed me the tombs at Westminster, the lions in the Tower, the rogues in Newgate, the mad people in Bedlam, and the merchants upon the 'Change, with the rest of the Town rarities worth a country fool's admiring, began about a month since, I suppose, to be tired of his office. Upon this, like a City sophister to a country cousin, he apologised for his departure, and so left me, saying he would wait upon me as often as the present urgency of affairs would permit; and if anything worth notice occurred to his knowledge he would communicate the same, or, if he could not spare to give me his company, he would dispatch intelligence by letter. So, being armed with good instructions and all necessary cautions, I shifted off my rural bashfulness and began to so embolden myself in a little time, by strange conversation, so that I could call a careless drawer, 'Blockhead', kick a saucy tapster on the breech, swear 'Zounds' at a Hackney coachman, or sit down amongst aldermen in a coffee-house without plucking off my hat. When I first left my mate, I thought myself in as disconsolate a condition as a widow for the first month after the loss of her husband, but I, like the mourning dame, found such new diversion as quickly obliterated my old friend, and soon made me as easy without his conversation, as the good woman is without her old bedfellow.

Being thus left to range the Town by myself like a man-hater that loved no company, or like a hangman that could get none, I happened near the 'Change to step into a tavern kitchen where I found, seated at a corner table, a knot of jolly, rough-hewn, rattling topers, who looked not as if they were born into the world but hammered into an uncouth shape upon Vulcan's anvil; their iron sides and metal-coloured faces seemed to dare all weathers, spit fire at the frigid zone, and bid death defiance. Bumpers of Canary went round as fast as one could drink and his neighbour fill, so that a stander-by might have easily guessed, by their streakable measure, that every glass had been a health to an emperor.

I soon found by their dialect they were masters of ships: 'Cheer up, my lads, pull away, save tide. Come, boys, a health to Moll Biscuit, the

baker's daughter, that swore a sea-chest was as soft as a feather bed.'
Then handling the quart, being empty, 'What, is she light? You, sir,
that's next, haul the bar-line and call the cooper's mate.' The drawer
being come, 'Here, you fly-blown son of a turd, take away this damned
crank bitch and ballast her well. Pox take her, there's no stowage in her
hold! Have you ne'er a larger vessel?'

With such sort of stuff was I diverted for a little time, till an old
gentleman coming into the kitchen, whose grave and venerable head
being frost-nipped with age was bleached as white as snow, his silver
hairs, which should have been a fence to his weather-beaten ears, being
so thin that they might be more easily numbered than his infirmities.
Happening to approve of my side of the fire, he sat down near me and
called for his half pint of that golden-coloured cordial over which our
fathers used to number up their juvenile pranks and make themselves
merry with reflections on their past happiness. And when he had
measured out a moderate dram of his age's only comfort, after a very
courteous manner he presents his service to me. This compliment I
returned with the respect due to his gravity, but could not forbear
fancying he was too complaisant to be a rich citizen, and that misfortune
had taught him to be civil to a stranger; for it may be generally observed
that a thrifty trader takes a pride in being surly, and seldom is burdened
with more manners than a ploughman.

After he had exchanged two or three words about 'What news?
What's o'clock? Methinks it's cold today,' and the like, I observed the
old gentleman, when he had discovered our neighbouring company, by
their talk, to be commanders of ships, looked at 'em with as much malice
as a man under suspicion of debt would at a gang of officers. Every
glance seemed to call 'em a pack of knaves, and at last his passion grew
so high that I observed by the trembling of his lips he was fallen into his
soliloquies, and I believe, was the truth known, he was cursing 'em as
fast within himself as a country hag does a farmer's hogs when he denies
her a pitcher of whey, or a dish of cheese curds.

Whilst the old gentleman seemed to be under this perturbation of
mind, one of Neptune's sunburnt subjects, trussed up in trousers of old
sailcloth, was ushered into the kitchen by a drawer, in order to deliver
melancholy tidings, as he thought, to Father Grizzle who, I soon
understood, had been drawn in to hold a fourth part of a vessel. The
boatswain had been dispatched to him with all expedition from Deal to
bring this following intelligence, which, after two or three marine scrapes

and congees, with a head shaking like a paralytical almsman, and a countenance as sad as a priest in Denmark that has lost his genitals, he begins after this manner:

'Ah, sir, I am beloath to let you know what I am come on purpose to tell you. I am sent as the ambassador of sad, sad news, indeed.' 'Prithee, friend,' says the gentleman, 'what is it? If my family be but safe, and my house not on fire, I thank my stars I shall not be much frighted, let it be what it will; for I have been used to so much bad news from men of your calling that I have not received a comfortable word from that unlucky element you belong to this four year. I never see a seaman come towards me, to speak to me, but I always fancy he's as ill an omen to my family as a raven that flies over my house and croaks three times in his passage; though now I know not what news thou can'st bring me that will trouble me. Therefore, such as it is, prithee, friend, let's hear it.'

'Ah, sir,' says the fellow (blowing his nose and wiping his eyes), 'the poor *Betty's* lost. Coming into the Downs, a storm of wind sprang up at N.W. and by W., as God would have it, enough to blow the Devil's head off. We made our larboard tack, and plied to windward, worked like dragons, and did all that men could do to save her, but could not weather the Goodwins, in which sand, to our great sorrow, as well as your lamentation, she lies now buried.'

'There let her lie,' says the old Dad, 'till doomsday. Here's to thee, friend, with all my heart! 'Tis the best news thou could'st have brought me; for if the old bitch of a *Betty* had survived the danger of the seas much longer, I believe she and the master together would have brought me to the parish. I hope,' says he, 'I shall be a warning to all fools how they are drawn in by a pack of knaves, to meddle with such business as is out of their knowledge. My share cost me two hundred pound, and not one prosperous but three bad voyages brought her owners into debt; and now, at last, lost upon the Goodwins. Goodbye t'ye good Mistress *Betty*, I am heartily glad to hear you're at bottom; for i'faith, I believe if thou had'st not sunk, in a little time I should. No more long bills for refitting, no master's long accounts for repairs of damage sustained in a storm. No, no, if ever they hook in the old fool again to make ducks and drakes with his money in salt water, I'll give 'em leave to draw a rope through his guts and tie him to a cable to make a buoy on; for I find merchants are a pack of sharpers, masters of ships a parcel of arrant knaves, a vessel but a doubtful confidant, and the sea a mere Royal Oak lottery.'

Having thus said, he paid for his nipperkin of Canary, and away he went, I staying a little while after him to observe the behaviour of the salt-water emperors, from whose ridiculous talk, and more ridiculous actions, I drew this following character:

Of a Master of a Vessel

A brawny lump that scarce knows good from ill,
Fatted on board, like hogs, with peas and swill,
Affects a hoarsness as a vocal grace,
Churlish his carriage and austere his face,
Lusty his limbs, and rusty is his skin,
A bear without, and a worse beast within.
If married, sure a cuckold, and if not,
A generous cully to each Wapping slut.
At sea an emperor, at land a slave,
A fool in talk, but to his owners, knave.
Tied, when on shore, to a huge silver sword
And struts about in Wapping like a lord.
With jilts in music-house he's pleased and glad.
When sober surly, and in liquor mad.
A bulky carcase with a slender soul,
But stout as Julius Caesar o'er a bowl.
In company pragmatical and rude,
Humble to his owners, to his seamen proud.
In calms or storms he seldom prays but swears,
Starving and drowning are his only fears,
And never thinks of heaven beyond the stars.
Mercator and his compass are his guides,
By them alone he thinks he safely rides.
A prosperous gale he looks for as his due.
He thanks no God, religion never knew,
And is no more a Christian than a Jew.
At land, although an idiot, when at sea
None must presume to be as wise as he.
Talk reason, and your argument's denied.
He swears you nothing know of time nor tide,
His words are laws, he is their sovereign lord,
An Aristotle's but an ass on board.

The burgoo novice, bred 'twixt stem and stern,
That knows to splice a line or spin rope-yarn
Shall by King Tar-Arse more respected be
Than an Erasmus, or the learned'st he.
His head's an almanac, which men may find
Filled up with tides, the weather and the wind,
Sun's declination, changes of the moon,
And how to know in India when it's noon.
A ship he takes to be the only school
And really thinks a land-man is a fool.
When warmed with punch and his mundungus weed
He praises briny beef and biscuit bread,
Condemns land dainties and the bed of down,
And swears a ship's more pleasant than a town.
So prisoners long confined would fain prevail
With freemen, to believe their stinking jail
Affords more satisfaction to the mind
Than all the pleasures they at large can find.
All that the sea-calf has on shore to boast
Is how he saved his ship from being lost,
Which the unthinking dolt, through insolence,
Ascribes to his own art, not Providence.
The most that to his honour can be said,
Of a tarpaulin rabble he's the head
And monarch of a wooden world, 'tis true.
But such a one as makes most land-men spew!
Let him rule on, his famished slaves command,
Dreading each storm that blows, each rock and sand.
Rather than such a king, I'll subject be at land.

From thence I went to a coffee-house where I had appointed my
acquaintance to meet with me at certain hours in the day, and there I
found a letter from my friend, to request my company to supper at a
private house in the City, where a gentleman had provided a commodious
entertainment for us and some other of his friends that evening.

When the hour assigned for our meeting came, I accordingly went
pursuant to my friend's directions, where I found a jolly company
assembled whose looks sufficiently discovered their affections to the
good creature, so that I had no reason to mistrust any obstruction of our

mirth from the appearance of the persons. Amongst 'em were two country parsons and a notable sharp Town Quaker, who I had reasonable foresight would produce some good diversion as soon as our cups, and the season of the night, had made us fit instruments for each other's felicity. I shall not tire you with a bill of fare, but, in short, a plentiful supper we had, to the great content of the founder (it being served up in such admirable order) and to the satisfaction of the guests. When we had tired our hands with stopping our mouths to assuage the fury of our appetites, and one of the parsons had put a spiritual padlock upon the mouths of the company and given a holy period to our fleshly sustenance for that evening, a magnificent bowl of punch and some bottles of right Gallic juice were handed to the table, which received, as the glass went round, a circular approbation. Our stomachs craving a hearty supply of wine for the digestion of our fish, made us at first pour down our liquor in such plentiful streams that it soon put our engines of verbosity to work, and made us as merry as so many schoolboys at a breaking up o'er a batch of cakes or a dishful of stewed prunes.

At last we came to a good-looking soldiers' bottle of claret, which at least held half a pint extraordinary; but the cork was drove in so far that there was no opening on't without a bottle-screw. Several attempted with their thumbs and fingers to remove the stubborn obstacle, but none could effect the difficult undertaking, upon which says the donor of the feast, 'What, is nobody amongst us so provident a toper as to carry a bottle-screw about him?' One cried, 'No'; another 'No, poise on't,' he had left his at home; a third never carried one, and so 'twas concluded no screw was to be had, the parsons being all this time silent. At last says the lord of the banquet to his man, 'Here, take it away, though I protest,' says he, ''tis a fine bottle, and I'll warrant the wine's better than ordinary, it's so well corked; but what shall we do with it? We cannot open it. You must take it down, I think, though I vow 'tis a great deal of pity. But prithee, bring us up some more bottles that may not puzzle us so.'

The oldest and wisest of the parsons, having observed the copious dimensions of the bottle, and well knowing, by experience, that sound corking is always an advantage to good liquor, 'Hold, hold, friend,' says he to the servant who was a-going out with the bottle, 'I believe I may have a little engine in my pocket that may unlock the difficulty.' And fumbling in his pockets, after he had plucked out a Common Prayer book, an old comb-case full of notes, a twopenny nutmeg grater, and made a remove of such kind of worldly necessaries, at last he came to the matter and out he brings a bottle-screw, which provoked not a little laughter through the whole company.

'Methinks, friend,' says the Quaker, 'a Common Prayer book and a bottle-screw are improper companions, not fit to lodge in one pocket together. Why dost thou not make thy breeches afford 'em different apartments?' To which the parson made this answer, 'Since devotion gives comfort to the soul, and wine in moderation preserves the health of the body, why may not a book that instructs us in the one, and an instrument that makes way for the other, be allowed, as well as the soul and body, for whose good they were intended, bear one another company?' 'But, methinks, friend,' says the Quaker, 'a bottle-screw in a minister's pocket is like the *Practice of Piety* in the hand of a harlot; the one no more becomes thy profession, than the other does hers.' To this the parson replied, 'A good book in the hand of a sinner, and an instrument that does good to a whole society in the hand of a clergyman, I think are both very commendable, and I wonder why a good man should object against either.' 'I am very glad,' says the Quaker, 'thou takest me to be a good man; then, I hope, thou hast no reason to take anything ill that I have spoken?' 'Nay, hold,' says the parson, 'I did not design it as a compliment to thee, for to tell thee the truth, I do not think thee near so good as those who, I believe, thou hast but a bad opinion of'; meaning, as I suppose, the Church clergy. To which replied the Quaker, 'Thou may'st see the government has a better opinion of us than it has of those people whom I imagine thou meanest, or else they would never have made our words of equal validity with your oaths. Therefore, I think we have reason to be looked upon as the most honest people in the kingdom.' In answer to this, says the parson, 'I remember a fable, which, with as much brevity as I can, I will repeat to the company in answer to thee.

'Once upon a time, the lion found there were many divisions amongst his four-footed subjects, insomuch that he could not, without some difficulty, preserve peace in his dominions, and allay the grumblings of each disaffected party. But amongst all the factious beasts in the forest the asses were most obstinate, and would never change their pace in obedience to those wholesome laws provided against their humdrum slothfulness. The lion, considering they were a serviceable creature notwithstanding their formality, and would bear any burden without complaining, let them have but their own ways and go their own pace, thought it very necessary to make a law that every ass should have his own will (which they had always had before, in spite of all the laws against it, and in answer to their petition that they should not be obliged to go shod like horses); but with this proviso, that if ever they tripped or stumbled, they should be soundly whipped for their fault. A little time after the commencement of this law, an ass meeting with a horse could not forbear boasting what great favourites the asses were at Court, upbraiding the horse with being iron-shod, and saying how they, by the law, were made free to travel upon their own natural hoof, which is much more easy. "You are mistaken," says the horse; "shoeing makes us walk more upright, and tread with more security; and pray, friend ass, remember this amidst your benefit, that you must be whipped if you stumble as well as we." '

Upon the application of this fable, the whole company burst into a laughter to the great discountenance of our merry Ananias, who had nothing left but blushes for a reply. But having a great desire to be even with his antagonist, lay so very close upon the catch that the parson was forced to put a guard upon his tongue, lest he should give him an advantage to recover his credit. Then at last, in a silent interval, the glass coming two or three times quick about made the parson neglect to take off his wine with his usual expedition, and set it down before him, which the Quaker observing, asked him what countryman he was. The priest returned him a satisfactory answer.

'Did'st thou not lately hear of a great living that was vacant in thy county, computed to be worth about four hundred pounds a year?' Upon this the parson began to prick up his ears, and enquired whereabouts it was, never minding his glass. 'Truly,' says the Quaker, 'I cannot tell directly where it lies, but I can tell thee 'tis in vain to enquire after it, for it is already disposed of to an eminent person of thy function, who is now in this Town, and of whom I have some knowledge. At a coffee-house he uses, I happened to hear him highly commending the hospitality and good housekeeping of the late incumbent. "It being," says he, "indeed so plentiful a benefice, that he might well afford it. And I hope," says he, "that I shall not be backward in following his example." '

The parson showed great dissatisfaction in his looks that such a living should fall, and be disposed on, without so much as his knowledge, not knowing but his own interest might have been sufficent to have carried it. The Quaker proceeded all the while in praising the orchards, gardens, barns, stables, fine rooms, large kitchen, noble parlour, convenient buttery, etc., which set the parson so agog that he listened and gaped as if he would have catched it in his mouth. But at last, says the Quaker, 'I heard him very much complain of one great inconvenience, indeed, and that was the misplacing of his wine-cellar, for which reason he would have it removed.' 'Why, where did the cellar stand?' says the parson. 'Just under the pulpit,' says the Quaker, 'and he looked upon it to be a great fault to preach over his liquor.'

The parson, who had let his glass stand charged all the time of the story, readily took the application. 'I confess,' says the parson, 'I very unadvisedly left a blot in my tables, and you by chance have hit it, and now you have done, it serves only to verify the old proverb, that fools have fortune.' This unexpected retort of the parson's quite dumbfounded the Quaker, and added a great deal of pleasure to the company; our merry disposed friend took breath after this sparring blow a considerable time, sitting as silent as a young swearer before his father, endeavouring as much to hide his failings as the other does his vices.

By this time, the stock of wine upon the table being exhausted, we began to apply ourselves to the punch, which, upon the wine we had already drunk, soon put our spirits into a fresh ferment, and made us now as noisy as gamesters in a cockpit, all bawling and betting on the behalf of one side or t'other. Insomuch that, with one impertinent question or other they had almost put the parson into a passion, during which uneasiness his yea-and-nay adversary asked him what he thought a Quaker to be. The parson, a little angry they had begun to tease him, made this response: 'A Quaker,' says he, 'is some of Old Nick's venom, spit in the face of God's Church, which her clergy cannot lick out with their tongues or rub off with their lawn-sleeves. Therefore the Church makes a virtue of necessity, and uses them as ladies do their black patches, for foils to magnify its beauty.' 'Indeed, friend,' says the Quaker, 'thou talkest as if the liquor had disturbed thy inward man. Prithee, tell me who thou thinkest was the first Quaker, that thou talkest with such profaneness against so good a profession?' 'The first Quaker?' says the parson, and after a very short deliberation answered, 'Balaam.' 'Balaam!' says the Quaker. 'How dost thou make that out?' 'It's plainly so,' says the parson, 'because he was the first that ever gave his attention to hear an ass hold forth.' The whole company expressed by their laughter an approbation of the jest, and it was agreed on all hands, that it might reasonably pass for a good punch-bowl answer.

The potency of the liquor, and the weakness of our brains, had now drawn our mirth to the dregs, so that we were more in danger of falling into disorder than we were of recovering our almost stupefied souls to their past pitch of felicity. Several of the company had wisely submitted their distempered heads to that great physician sleep, who can alone recover the patient's giddy brains of his epidemical fever. At last, down dropped the body of Divinity, in the condition of a weaker brother, and left the Quaker one of the survivors, who, with great joy, brandished a triumphant brimmer round his head, as a trophy of the inebrious victory he had obtained over a father of the Church.

My friend and I thought it now high time to be moving off, lest Bacchus and Morpheus together should close our eyelids, as they had done some others, and make us become as troublesome to the family as the rest. Accordingly, we made the gentleman a compliment for his kind and liberal entertainment, and took leave of the company, which we left in chase of their senses; some snoring and some talking, so that they made as good music as a parcel of giddy-headed sportsmen at the winding up of a venison feast. My friend and I (our ways lying different) parted at the door and he retired to his own lodging; but when I got home, and in my chamber, the witty repartees and pretty conversation of the parson so ran in my head that I could not go quietly to bed till I had communicated to paper the following description of a merry Levite in his cups:

When Bacchus once the priest subdues
    With his prevailing liquor,
The man, in spite of art, breaks loose,
    Abstracted from the vicar.

Sober, he kept the formal path;
    In's cups he's not the same man,
But reeled and staggered in his faith
    And hiccuped like a layman.

A many pretty things he spoke
    Deserving our attention,
Not Scripture fit to feed a flock,
    But of his own invention.

Yet whether truths said o'er his glass,
    Of which I took great notice,

Were, or in, *vino veritas*
  Or 'n *verbo sacerdotis*

We could not tell, yet praise was due.
  Though unto which to give it
I vow I know not of the two -
  The liquor or the Levite.

His scarlet cheeks inflamed with drink,
  Together with his white head,
Made him appear just like a link
  When at one end 'tis lighted.

He drank in earnest, broke his jest,
  No Scripture phrases uttered.
The man he played, and not the priest,
  But put the best side outward.

Till drowned at last in Bacchus streams,
  The prophet's weak condition
Lulled him to sleep, to dream strange dreams
  Or see some wondrous vision.

Having thus exonerated my brains of that troublesome excrement which the liquor had begot in the guts of my understanding, I plucked off Nature's disguise with as much expedition as a young bridegroom, and leaped into bed; though I had no matrimonial drudgery to anticipate my rest, but gently slid into a sweet sleep, without burdening my thoughts with reflections on the cares of a wicked world, or my own past miscarriages. So I enjoyed the silent refreshment of an uninterrupted repose till next morning. Then, waking at my usual hour, I made a new resurrection for the day, and slipping on my breeches over my nakedness, in imitation of our first parents' fig-leaves, I refitted myself for a walk in as little time as a beau spends in powdering his periwig. When I had thus washed me and combed me, and put myself in a cleanly condition of appearing abroad, I determined to give myself an hour or two's breathing in Gray's Inn Walks in order to carry off the dregs of the ante-day's debauchery. Accordingly I steered my course to the lawyers' garden of contemplation, where I found (it being early in the morning) none but a parcel of superannuated debauchees huddled up in cloaks, frieze coats and wadded gowns, to preserve their old carcases from the searching sharpness of Hampstead air. They were creeping up and down in pairs and leashes, no faster than the hand of a dial, or a country convict walking to execution. Some talked of law, some of religion, and some of politics, arguing the matter in hand with so warm a zeal in defence of their opinions that I thought every now and then some of the feeble peripatetics would have made a combat of skeletons and have rattled their old bones together, in order to decide with their hands what their tongues could not determine.

After I had taken two or three turns round, I sat myself down in the Upper Walk, where just before me, upon a stone pedestal, was fixed an old rusty horizontal dial, with the gnomon broke short off. A bullet-headed Boglander coming up into the same walk, at last entered the bow or half moon where I sat and the dial stood, and after he had spent near a quarter of an hour, 'Be my fait,' said he, 'E did never see tuch a ting id my lifesh. I pray ye, Dear Joy, egra, vat ish de ush of it?' I could not forbear smiling at his ignorance, and told him 'twas a sundial to show the hour of the day. 'I pray,' said he, 'will you tell me vat it ish o'clock den?' It being a cloudy morning and the sun quite obscured, I replied I could not show the hour unless the sun shone out. 'Ub bob bou,' says he, 'erra be Chreesht den it ish not half so gude as e vatch, for dat vill show me de hour without sunshine.' And away he shuffled upon an Irish trot, seeming to be much conceited with his expression as if he had spoke like a Ben Jonson.

The ignorance of the common Irish hath rendered them a jest in all nations, though amongst the gentry there are many brave and well-qualified persons, who have given sufficient testimonies both of their courage and their learning. Therefore, as the foregoing story will opportunely introduce a character of an illiterate silly Irish peasant, the following piece of microcosmography is only intended upon the most ignorant of 'em, abstractly considered from all such of the same country who have had the advantage of a better education.

The Character of an Irishman

He is commonly a huge fellow with a little soul, as strong as a horse and as silly as an ass; very poor and very proud; lusty and yet lazy; foolish but yet knavish; impudent but yet cowardly; superstitiously devout yet infamously wicked; very obstinate in his faith, but very loose in his morals; a loyal subject to his prince, and a humble servant to his master, for he thinks 'tis his duty to make a rogue of himself at any time to serve the one, and a fool of himself at any time to serve the other; that is, to back a plot, or make a bull, he's the fittest calf in Christendom. He has a natural propensity to pimping, and at his first coming into England most certainly lists himself into a whore's service and has so much a day out of her earnings to be her *garde de corps*, to protect her in her vices. His next degree of ascension is to be a bailiff's follower, so that by catching strumpets by the belly, and debtors by the back, he makes a decent shift, betwixt pimping and bumming, to sing 'hall-la-loo' over usquebaugh, and thinks himself as great as an Indian emperor over a bottle of rum.

He has as great a veneration for his sword as a Spaniard; he'll do nothing that's mean without it, nor anything that's brave with it. Yet no man is readier to draw it, to show his forwardness to fight, and none more glad to put it up to show his willingness to be friends. Though born within mud walls and a stranger to the hornbook, he's no less than a gentleman; and if once in the army, though no more than a powder-monkey, no less title will content him than to be Captain MacSomebody. He has as little kindness for his native country as a Scotchman; when once he's come out of it, seldom cares for returning.

We cannot say in conversation he's a forward man, for he generally talks backwards. He begins what he has to say at the latter end and seldom comes home to the beginning, but ends in the middle. He's an unfit servant for a family where they eat much pease-porridge, for though a very windy fellow himself, he has a great aversion to a fart. He is often under the misfortune in England of bemoaning the loss of a countryman, for the law usually every month disposes of one of them to keep the gallows from cobwebs. He's much of the nature of pumpkins, and thrives best within filthy places. Base means to live he loves most, and honesty's a soil that won't agree with him. He is never well but when he's an ill-man; and the worse he grows the better man he thinks himself. He's a rare messenger to be sent on a fool's errand, for though he bares the image of a man, he performs his actions like a horse, without thought or reason. To conclude: he's a coward in his own country, a lusty stallion in England, a graceful footman in France, a good soldier in Flanders, and a valuable slave in our western plantations, where they are distinguished by the ignominious epithet of White Negroes.

By the time I had digested this character in my thoughts, as I sat musing by the dial, I found by the sundry Turkish and Arabian scaramouches who were gracing the walk with their most glittering appearances, that the beaus began to rise and come forth in their morning plumes, in order to attract the eyes of some mercenary belfas. These airy freaks and distinguishable graces, I could perceive, would more easily be subdued by the prevailing power of a guinea, though offered by a withered hand belonging to an ill-shaped carcase, than be tempted with the charms of an ostentatious owl who had emptied his pockets to cover his back with gay ornaments, like a peacock.

The sundry sorts of unusual figures I beheld, transported my thoughts beyond the Equinoctial, and made me fancy I was travelling in some strange distant territories where men, unpolished, show the rudeness of their natures by the uncoothness of their garbs. Some had covered their tender skulls with caps in the fashion of a Turkish turban, and with such gaudy figures woven into their gowns so that they looked, at a small distance, as if they had been frighted out of their beds by fire, having not time to dress, and had wrapped themselves up in tapestry hangings and Turkey-work tablecloths, as the readiest shift they could make to cover their nakedness. Others had thrust their calves' heads, some in bags like poke-puddings, and some in caps fashioned like an extinguisher, and hung down half-way their backs, which made 'em look like pages to some strange ambassador come from *Terra Incognita* on purpose to let England see what ridiculous garbs are worn by the devil knows who, at the very fundament of the universe. They masqueraded in morning gowns of such diversity of flickering colours that their dazzling garments seemed like so many rainbows woven into a Scotch plaid, and looked so extravagantly vain and foppish that certainly, had they not been influenced by some giddy-brained young girls to have discredited their masculine natures with this female kind of prodigality, the thoughts of men could have never entertained such butterfly conceptions as to imagine any reasonable creatures so silly as to worship or admire the person of a man because they see him in a fool's cap or fool's coat. Each man thought it added an excellence to his proportion, to have all the colours in heraldry blazoned upon his back; or as if it were a piece of plain dealing to discover to the world, by a tawdry outside, his inward vanity and emptiness. Nobody might expect more in his conversation than to oblige their eyes with a new fashion or hear a verbal panegyric on some French tailor.

'Tis pity that pedestals are not erected in the garden for the novices to mount on in their several disguises, and there fix themselves in their fencing and dancing-school postures. They'd serve rarely for antic images to adorn the Walks, and no question but the painted things, according to the end they propose by their finery, would be wonderfully gazed at by the ladies, and be thought worthy of each strumpet's admiration. For the reader's further satisfaction, I will let him more plainly see what sort of animal I mean, by summing up his outside and inside in a brief character.

A Beau

He is a Narcissus that is fallen in love with himself and his own shadow. Within doors he's a great friend to a great glass, before which he admires the works of his tailor more than the whole creation. Without doors he adores the sun like a Persian and walks always in his rays, though at midsummer, to please himself with a moving copy of his own proportion. His body's but a poor stuffing of a rich case, like bran in a lady's pincushion, that when the outside is stripped off, there remains nothing that's valuable. His head is a fool's egg which lies hid in a nest of hair. His brains are the yolk, which conceit has addled. He's a strolling assistant to drapers and tailors, showing every other day a new pattern and a new fashion. He's a walking argument against immortality, for no man, by his actions or his talk, can find he has more soul than a goose.

He's a very troublesome guest in a tavern, and must have good wine changed three or four times, till they bring him the worst in the cellar, before he'll like it. His conversation is as intolerable as a young counsel in term-time, talking as much of his mistresses as the other does of his motions, and will have the most words, though all that he says is nothing. He's a bubble to all he deals with, from his whore to his periwig-maker, and hates the sordid rascal that won't flatter him. He scorns to condescend so low as to speak to any person beneath the dignity of a nobleman. The Duke of Such-a-place, and my Lord Such-a-one, are his common cronies, from whom he knows all the secrets of the Court, but dares not impart 'em to his best friends, because the Duke enjoined him to secrecy.

He is always furnished with new jests from the last new play, which he most commonly spoils in repeating. His watch he compares with every sundial, swears it corrects the sun, and plucks it out so frequently in company that his fingers go oftener in a day to his fob than they do to his mouth; spending more time every week in showing the rarity of the work than the man did in making on't, and being as fond to tell the price of it, without desiring, as he is to tell the hour, without asking. He is as constant a visitor of a coffee-house as a Drury Lane whore is of Covent Garden Church, where he cons over the newspapers with as much indifference as the other prays, reading only for fashion's sake, and not for information.

He's commonly of a small standing at one of the universities, though all he has learned there is to know how many taverns there are in the town and what vintner has the handsomest wife. Though his parents have given him an expensive education, he's as dumb to rhetoric as a fool to reason; as blind to philosophy as an owl in the sunshine; and as deaf to understanding as a priest to charity. He often hopes to pass for a wit by calling other people fools, and his fine apparel is his only armour that defends him from contempt. He's a coward amongst brave men, and a brave fellow among cowards; a fool amongst wise men, and a wit in fools' company. All that I know he's good for is to give a poor fellow a dinner, so that he will do him homage, and to help to serve the turn of an insatiate woman, instead of a dildo.

By the time I had finished the picture of my beau, the belfas in their morning gowns and wadded waistcoats, without stays, began to flow as fast into the Walks as whores into the eighteen-penny gallery at the third act, tripping about in search of their foolish admirers, like so many birds on a Valentine's Day in order to find a mate. I was mightily pleased at the various diverting scenes with which I was entertained in this natural theatre, where I had so large an opportunity of observing the vanity of both sexes in a greater perfection than the drama, by faint imitation, is capable of representing. I cannot here make so good a use of it as I would do, because I am obliged to take notice of something of greater moment. I shall therefore only give you a short character of a modish lady in verse, and so quit the Walks to pursue my further intention.

> Pride, beauty, prattle, lech'ry and conceit,
> Airy deportment, and the want of wit,
> Small waist, plump buttocks, and a face divine,
> Wretchedly foolish, and extremely fine.

At Hackney, Stepney, or at Chelsea bred;
In dancing perfect, and in plays well-read.
The only daughter of some trading fop,
Trained half in school, and t'other half in shop.
Who nothing by her parents is denied
T' improve her charms or gratify her pride,
Spoiled by her father's fondness and his pounds
Till her wild fancy knows at last no bounds.
Impatient of extremes, with pride half crazed,
Then must her head a storey higher be raised.
In her next gaudy gown her sweeping train
Is ordered to be made as long again.
All things must vary from the common road
And reach a size beyond the decent mode.
Thus monstrously adorned to make a show,
She walks in state, and curtseys very low,
And is a proper mistress for the fool, a beau.

From thence I took a turn into the City, where people were running about with as much concern in their countenances as if they had received news of the French landing, or that an army of Irish Papists had taken possession of Stocks Market, in order to massacre the Protestants, and plunder the City.

At last I went to Jonathan's Coffee-house by the 'Change, to enquire into the meaning of this strange disorder. There I saw a parcel of men at one table consulting together with as much malice, horror, anger and despair in their looks, as if a new pestilence had sprung up in their families, and their wives had run away with their journeymen to avoid the infection. And at another table was a parcel of merry, hawked-looked blades, laughing and pointing at the rest, as if, with abundance of satisfaction, they triumphed over the others' afflictions. At last, upon a little enquiry into the matter, I found the honest brotherhood of the stockjobbers were in a lamentable confusion, and had divided themselves in two parts, fools and knaves. A few of the latter (having been too cunning for a great many of the former) had drawn in the fools, some two, some three, some four or five hundred pounds deep, to the ruin of many and the great disadvantage of more; who having been under the reputation of knaves all their lives' time, have at last, by the unexpected ill-success of an unlucky project, undeceived the world at once, and proved themselves the arrantest fools in the whole City. And for the reader's better information I have drawn one of these sublunary busybodies into a brief character, with which I shall conclude.

A Stockjobber

He is a compound of knave, fool, shopkeeper, merchant, and gentleman. His whole business is tricking. When he cheats another he's a knave; when he suffers himself to be outwitted he's a fool. He most commonly keeps a visible trade going, and with whatsoever he gets in his shop he makes himself a domestic merchant upon 'Change by turning stock-adventurer, led on by the mighty hopes of advancing himself to a coach and horses, so that he might lord it over his neighbouring mechanics. He's as great a lover of uncertainty as some fools are of the Royal Oak lottery, and would not give a farthing for an estate got without a great deal of hazard. He's a kind of speculum wherein you may behold the passions of mankind and the vanity of human life. Today he laughs, and tomorrow he grins; is the third day mad, and always labours under those twin passions, hope and fear, rising one day, and falling the next, like mercury in a weather-glass, and cannot arrive to that pitch of wisdom as to know one day what he shall be the next. He is never under the prospect of growing rich but at the same time under the danger of being poor, and is always to be found between hawk and buzzard. He spins out his life between Faith and Hope, but has nothing to do with Charity because there's little to be got by't. He's a man whose great ambition is to ride over others, in order to which, he resolves to win the horse, or lose the saddle.

XVII

HAVING RECEIVED A note from my friend to meet him at the sign of the Dolphin in Lombard Street (which fish, by mistake of the painter, is rendered more like a crooked billet than the creature it's designed to represent), at the time appointed, I accordingly went where my friend over a penny nipperkin of molasses-ale sat ready to receive me. When an accustomary salutation had passed between us (it being about the time when strolling pastry cooks, who keep their shops in their baskets, pay their visits to their customers), we began to consult about our dinner, being posted in a very convenient house for that purpose. At last we agreed to corroborate our bodies with a slice of that martial venison, beef; fit food for either saint, soldier, or sailor; the King of Meats, and the most delicious of all dainties, saith S_____ the poet, and Marriott the counsellor. When we had suppressed our hunger, the most powerful of all appetites, and tired our jaws with tedious mastication, we began to fall into talk about our neighbouring scavengers, whose houses are the stalls of that filthy dross which defiles the virgin, corrupts the priest, contaminates the fingers of the judge, is the cause of every ill, and the very seed of human misery; the mistaken happiness of mankind which brings with it, wheresoe'er it comes, a thousand curses worse than poverty.

'Prithee,' says my friend, 'don't rail so against money. It's a talk becomes nobody but a mendicant, who is always endeavouring to put other people that have it out of conceit with it, so that they may the more willingly part with it to those that want it. There's a great deal to be said on the behalf of money, and if you were but to hear a rich parson preach a lecture upon it, according to his real sentiments, he would teach you, perhaps, to have as good an opinion of it as e'er an alderman of the City. You must consider our ancestors had as great a veneration for this sort of dirt, as you call it, as the present age can possibly bear towards it. This you may find by the excellent virtues they ascribe to it in their old sayings, viz., "Money answers all things"; "Money makes the old wife trot"; "Money makes the mare to go"; "What words won't do, gold will". And a great many other adages I could recollect, with a little thinking, which would show sufficiently that our forefathers were as much given to value this "root of all evil", as some term it, as any of our modern misers can be. Therefore, if you'll take counsel of a friend, instead of slighting it, endeavour to get it, and never rail against it till you are assured you have enough to serve your turn. To despise riches when they are out of your power savours more of envy than philosophy, but to seem not to value wealth when you have it in possession is an argument of generosity.'

I thanked him for his instructions, which were a little out of my way at present to put in practice, and then began to enquire of him what method those great dealers in money chiefly take for the improvement of such mighty sums which were trusted in their power. In answer to which, my friend gave me this following information. 'The best of their harvest,' says he, 'is now over. Ever since the alteration of the coin has put a period to the project of diminution, their trade has been in a declining condition, but they have, most of them, so feathered their nests by the old treasonable snip-snap, that they have no occasion to fear the greatest disadvantages the difficulty of the times can bring them under. As an argument of their dealings in that profitable affair, I will give you a convincing instance of my own knowledge.

'I had, in the very heat of those mysterious times, a bill upon an eminent banker, not far off, to receive twenty-five pounds. Waiting in the shop till he had dispatched his business with some other persons who had stepped in before me, in comes a spark in a good camlet cloak, lined with red, a sword, long wig and beaver hat, and gave the banker a bag of money, desiring him to lay it by for him, and he would call for it on the morrow morning. He took it from him, and laid it down upon a seat on the other side of the counter. The person that brought it becoming his habiliments but awkwardly (looking like the tinker in Jevon's farce in a lord's apparel), occasioned me to take more than ordinary notice of his face, which I was assured I had often seen, but could not, till he was gone, recollect where. At last I fully satisfied myself. About a twelve-month before, he was a cobbler at Westminster, who had mended many a pair of shoes and run off many an errand for me. I then lodged within three or four doors off where he kept his stall, in which he used to be as merry over his work with the ballad of Troy-town as ever was country dame over her spinning-wheel, or a musical bumpkin with his Jews' trump.

'When the banker had told over the several sums, and satisfied the demands of the first comers (showing as much double-handed dexterity in telling of money as a hocus-pocus can well show in the conveyance of his balls), I then accosted him, and showed him my authority for another sum, which he was ready to pay upon sight of the bill, as if he were never better pleased than when he was getting rid of his money. And taking up the bag my old acquaintance had left, he attemped to pay me in scrupulous and diminutive pieces that I thought nothing but a knave would offer to pay, or a fool be willing to receive. Upon which, I refused to take it. He urged the money was passable, telling me that a gentleman left it with him but just before, which he thought, I suppose, I had not observed.

' "Pray," said I, "what was that gentleman?" He answered me, "An Essex gentleman of six or seven hundred pounds a year." Said I, "I saw the person that left it, and if he be worth such an estate as you speak of, he has got it in a very little time, for within this year and a quarter he has soled me a pair of shoes for sixteenpence, and I am sure he had not land enough then to raise a bunch of carrots in, or money enough to spare to buy the seed. Therefore I fancy you are mistaken in the man." "Oh dear! sir," says he, "your eyes are strangely deceived; he's a very worthy honest gentleman. I have had money of his in my hands, at times, this seven years. But, however, sir, if you don't like this money, I'll see if I can look you better." And with that he goes and finds me out good market money to my content, which, I suppose, I should have had some difficulty to have got, had it not been for my accidental discovery.'

'Well,' said I, 'but this golden age is past, and what methods do they take now to improve their cash?' 'The chief advantage,' says he, 'that they now make, is by supplying the necessities of straitened merchants and great dealers to pay the duty of goods imported rather than they should fall under the discredit, as well as disadvantage, of being run into the Queen's Warehouse, or by assisting of 'em in the purchase of great bargains, or the like, for which they make 'em pay such unreasonable extortion, that they devour more of the merchant's profit than snails, worms or magpies do of the farmer's crop, or the gardener's industry. In relation to this, I'll inform you of a pretty disappointment that lately happened to one of these unconscionable usurers, who insisted upon a very extravagant gratuity for the loan of a very considerable sum to a very eminent merchant:

'A person of quality having made a topping banker in Lombard Street his cashier, and having occasion to talk with him about some pecuniary affairs, ordered his coachman to drive him to his shop, where he found the banker talking very busily with a merchant. The banker, in respect to his quality, came immediately to his coach-side to know the gentleman's pleasure, who desired him first to dispatch his business with the person he was before talking to, and he would tarry in his coach till he had done, for he was in no great haste. Upon this, the banker retiring into the shop, they proceeded again to the matter in hand, which was about lending the merchant a sum of money, who was very unwilling to come up to the banker's unreasonable demands for the use of it, which the merchant required but for one month. The banker, being well acquainted with the present necessity of the merchant for money, though a very rich man and a great dealer, stuck close to his first proposals, and would abate nothing of the extortion he required, which occasioned 'em at last to talk so warmly that the gentleman overheard their discourse, and calling his footman whispered to him, and bid him dog the gentleman till he had fixed him, and bring an account of where he left him to Lloyd's Coffee-house.

'The merchant being very unwilling to comply with the banker's avaricious terms, went out of the shop in a huff and told him he would see what he could do elsewhere before he would submit to so inhuman an exaction. As soon as he was gone, the footman observed the commands of his master, who, after he had talked a little with the banker, bid his coach wait till he walked over to Lloyd's. There, in a little time, his footman brought him intelligence that the gentleman he ordered him to follow was gone into a great house in Mincing Lane, which he believed was his own habitation, because, when the door was opened to him, he went readily in, without asking the servant any questions. Upon this the gentleman steps into his coach and orders his footman to direct the coach to the house, where the gentleman orders his man to knock and ask the servant that should come to the door, whether their master was within, who answered, Yes, but that he was just sat down to dinner.

'The gentleman bid the servant not disturb him, but desired to walk into a room, and he would stay till he had dined. Upon which they showed him into a parlour where he waited but a little time before the merchant, upon his servant's information, came to him. The gentleman finding it to be the same person, asked him if about an hour since he was not treating with such a banker about such an affair. He told him, Yes, he was, and seemed to be surprised the gentleman should know anything of the matter. To make the merchant easy, he discovered by what means he became acquainted with what had passed between him and the banker, expressing himself to the merchant after this manner:

'"I have," says he, "in the banker's hands you were talking to between three and four thousand pounds, and if he can think it safe to trust part of my money in your hands for the sake of an unreasonable advantage, I don't know why I may not trust you as well myself upon more reasonable terms. He pays me no interest, and I cannot think him an honest man that will be so severe with another in whose hands I have reason to believe he thinks his money safe, or else he would not venture it at all, though on the most advantageous conditions. Therefore, since he was so hard with you, if you will let me know what sum your occasions require, I will give you my note upon the same person to pay you the money, which you shall use for any reasonable time without a penny interest or gratuity."

'The merchant, amazed at so generous an offer from a stranger, expressed himself in all the thankful acknowledgements imaginable, and gladly accepted of his kindness, telling him six hundred pounds would do his business, for that three or four ships were come in, on board of which he had considerable effects, and that the money was to help pay the customs. The gentleman accordingly, as the merchant's straits required, draws him a bill upon the banker for six hundred pounds, and afterwards found such agreeable honesty from the merchant that he drew all his money out of the banker's hands, and put it into the merchant's, by which means he is become one of the richest men and greatest merchants in the City; and the banker lost a friend, to his great injury, as a just reward of his covetousness.

'These base and unchristian-like impositions are so practical amongst the bankers and money-scriveners that Mr D.J., Lecturer of St _____ Parish, thought it his duty to reprove 'em publicly in Lombard Street Church for their abominable usury and extortion. This they so highly resented, being touched to the quick, that instead of reforming their Jewish and unlawful practices, they protested against his doctrine, like a parcel of incorrigible sinners, and turned the conscientious priest out of his lectureship for the faithful discharge of his holy function. He gave 'em a notable, though unwelcome, reprehension in his farewell sermon, choosing these words for his text: "Am I therefore become your enemy because I tell you the truth?" Therefore, since to the utmost of my power I have enlightened your understanding of these City money-jobbers, I hope you will sum up a short character of one of them in verse, to oblige the world, and I make no doubt but 'twill be very acceptable.' This, according to my friend's request, I have done for the further satisfaction of the reader.

The Character of a Banker

Himself the scavenger, his house the cart
    Where plodding men throw in their drossy pelf.
Thus, like a farmer, he from rich men's dirt
    Raises a happy living to himself.

With others' cards a cunning game he plays —
    They stand the hazard, whilst he gains his end.
He borrows still, and still no interest pays,
    And ne'er without a damned extortion lends.

Though proud and stately, whether rich or poor,
    Is to all men, except himself, unknown.
Amidst his borrowed treasures he's no more
    Than slave to others' riches, not his own.

His dealings are so dark a mystery,
    No man can truly tell, though ne'er so wise,
Whether he thrives or that he honest be,
    Until the black-palmed miser breaks or dies.

With one man's money, he another pays.
    To this he cuts, and to the other deals.
Small accidents his credit oft decays —
    Then farewell fingers, God have mercy heels.

The beggars curse him as they pass his door,
    Envy the heaps of riches which they see,
Beg but in vain, then wish the banker poor,
    Who rolls in wealth, but has not charity.

Great sums each day are on his counters told
   And piles of bags his fettered trunks contain,
But, yet for his silver and his gold,
   He's but the mimic of a vast rich man.

I have a relation in town who, about twelvemonths since, had the
courage, in spite of cuckoldom, to suffer a parson to rob him of his
native liberty and bind him fast with fetters of matrimony to man's
misery, a wife. And the first fruits of their drudgery being lately crept
out of its original habitation into this world of affliction, the joyful
father, bringing me the glad tidings of my new squab relation, very
closely solicited me to do the penance of a godfather, that the little
epitome of the Dad might be craftily cleansed from the sin of his birth
and the iniquity of his conception. Wanting ill-nature enough to resist his
importunities, I submitted to his request, and engaged myself for once to
stand as a Tom-doodle for an hour or two, to be bantered by a tittle-tattle
assembly of female gossips.

The time appointed for the solemnisation of this ancient piece of
formality being come, after I had put on a clean band and bestowed two
pennyworth of razoridge on the most fertile part of my face, whose
septenary crop required mowing, away I trotted towards the joyful
habitation of my friend and kinsman, but with as aching a heart as a wise
man goes to be married, or a broken merchant comes near the Compter.
At last I came to the door, which I passed by, backwards and forwards,
three or four times, as a bashful lover does by his mistress's lodgings,
before I had courage enough to enter, fancying every time I went up to
the door, that I heard a confusion of women's tongues come through the
keyhole, which struck with such a violence upon the drum of my ear that
'twas ready, when I listened, to knock me backwards. At last I plucked
up a spirit like a City draper going to dun a man of quality, and gave a
rap at the door which brought Nurse Busybody to give me admittance.
She introduced me into a back parlour and called her master, of whom
I enquired after the welfare of the woman in the straw, and he answered
me, according to the old phrase, 'As well, God be thanked, as can be
expected of a woman in her condition.'

I told my kinsman I dreaded the fatigue I was bound to run through,
who heartily pitied my condition, and advised me to put on the best
assurance I could, telling me he was equally obliged to be a partner in
my sufferings, for that he expected to be tongue-teased, by the time the

wine had gone a little about, as bad as a man that had beat his wife before a whole jury of matrons. The women (Heaven be praised!) were ushered upstairs, so that I was in no great danger of having my ears stretched upon the rack of verbosity till the sacerdotal administration of the sacrament was over.

By this time in came my brother nominator (who was to stand the bears with me), and after we had made ourselves a little acquainted, by enquiring of each other 'What news?' and the like, we began to look forward and consider of the difficulties we were to run through. 'Pooh,' says he, 'never fear. I warrant you we'll deal with 'em well enough, let me alone to bring you off; I have been used to't. This is sport,' says he, 'that I have been at so often that I believe half the children in the parish call me godfather. I am as well known to all the gossips hereabouts as St Augustine is to the parson, or Amen to the clerk. Do but take my method amongst 'em, and you will gain their hearts forever, and be accounted as pretty a man by 'em as ever came into a woman's company, or listened to the tattles of a female convention. So, be sure you highly praise the fair sex, and speak very honourably of the state of matrimony, rail soundly against all those jealous-pated coxcombs that abuse their wives, though with good reason, and declare every man that think himself a cuckold deserves to be made one, and that it is always men's own faults that they are so. Be sure to remember a woman's freedom is an argument of her honesty; that the still sow eats all the draught; that a woman ought to have a cheer-up-ing cup as well as a man; that she may go into a tavern with another without her husband, and may be very honest for all that; and that she may like another man's company for his good humour, merry jests, and witty conversation, without doing an ill thing, or abusing her husband.

'Tongue the old women when you kiss 'em, and suck the lips of the young ones like a horseleech. If you hear a woman rail against her husband before you, second her, and say he's a very morose man to use so good a woman after so ill a manner. Be sure you preach up female authority, that a husband ought to mind nothing but his trade, and let the wife alone to govern the family. Say that no woman who wants children by her husband, ought to be blamed if she raises seed with discretion by another, since it takes off from her the reproach of being barren, not forgetting the old saying, "There's no harm done when a good child's got." Follow but these instructions, and lard your talk now and then with a little waggery, wrapped up in clean linen, and you need not doubt but you will find yourself an acceptable a man amongst 'em as if they had heard that nature had bestowed as great a fool's blessing upon you as ever they desired to partake of.'

I thanked him kindly for his serviceable documents, and was mightily satisfied I had so experienced a partner to assist me at the solemnity, not fearing but so good an example would be a means of carrying me cleverly through the whole ceremony without baulk or discountenance. By this time in came the parochial sprinkler with Mr Amen at his heels, who were ushered upstairs among the assembly of helpmates. Now, thought I, the curtain's to be drawn, and the show is ready to begin presently. Whilst I was thus thinking, down came the nurse to desire us to walk up. She had so adorned her withered countenance with tape-laced head-cloths that her weasel face looked as disproportioned to her commode as a tomtit's egg put into an owl's nest. She had a scallop-laced handkerchief round her neck, that looked as old-fashioned as if Eve had spun the thread and made the lace with the same needle she sowed her fig-leaf apron with, and a white safeguard round her, tied down behind with tape, so that she looked all over as white as the very ghost of Bateman in the droll.

As soon as we came into the room, and had bowed our backs to the old cluster of harridans and they in return had bent their knees to us, I sneaked up to the parson's elbow, and my partner after me, and there I stool as demurely as if I had just turned Jew and was circumcised before all the company. The parson, plucking out a pocket-tool belonging to his trade, began in solemn-wise the preface to the business in hand, whilst old Mother Grope stood rocking of the bantling in her arms, wrapped up in as rich a mantle as if both Indies had clubbed their utmost riches to furnish out a noble covering for my little kinsman, who came as callow into the world as a bird out of an eggshell. At last the babe was put into my hands to deliver (though not as my act and deed) to the parson, who having consecrated some new river-water for his purpose, washed away original sin from my new nephew and brought him amongst us Christians into a state of salvation. But when my froward godson felt the cold water in his face, he threatened the priest with such a parcel of angry looks that, if he had been strong enough, I dare swear he would have served him the same sauce, and if under the same ignorance would have returned him but little thanks for his labour. After we had joined together in a petition for the good of the infant Christian, the religious part was concluded, and now kissing, feasting and jocularity were to follow in their proper places. I left it to my partner to be the leading man, resolving to be a true copy of his impudence to the utmost of my capacity.

The first example he set me was to kiss the godmother, who had a very passable face and tolerable mien, and as for her age, I believe she was near upon the meridian. I followed his directions to a tittle and kissed so very close that I am confident the inside of her lips could do no less than take off an impression of her teeth, as deep as a child leaves when he bites a mouthful of bread and butter. As soon as ever the parson had refreshed his spirits with a bumper of Canary, dedicated to the woman in the straw, and the clerk had said 'Amen' to his master's good wishes after the like manner, each of 'em accepted of a paper of sweetmeats for his wife or his children, and away they went, leaving the rest of the company behind to make a rehearsal of the good old custom, always practicable at these neighbourly sort of meetings.

The next piece of lip exercise my partner set me, was to make a regular service of kisses round the room, keeping such exact time in the discharge of this ceremony, not daring to stay too long in a place for fear the rest should have taken it ill, that if he had but smacked as he kissed, he would have kept much the same measure, have made much the same music, as a church clock that clicks every quarter of a minute. By the time he had ended his first ceremonious essay to please the ladies, and had swept off with his lips the dry scurf which loosely hangs upon the muzzles of the old women, and had sucked a vermilion colour into the lips of the young ones, I began to succeed him in the drudgery of osculation, which I went about with as ill a will as a security pays a debt he never drank. For though there were two or three as tolerable temptations as a man would desire to meet with (between a pair of iniquitous counsel-keepers), yet the public formality of the matter so took off the pleasure of lip-lechery that, instead of a satisfaction, I thought it but a very troublesome ridiculous piece of ancient superstition.

One old woman, having the palsy in her head, happened, by a sudden resolution of the sinews which govern the under-jaw, to snap my under lip between her gums, that had it not been for shame, I had cried out; but, as Providence would have it, she had ne'er a tooth, or else I believe she would have spoiled my kissing for a fortnight. This acccident begot in me ever since such aversion to the kissing of old women that, I sincerely protest, I had rather kiss twenty young ones, twenty times apiece, than to run the like hazard of having my lips disfigured.

The next part we agreed to perform was a very costly piece of ceremony, which was to pay our acknowledgements to Mother Bawdy-Flirt, who brought the little prisoner out of his dark dungeon into light and liberty, and so on to Nurse Caudle-Cook who, through greediness of the present, gave my fingers such a mercenary grip as if she had mistaken my hand and thought she had got fast hold of the rudder of my affections. Having very orderly proceeded thus far without a baulk, I was as glad I had overcome this the most difficult part of my journey as a pilgrim going to the Jubilee is that he has passed the Alps. The greatest uneasiness that remained now was only a little tittle-tattle, which I did not doubt but the wine would inspire me with courage enough to cope with.

When this was over, the next piece of folly that my kinsman was guilty on, in submission to his wife's vanity, was to usher the assembly into the next room, where was a very good hot supper ready upon the table, and two or three dozen of several sorts of wine to entertain their ladyships. Before they sat down, the parson's business forcing him to take an early leave of the company, and I having the most canonical countenance, the gossips pitched upon me to bless the good creatures. And, to tell you the truth, being at a nonplus for a grace, and thinking it a scandal to acknowledge it, I was forced to blunder out one extempore as well as I could, for fear of being taken for a heathen, which, because of the newness of it, I'll present it to the reader:

Bless the good ladies and good food
    That Heaven has set before us,
And may we men prove all so good
    The women may adore us.

May these, thy fruitful dames, live long,
    Grow ev'ry day more handsome,
And may their husbands prove as strong,
    I' the back, as second Samson.

May they dance merrily each night
    Without pipe or tabor,
And Mother Midnight bring to light
    The fruit of all their labour.

God save the Queen, and send quite through the Realm,
Men may obey, and women rule the helm.

This lucky thought so obliged the whole congregation of tattle-baskets
that I found, by the satisfaction they expressed in their countenances,
scarce a woman in the company could forbear clapping me. And the
good wives falling-to, as eagerly as so many liverymen at a hall-feast,
were all so ready to help me with a choice bit that I had a plate piled up
in half a minute, enough to have feasted a whole family of French
Protestants just landed.

As soon as the edges of our hungry appetites were taken off, and our
mouths were a little at leisure to employ the glass and give way for our
tongues to express our sentiments, the women were presently so
wonderful busy in drinking the chaplain's health that they had like to
have forgot the sow and her pig if it had not been for the woman's
oracle, the midwife, who put 'em in mind of it. By that time, three or
four glasses had washed away their counterfeit or acquired modesty
which restrained 'em from that freedom of the tongue which their natures
prompt them to. We had as great a jargon of confused talk arise amongst
us as ever you heard amongst a crowd of female neighbours gathered at
a woman's door that had just hanged herself. They talked as much of the
ill qualities of their servants, and good humours of their children, as a
parcel of country gentleman got over a tub of double ale do of their dogs
and their horses.

Whenever they talked of any of their own sex that were not present,
a man that had been wholly unacquainted with the conversation of
women would have thought they had been setting forth the the faults and
infirmities of some she-devil, and that nothing which bore human shape
and nature could have been liable to so many odious imperfections. She,
'tis very likely, was much handsomer and more virtuous than the ill-
natured she who had accumulated such a number of defects and vices
and laid 'em to her charge, who was not present to justify herself against
'em. The failings of their husbands, also, was a great subject of their
discourse, with now and then a whisper, which, I suppose, was touching
some secret disabilities or neglects, which were not proper or consistent,
though with the most free and unrestrained modesty, to speak in public.

At last a great talk arose about a woman who had been married two
years, and not proving with child in so long a time, had lately made an
elopement from her husband with a courtier who had got her close in his

lodgings at Kensington, even to the distraction of the poor cuckold, who offers to take her again, but she won't live with him. 'Fie upon her,' says old Mother Tumble-Tuzzy, 'for a naughty woman. If she had taken my advice, I am sure it had been better for her. If things were as she told me, I am sure she had no great reason to complain; but in short, I don't believe she loved her husband, for if she did she would never have done so by him. I'll swear I pity the man with all my heart. I look upon him to be as honest a man as any dwells in the parish, and indeed, I believe he loved his wife very well. Aye, indeed, neighbour, much better than such a minx deserved.' 'Why so, madam,' says a third, 'why should you rail against the poor woman behind her back? She might have reason enough to do what she did, for aught you know.' 'Reason! Marry hang her,' says a fourth, 'what reason could she have to bring herself under this scandal, and her husband, poor man, under all this shame and sorrow? If she could not be contented with what the good man could give her, there are journeymen and apprentices enough in the house, that she need not have been such a slut to have run away from him.'

'Oh fie,' says another, 'why sure you would not have had her disgrace herself with so mean a thing as a servant, would you?' 'Servant!' replied the former. 'Marry, come up, my dirty cousin! How little you make of servants, as if 'twas impossible an apprentice or a journeyman could have a longer nose than his master! You see the Court ladies have wit enough to be content with their own coachmen and footmen, and not come into the City to expose themselves. Besides, a servant looks upon it to be so great an honour that he will take thrice the pains to oblige a woman as a man will that's her equal. For that reason quality have sense enough, you see, to choose such men for their gallants as are much beneath them, because they have 'em more at their beck. And since we follow their fashions, I don't know but it would be better for us if we followed their example too.' 'Nay, truly, neighbour,' says the other, 'I must confess there is something of reason in what you say. But, indeed, I think 'tis a burning shame that a man who knows how 'tis with him, should be so foolish to marry a woman and bring her to these hardships; for they ought to consider, that's the truth in't, we are flesh and blood as well as they.'

In this sort of hopeful tittle-tattle they tired their lungs and wasted their time, till they were most of them got as boozy as so many bumpkins at a wake, or tippling loyalists upon the King's birthday. The merry dames, by this time, having at one sitting pretty well filled their carcases and emptied their minds, they began to call upon me, their chaplain, to give them a discharge. This put me to a second nonplus, believing they had drank themselves at supper past all grace; but I found myself mistaken, forgetting that hypocrites are always most devout when they are maudlin. Finding I had no way to avoid the office, I made a shift to blunder through this ceremonious piece of thanksgiving, after the following manner:

> Our hearty thanks we humbly pay
>   For the blessings we have tasted!
> Lord send such christ'nings every day,
>   That we may thus be feasted.
>
> We bless thee for each merry dame
>   And her good conversation.
> Oh bring 'em yearly to the same
>   Blest end of their creation.
>
> May they abound in girls and boys,
>   Yet still, and still, be kissed-on,
> That we may meet and thus rejoice
>   To make each babe a Christian.
>
> Bless all good women in their married state!
> Make their pains easy, and their pleasure great.

This so obliged the assembly of fruitful matrons, that I dare swear I might have picked and chose as the Turk does in his seraglio. I was now esteemed as the prettiest, wittiest and best humoured gentleman that ever they were in company with in their lives; and what a thousand pities it was I should be a bachelor. Every one offered to help me to a wife, so I began to be afraid they would have made a priest of the midwife, and married me in spite of my teeth before I could get out of their company. I dare swear, if we had had but a fair opportunity, my partner and I might have made as many cuckolds this one night as ever were made by a couple of churchwardens during the whole time of their office; and they have generally as great a command of the parish as any that dwells in't, except the parson.

This generous entertainment we had hitherto had, was not sufficient to plague my poor kinsman enough; and to gratify the ridiculous prodigality of the good woman in the straw, it being the first testimony of her fertility, after all this, the extravagance must be summed up with a service of sweetmeats which every gossip carried away in her handkerchief. Then were my brother-witness and I forced to conclude all with a final repetition of old Judas's ceremony, and so sent 'em packing home to their own dear spouses, to tease their ears with a rehearsal of their welfare.

What now remained for me to do, was to go upstairs to bid my bedridden relation much joy of her new Christian, and to receive thanks for the trouble she had put me to. I kissed the good woman with a good will enough, but having no great kindness for the creature so newly calved as my little kinsman, I could not salute him, but with as indifferent an appetite as I did the old woman. For bull-veal, so very young, and cow-beef, so very old, are two sorts of flesh I could never heartily approve on; for I always fancy the one's a little too tender and smells of the cask, and the other a little too tough and stinks of a coffin.

Having now struggled through every difficult part of these accustomary formalities, I had nothing to do but to thank them for their liberal entertainment, wish the woman well again, and both much happiness in their male offspring, and so take my leave. This I did accordingly, and was as greatly overjoyed when I got out of the house as ever convict was that had broke jail, or detected pickpocket that had escaped a horse-pond.

When I came to my lodging, I began to consider what further use I could make of the sundry passages and pleasant humours I had observed among this female congregation, and at last agreed with myself 'twas a rare opportunity to take off a true impression of a gossip, which I desire the reader to accept.

The Character of a Gossip

Seven years in wedlock first she must have spent,
And must have made her spouse as long repent
That such a curse was e'er from Heaven sent.

By nature made to teem, to tease and vex,
No longer happy than she can perplex,
Lustful towards men, and envious t'wards her sex.

Homely, disdainful, talkative and proud,
Foolish, self-willed, too stubborn to be bowed,
Fiery as light'ning, and as thunder loud.

A junket follower and a friend to wine,
Who to her betters will no place resign,
And hates the gossip that appears more fine.

Of her own faults she others does accuse,
Her neighbours' failings are her chiefest news,
And rails against the vice she most pursues.

Her spite at ev'ry well-bred she takes aim.
The model woman is a close sly dame
Who though she opens not, yet hunts the game.

She's the still sow that drinks up all the draught,
Though so reserved in tongue, she's loose in thought
And is the more suspected to be naught.

If handsome, then the envious tatler cries,
'Her face is well enough, she's pretty eyes,
But has an ugly fault, else people lies.

'What I have heard I'm very loath to speak.
Besides all that, she gives her cheeks the lick
And is as ill-conditioned as Old Nick.

'Were I man, such beauty I'd adore
As should be only natural and no more,
For she that paints will doubtless be a whore.

'Beauty's but fancy silly boys pursue,
Men love a woman that is just and true;
She's only handsome that will handsome do.'

She blames the dame that like herself is free,
Who loves good liquor and much company —
One gossip with another can't agree.

To drink a private cup she holds no harm,
And finds in brandy such a secret charm
It cheers her heart and keeps her stomach warm.

Abroad she walks to see and to be seen,
And if the good man asks her where she's been —
'With a gallant, Tom Coney; and what then?

'Fools must ask questions: I'm your wife, 'tis true,
But am of age and know sure what I do,
Can go and come without the leave of you.

'Art jealous, love? You need not be afraid.
Had you a wife like such a one, egad,
You then, indeed, might fear an aching head.

'But I (as God well knows my heart) despise
The very thought.' Although she knows she lies,
Being maudlin, then to please the fool she cries.

Thus charms the man with her dissembling spell,
A thousand lies can in a moment tell,
And, when she pleases, make things ill or well.

Thus she the breeches wears, and rules the roost,
Of which she does at all her meetings boast,
'The man's no more, God help him, than a post!'

She tells how all things on her care depends.
She buys and pays, she borrows and she lends,
Hoards what she pleases, what she pleases spends.

None could his ugly humours bear but she.
Besides, she's sure he cannot but agree
She understands the trade as well as he.

She pleases customers much better far.
He oft neglects his shop; he does not care
Pounds would be often lost were she not there.

'Believe me, neighbour, he's so peevish grown
E'er since he has been troubled with the stone,
That 'twould be happy for him if he was gone.

'Poor man, I pity him with all my heart,
And wish I could but ease him of his smart.
He cannot say but I have done my part.'

Thus can she lie, dissemble, and be drunk,
Rail at tobacco; yet, for the toothache funk,
And want no odious symptom of a punk.

May my throat meet a halter or a knife,
Or any way, good Heaven, dissolve my life
Rather than plague me with so damned a wife.

XVIII

A DEEPER CONCERN hath scarce been known to affect in general the minds of grateful and ingenious men, than the melancholy surprise of the worthy Mr Dryden's death hath occasioned through the whole Town, as well as in all other parts of the kingdom, where any persons either of wit or learning have taken up their residence. Wheresoever his incomparable writings have been scattered by the hands of the travellers into foreign nations, the loss of so great a man must needs be lamented amongst their bards and rabbis, and 'tis reasonable to believe the commendable industry of translators has been such, to render several of his most accurate performances into their own language, that their native country might receive the benefit, and themselves the reputation of so laudable an undertaking. And how far the wings of merit have conveyed the pleasing fruits of his exuberant fancy is a difficult conjecture, considering what a continual correspondence our nation has with most parts of the universe. For it is reasonable to believe all Christian kingdoms and colonies, at least, have been as much the better for his labours as the world is the worse for the loss of him.

Those who were his enemies while he was living (for no man lives without), his death has now made such friends to his memory that they acknowledge they cannot but in justice give him this character, that he was one of the greatest scholars, the most correct dramatic poet, and the best writer of heroic verse, that any age has produced in England. And yet, to verify the old proverb that 'Poets, like prophets, have little honour in their own countries', notwithstanding his merits had justly entitled his corpse to the most magnificent and solemn interment the beneficence of the greatest spirits could have bestowed on him, 'tis credibly reported the ingratitude of the age is such that they had like to have let him pass in private to his grave, without those funeral obsequies suitable to his greatness, had it not been for that true British worthy, who, meeting with the venerable remains of the neglected bard passing silently in a coach, unregarded to his last home, ordered the corpse, by the consent of his few friends that attended him, to be respited from so obscure an interment; and most generously undertook, at his own expense, to revive his worth in the minds of a forgetful people, by bestowing on his peaceful dust a solemn funeral answerable to his merit. This memorable action alone will eternalize his fame with the greatest heroes, and add that lustre to his nobility which time can never tarnish, but will shine with equal glory in all ages and, in the very teeth of envy, bid defiance to oblivion. The management of the funeral was left to Mr Russell, pursuant to the directions of that honourable great man, the Lord Jeffreys, concerned chiefly in the pious undertaking.

The first honour done to his deserving relics was lodging 'em in Physicians' College, from whence they were appointed to take their last remove. The constituted day for the celebration of that office which living heroes perform in respect to a dead worthy, was Monday, the 13th of May, in the afternoon, at which time, according to the notice given, most of the nobility and gentry now in Town assembled themselves together at the noble edifice aforesaid, in order to honour the corpse with their personal attendance.

When the company were met, a performance of grave music, adapted to the solemn occasion, was communicated to the ears of the company by the hands of the best masters in England; whose artful touches on their soft instruments diffused such harmonious influence amongst the attentive auditory that the most heroic spirits in the whole assembly were unable to resist the passionate force of each dissolving strain, but melted into tears for the loss of so elegant and sweet a ravisher of human minds. Notwithstanding their undaunted bravery, which had oft scorned death in the field, yet now, by music's enchantment at the funeral of so great a poet, the company were softened beneath their own natures into a serious reflection on mortality.

When this part of the solemnity was ended, the famous Doctor Garth ascended the pulpit where the physicians make their lectures, and delivered, according to the Roman custom, a funeral oration in Latin on his deceased friend; which he performed with great approbation and applause of all such gentlemen that heard him, and were true judges of the matter; most rhetorically setting forth those eulogies and encomiums which no poet hitherto, but the great Dryden, could ever truly deserve.

When these rites were over in the College, the corpse, by bearers for that purpose, was handed into the hearse, being adorned with plumes of black feathers, and the sides hung round with the escutcheon of his ancestors, mixed with that of his lady's. The hearse was drawn by six stately Flanders horses, and everything was set off with the most useful ornaments to move regard and affect the memories of the numberless spectators, as a means to encourage every sprightly genius to attempt something in their lives that may once render their dust worthy of so public a veneration. All things being put in due order for their movement, they began their solemn procession towards Westminster Abbey, after the following manner:

The two beadles of the College marched first in mourning cloaks and hatbands, with the heads of their staffs wrapped in black crêpe scarves, being followed by several other servile mourners whose business was to prepare the way that the hearse might pass less liable to interruption. Next to these moved a concert of hautboys and trumpets, playing and sounding together a melancholy funeral march, undoubtedly composed upon that particular occasion. (After these, the undertaker with his hat off, dancing through the dirt like a bear after a bagpipe. I beg the reader's pardon for foisting in a jest in so improper a place; but as he walked by himself within a parenthesis, so I have here placed him, and hope none will be offended.) Then came the hearse, as before described, most honourably attended with abundance of quality in their coaches and six horses, that it may be justly reported to posterity no ambassador from the greatest emperor in all the universe, sent over with the welcome embassy to the Throne of England, ever made his public entry to the Court with half that honour as the corpse of the great Dryden did its last exit to the grave.

In this order the nobility and gentry attended the hearse to Westminster Abbey, where the choir, assisted by the best masters in England, sung an epicedium. The last funeral rites being performed by one of the prebends, he was as honourably interred between Chaucer and Cowley, where, according to report, will be erected a very stately monument, at the expense of some of the nobility, in order to recommend his worth and to preserve his memory to all succeeding ages.

The cause of his death being very remarkable, it will not be improper in this place to take notice of it, as a means to put the world in mind of what slender accidents are sufficient to change the state of man, and hurry him into the dark somewhere of Eternity. The occasion of his sickness was a lameness in one of his feet, springing from so trivial a cause as the flesh growing over one of his toe-nails which, being neglected, begot a soreness and brought an inflammation in his toe; and being a man of gross body, a flux of humours falling into the part made it very troublesome, so that he was forced to put himself into the hands of an able surgeon, who, foreseeing the danger of a mortification, advised him to part with the toe affected, as the best means to prevent the ill-consequence likely to ensue. This he refused to consent to, believing a cure might be effected by less severe means than the loss of a member, till at last his whole leg gangrened, which was presently followed by a mortification, so that nothing remained to prevent death but an amputation of the member thus putrefied. This he refused to consent to, saying that he was an old man and had not long to live by course of nature, and therefore did not care to part with one limb, at such an age, to preserve an uncomfortable life in the rest, and therefore chose rather to submit to death. This, in a little time after, according to the foresight of his surgeons and physicians, did unhappily happen.

Having thus given the reader the manner of his death, as well as the order of his funeral, I could not withhold my muse from presuming to attempt an elegy, or funeral song, in respect to the memory of so worthy an author, whose name and works will outlive Time, and stand up with Eternity:

To the Pious Memory of the Most Sublime
and Accurate Mr John Dryden

To those blest unknown distant regions where
    Great Pindar, Homer, and sweet Virgil, live,
The immortal Dryden's fled; and justly, there,
His nervous poems does with theirs compare,
    Whilst more discerning gods to him the laurel give.

May envy let his dust in quiet sleep,
    And fame eternal in his volumes dwell,
Whilst Chaucer's sacred tomb his ashes keep,
Let lovers o'er his golden writing weep,
    And thus the melting force of his strong numbers feel.

Great was his learning, and sublime his thoughts.
    Powerful his fancy, matchless was his wit,
Num'rous his excellencies, few his faults:
And these he placed as foils and beauty spots,
    To give more sprightly lustre to the lines he writ.

His soul was, sure, some god wrapped up in clay,
　　From Heaven descended to inform mankind,
Whose mighty genius did no time delay
But most industriously improved each day
　　To show the world the beauties of his fruitful mind.

No ancient muse, in Greece or Rome e'er bred,
　　Could sweeter or more god-like strains impart.
The heavenly soul's unborn that can exceed
Those soft enchantments in his verse we read,
　　Where we find nature heightened with the purest air.

Envious competitors, the worst of foes,
　　His pen hath conquered, that they can't but own:
He so excelled in poetry and prose,
That each great task indisputably shows
　　None was like him inspired — his equal's yet unknown.

The chiefest glory of his native land,
　　Whose soul such large angelic gifts possessed,
'Twas hard to think that any human hand
Could such bold strokes, such lofty flights command,
　　Yet harder to determine what he writ was best.

Satire and praise flowed equal from his pen.
　　Dramatic rules no Shakespeare better knew:
The stately epic and the lyric strain.
In each he had so excellent a vein
　　That from the best of judges admiration drew.

Great King of Verse whose merit raised thee high
　　And won thy brows fresh laurel crowns each day,
Thy works immortal are and cannot die.
Why not thyself exempt from Fate, Oh why?
　　Unless the world's unworthy of thy longer stay.

Or was it 'cause thy soul was so divine
　　The barren Earth could not thy works reward,

Or that the power and beauty of each line
Made thee, the author, like a deity shine,
   And that the gods foresaw, like them, thou'lt be adored?

Or did the slights of an ungrateful age
   Hasten th' aspiring soul to take its flight,
And leave this worthless sublunary stage
Where pride and lust do mortal minds engage,
   And keep the giddy world from doing merit right?

What called thee hence, or whither thou wilt soar,
   None but Eternity itself can tell.
We know for mankind thou canst do no more,
But Heaven for thee has its best joys in store
   To recompense those tasks thou hast performed so well.

Let every pen more worthy of the theme,
   Thy elegy or epicedium sing.
The mournful verse may equal the esteem
The learned and witty should express for them,
   Who did to human knowledge such improvements bring.

Great soul! No pen less powerful than thy own
   Can thy deserved immortal praise set forth,
Which time will magnify when thou art gone,
As every age successively comes on,
   And to mankind discover by degrees thy worth.

Could dust be sensible within the grave,
   How joyful would thy peaceful neighbours be
Such venerable company to have,
Whose meritorious works will surely save
   Thy mem'ry from decay to all Eternity.

Chaucer and Cowley gladly would receive
   Thy frozen clay into their silent tomb,
Desiring their applause with yours might live,
In hopes your fame Eternity might give
   To theirs, and that your laurels might together bloom.

Since Fate (to wise men's grief) has called thee hence,
    It justly in thy absence may be said
No Grecian bard e'er showed such excellence.
None has so well bestowed such reams of sense
    As the great Dryden hath, but now, alas, he's dead.

For such an universal loss sustained
    May the like sorrow through the world be shown.
Let everything in nature be constrained
To weep, let full-charged clouds assistance lend,
    And flaming orbs above their fiery tears drop down.

I shall now return to Chancery Lane End, where I stood to see the funeral pass by, observing there some passages of Hackney coachmen and the mob worth delivering to the reader. The great number of qualities' coaches that attended the hearse so put the Hackney whore-drivers out of their bias that against the King's Head Tavern there happened a great stop, occasioned by a train of coaches which had blocked up the narrow end of the lane, obstructed by an entangled number of movable bawdy-houses who waited to turn up the same narrow gulf the others wanted to go out of. Some ran their poles into the windows of another's coach, wherein fat bawd and whore, or mother and daughter, squeaked out, for the Lord's sake, that some merciful good man would come to their assistance.

One impudent corrector of jade's flesh had run his pole against the back leather of a foregoing coach, to the great damage of a beau's reins, who peeping out of the coach door, with at least a fifty-ounce wig on, swore, damn him, if he came out, he would make as great a slaughter amongst Hackney rogues with his sword as ever Samson did amongst the Philistines with the jaw-bone of an ass. Whilst he was thus cursing and swearing like an old sinner in a fit of gout, his own coachman flinging back the thong of his whip in striking of his horses, gave him such a cut over the nose that he jerked in his head as if he had been shot, not knowing from whence the blow came, and sat raving within his leather territories, like a madman chained down to his seat in order to be carried to the famous Doctor Norris to be cured, not daring to look out, for fear, after the like manner, he should a second time pay for his peeping.

The coachmen all the while saluted one another with such diabolical titles, and confounded one another with such bitter execrations, as if everyone were striving which should go to the devil first. They attacked each other with such a volley of oaths that if a parcel of informers had stood by as witnesses to their profaneness, and would have taken the advantage, there would scarce have been one amongst 'em that would not have sworn away his coach and horses in half the time of the disorder. At last, by sundry stratagems, painful industry, and the great expense of whip-cord, they gave one another way, and then with their 'hey-ups' and ill-natured cuts upon their horses, they made such a rattling over the stones that had I been in St Sepulchre's belfry upon an execution day, when the prisoner's bell rings out, I could not have had a more ingrateful noise in my head than arose from their lumbering conveyances.

No sooner had they dispersed themselves towards the several places they were bound to by their fares, but one of the prize-fighting gladiators from Dorset Gardens Theatre (where he had been exercising the several weapons of defence with his bold challenger, upon a clear stage without favour) was conducted by in triumph, with a couple of drums to proclaim his victory. He was attended with such a parcel of scarified ruffians, whose faces seemed to be as full of cuts as a ploughed field is of furrows; some of their countenances chopped into the form of a Good Friday bun with cuts across one another, as if they were marked out for Christian champions. Others had as many scars in their beargarden physiognomies as there are marks in a chandler's cheese scored out into pennyworths.

These were hemmed in with such a cluster of journeymen, shoe-makers, weavers and tailors, that no bailiff from an Inns of Court bog-house, or a pickpocket carrying to be pumped, could have been honoured with a greater attendance. Through this the victorious combatant came off with flying, yet 'twas with bloody, colours; for, by the report of the mob, like a true cock, he won the day after he had lost an eye in the battle. They mauled one another stoutly, to the great satisfaction of the spectators. I think it will not be amiss if in this place I present the reader with a character of a prize-fighter; it being properly enough introduced, I have thought fit to put it into lyric verse, as follows:

> Bred up i' th' fields of Lincoln's Inn,
>   Where vinegar reigns master,
> The forward youth doth thence begin
> A broken head to lose or win
>   For shouts, or for a plaster.

For North or West he doth contend,
   Sometimes his honour looses,
Next night his credit is regained,
Thus fights till hardened in the end
   To bloody cuts and bruises.

When at his weapons grown expert
   By bangs and rough instruction,
To make a trial of his heart
At sharps he doth himself exert,
   And dallies with destruction.

Proud of his courage and his skill,
   No champion can out-brave him;
He dares to fight, yet scorns to kill,
He guards so well, and lives so ill,
   That few know where to have him.

He glories in his wounds and scars
   Like any Flanders soldier,
And as one talks of foreign wars,
The t'other boasts of Hockley jars
   Wherein no man was bolder.

He fought before some Duke or Lord,
   With hardy Tom, the weaver,
And cut him off the stage at sword;
The Duke his manhood to reward
   Presented him a beaver.

He lies and tells his bloody feats
   And bounces like a bully,
Though all his prizes were but cheats.
Yet when he with a coward meets
   He knows he has a cully.

Thus hacks in jest and finds, at best,
   But little money coming.
And when his youthful days are past

His only refuge is at last
To follow theft or bumming.

The Town received notice, by an advertisement in the *Post Boy*, of a great cause to be tried on the following Wednesday, at the King's Bench bar at Guildhall, between one of St Hugh's false prophets (who can foretell more in an hour than will prove true in an age), plaintiff, and a famous student in the celestial sciences (most highly learned in the languages of the stars), defendant. The former had, *secundum artem*, pursuant to the old custom of almanac-makers, most closely attacked the latter about several profound points in the mystery of astrology, in which many fools put more faith than they do in the Twelve Articles. And wisely knowing a volley of scurrility (where scoundrels are to be judges of the battle) would do more execution against a rising competitor, and wound the reputation of such an adversary far deeper than the dint of argument drawn from the rules of art assisted by sound reason, he thought it therefore his safest method to stuff his almanacs as full of hard calumny and ill-words as the art is full of fallacy and lying. Accordingly began the quarrel in public in as sweet, obliging language as ever a Billingsgate termagant bestowed in anger upon a provoking sister in the turbulent times of herrings, sprats, or the mackerel season, as if sense and manners were incongruous with star-fumbling, and railing and lying were the two supporters of astrology.

This malicious sort of treatment from his predicting brother philomath so animated the defendant that he could not forbear flinging off all modesty and patience. So he resolved to contend with his new enemy at his own weapon, scurrility, and give him a true taste, in return for those compliments and stabbing abuses which none but the worst of men would give, or the best of Christians pass by without notice. Accordingly, he arms his ephemeris with such a justification of himself and, whetting his ill-nature upon the very grindstone of revenge, chewed his words, as spiteful enemies do their bullets, till he had made 'em so very rough and ragged that wherever they entered they made the wound incurable. The defendant having the best end of the staff, and being vexed, exercised his weapon with more cunning and dexterity, and so mauled his opponent that, 'tis thought, had he any in his skull, he would have knocked his brains out. Being thus so hard set, he was forced to a very dishonourable retreat, insomuch that he began to consider his money was a better security than his wits, and the law a much better refuge under this defeat than Ptolemy or Copernicus. Accordingly he commenced a suit with his antagonist by arresting him in an action of scandal, laying his damages at five hundred pounds, for the loss of a good name which he never enjoyed.

The day being appointed for the trial, amongst the rest of the fools, my curiosity must needs lead me to hear the matter determined. When I came into the Hall, all the fortune-telling wiseacres in the Town, both male and female, were drawn in a cluster from all the by-alleys in Moorfields, Whitechapel, Salisbury Court, Water Lane, Fleet Street and Westminster. I perceived, notwithstanding their skill in conjuration (by which they pretend to tell fools their fortune, and help the credulous ignorant to lost spoons, thimbles and bodkins), yet they could not, by their art, foresee which of the two contending planet-peepers was most likely to obtain the victory.

Several great counsels were feed, on both sides, for the trial, looking upon the ordinary means, which other people use as the best security in such cases, to be much safer than a dependence on the stars to discover, by their aspects, what should be the issue of the great difference between 'em. Several of the counsel were conning over the almanacs, wherein they had set forth the virtues and merits of each other to such an admirable perfection. I perceived (by the looks of the lawyers) they were so affected with the cause that, I believe, had it been tried it would have given the court as much diversion as the ridiculousness of a foolish contention, or the banter of the counsel, could have possibly afforded. Public notice of the trial having been given in the *Post Boy*, great numbers of well-wishers to the mathematics had recourse to the Hall, in order to give their attention.

There was more staring at the conjurers as they walked than there was at the two giants as they stood; which shows the former are the greater monsters in the eyes of the people. But as 'tis common for astrologers to make fools of that part of the world that will give them an opportunity, so, indeed, they served us who came with an expectancy to hear them make fools of themselves in a public court, as they had made so many in the kingdom. But a little before the cause was to be called on (I suppose through the prudence of some friend or other who was willing to prevent their being further exposed), they were advised to endeavour at some agreement. Whereupon, some terms of accommodation being proposed, they stopped the trial and adjourned to a neighbouring tavern, to the great disappointment of the court, as well as company.

I, being curious to know what end they made of the matter, followed into the same tavern and took up my sitting in the public kitchen, where I had been but a little time before a parcel of approved students in physic and astrology came in, whose looks were as legible to a man of common reason as the neck-verse is to the ordinary of Newgate. For by contracting their faces into ill-looks, to render themselves more terrible to silly wenches and such sort of ignorant creatures who give credit to their delusions, they had, by time and practice, framed such diabolical air in their crabbed physiognomies that nobody can well guess 'em anything but conjurers by their countenances. As 'tis generally observed when several of the same profession are in company together, the main topic of their discourse must be something relating to their own art, trade, or mystery, for most people take a pleasure in talking of what business they are most conversant with. So it proved by these the deceivers of human ignorance, who were standing up very highly for their art, and what wonderful things might be, as well as had been done therein.

A gentleman sitting next 'em in the kitchen who, I suppose, had a very slender opinion of these Egyptian kind of jugglers, took upon him now and then to slip in a word amongst 'em that so puzzled the matter in hand that the whole knot of wizardly cacodemons were all dumb-founded. Yet they would peremptorily assert that things might infallibly be foretold by the stars, and that the incredulity of those persons who opposed judicial astrology proceeded only from their ignorance. And, if they would but study it as much as they had done, they would be thoroughly convinced that a certain foresight of things to come might be read in the great library of the heavens as certainly as the change of weather might be foretold by a weather-glass. Upon this the gentleman, having seen 'em in the Hall, surprised 'em with this following question:

'Pray,' says he, 'do you think it possible by the art of astrology to tell me if I am robbed, what's become of the thief?' 'Yes,' answers one, 'we can, and direct you, by our knowledge in the stars, which way you shall find him.' 'I am very well satisfied now,' replied the gentleman, 'you must be a pack of deceitful knaves, or a parcel of very silly fools. For if you are able to tell me, by consulting your planetary friends, what sort of a man hath done me wrong, and which way I shall find him when he's fled from justice, what's the reason you cannot discover such persons which the government have truly described, ready to your hands, and have given you the advantage of their names too, with an assurance sometimes of five hundred, sometimes a thousand pounds reward for the

great service you would do the nation to apprehend such persons, which
every good subject ought to be industrious to find out and bring to
justice? Therefore, 'tis plain, if you will pretend to make a serviceable
discovery to an ignorant subject for half a crown, and may have a
thousand pounds to serve the government with the same facility, 'tis a
great argument you are juggling knaves to undertake the former and
cozen people of their money. Or else that you are arrant fools to neglect
the latter, wherein your recompense may be eight thousand times as great
for very little more than the same trouble. For between half a crown and
a thousand pounds there's just the same disproportion.'

This put all the star-gazers to the great nonplus for an answer, which
the gentleman, observing, took a further advantage of their weakness and
applied himself to 'em again, after this manner: 'I suppose, gentlemen,'
says he, 'you are waiting here in order to hear, by and by, how the cause
will go between the two famous conjuring antagonists.' 'No, sir,' says
one, 'I find you are no astrologer by your guess; the trial is put off by
consent till the next sitting of the court, in order to an accommodation.'
'But I suppose, sir,' replied the gentleman, 'you came with an expectancy
of hearing it debated this very day?' 'Yes, sir,' says one of them, 'we did
so.' 'Why then, sir,' says the gentleman, 'you astrologers may be out of
your guess as well as other people, or else why could you not foresee by
your art how the cause would go, or, if you came today to hear it
determined, that you'd all be made fools on?' 'Because,' says one, 'we
took the report as a granted truth, and never consulted the stars at all
about the matter.' 'Truly,' replied the gentleman, 'if you had, I believe
you would have found yourselves as much the wiser as he that consults
Cornelius Agrippa about raising an homunculus; and so farewell to you.'

When he had made his exit, my sober reflection on what he had said,
whilst I was seriously a-wasting a pint of wine and a pipe of tobacco,
drew these following lines into my head, which being applicable to the
matter in hand, I have given to the reader:

> Little their learning, less their sense,
> Who put in stars such confidence
> As think those senseless bodies can
> Govern the life and fate of man.
> How can we boast our life is free,
> If under such necessity?
> That beings quite inanimate

The will of man should actuate,
And unlearned dunces should foretell
Who shall do ill, or who do well?
Predict our fortunes, when 'tis known
The juggler ne'er could tell his own?
If they such mighty things could do
As prove their blind conjectures true,
And make it manifest in print,
Wise men might think there's something in't.
Instead of that, their prophecies
To one true word have twenty lies,
And what by guess they do foretell
Each prudent man foresees as well.

For fools to think the sun or moon
Can help 'em to a stolen spoon,
Or that to ease the loser's grief
The planets will declare the thief,
The novice may as well believe
The scissors turning with the sieve,
As pin his faith on conj'rers' dreams
Of planets, houses, and their schemes,
Which the fox seems to put in use
Only to colour his abuse,
And keep the client's thoughts in play
Till he has studied what to say.
And though an art he does profess,
Yet chiefly what he says is guess,
By which he does fools' pockets pick,
Who think him cunning as Old Nick.
The truth he tells you, is no more
Than what he sifts from them before,
Who, awed by his affected look
(And scrawls within his conj'ring book),
Forget the insight they have gi'n him,
And think at last the Devil's in him.

A wag that had sustained a loss,
And coming to the wizard's house,

Some nasty sloven, or else slut,
Had at his threshold eased a gut.
The conjurer coming to the door,
In mighty passion cursed and swore
That if he knew who 'twas had laid it,
He'd make 'em rue the day they did it.
'Nay,' says the man, 'if you've no way
To tell who did your door beray,
I'll e'en again put up my purse,
For you can't help me to my horse.'
Would all like him consider right,
They'd bid astrology good night.

The referees, for want of an umpire, which the plaintiff would not admit of, could bring the matter to no manner of conclusion, so the accommodation proposed was rendered quite ineffectual. And at the next sitting, in favour of their being astrologers, their cause was called on by the court about eleven at night, when the moon and stars were in their greatest glory and bore dominion, in Sol's absence, within our horizon. Both parties put great confidence in the present position of the heavens; and, according to the astrological judgement they had both made of the stars, neither could find pointing towards him such an evil direction but that each had equal hopes, from the propitious aspects of the planets, of overcoming his adversary. But they could not thoroughly determine, by the surest rules of their art, who should have the best on't. One trusted so very much in the stars that his friend had much ado to persuade him to fee counsel, which occasioned some of the wizardly fraternity to conjecture that he expected the planets should have pleaded for him. The plaintiff, erecting a scheme a little before trial, found, by the position of the heavens, the judge would be the Lord Ascendant in the matter, and that the jury were the Twelve Signs towards which the planets of the law, the counsel, were to direct their influence. Accordingly he took care to secure, by the interests of Sol, the very Mars and Mercury of the laws, to give his cause their assistance, whilst the defendant had engaged none but Saturn on his part to bid defiance to his adversary.

All things being put in as good order as they were able, the verbal engagement was begun so strenuously on the plaintiff's behalf (who, according to the custom of suchlike wars, always made the first onset) that a bystander might have easily foreseen who would gain the victory, without the rules of astrology. The nimble weapons of offence and defence (being almost tired with long pleading in many foregoing causes) made not half the pastime as the audience expected. They were apprehensive of hearing the conjurers bandied about the court from one to another by their bantering advocates, as they had chosen to make the weighty difference of their wrangling clients the court's diversion. This the lateness of the night, and the weariness of the counsel, it was supposed, prevented; to the great disappointment of many young students, as well as old practisers in the noble art of pump and wheedle, of which, in this capacious town, there are of both sexes an abundance, not only pretenders but real artists.

In half an hour's time, from the beginning of the debate, the business, without much trouble, was brought to a determination. The plaintiff, however his stars favoured him, obtaining a verdict, the compassionate jury (not knowing but sometime or other it may be their own case) gave him five pound damages for the great abuses he had honestly deserved by a just provocation.

The decision of this controversy proved very unlucky to both enemies, for they were neither of them well satisfied with the justice done to both parties. The plaintiff was very angry his damage was no more, and the defendant very much displeased they had given him so much, so that the jury would have had a very hard task to have pleased both, since they were so unfortunate in their concurrence that they could content neither.

> When conjurers their purses draw
> And like two blockheads go to law,
> They show, by such expensive wars,
> There's little wisdom in the stars,
> And that they act, who know the heavens,
> Like us, by sixes and by sevens.
> For if one wizard had foreseen
> The other should the battle win,
> He'd cry 'Peccavi' and not come
> Before a judge to know his doom.
> I think from thence the world may see
> They know by th' stars no more than we.

Finis

Glossary

abroad	out of doors, at large.
abstractedly	separately.
ad's blood	a minced form of 'God's blood', used in oaths.
ad's heart	a minced form of 'God's heart', used in oaths.
adsheartlywounds	a minced form of 'God's heart and wounds', used in oaths.
Aesculapius	god of healing, portrayed holding a serpent coiled around a staff.
Aesop	(? 6th cent. B.C.) In legend, a slave and fabulist.
Agrippa,	Henricus Cornelius (1486-1535). German scholar, heretic, and writer on the occult, whose notorious *The Vanity of Arts and Sciences* (translated, 1569) was reprinted many times in the seventeenth century.
airy	light, breezy.
Ajax	in mythology, a courageous warrior who contended with Odysseus for the arms of Achilles after that hero's death.
Albumazar	(805-885). Arabian astronomer and author, portrayed as a rascal in a play by Tomkis which was thought by Dryden to have inspired Jonson's *Alchemist* (1612).
Amazons	in mythology, a race of female warriors.
ambs-ace	double ace (the lowest throw at dice); bad luck.
Amminadib	a Quaker.
Amphion	in mythology, a wonderful musician who fortified the city of Thebes by playing his lyre.
Ananias	a Quaker.
angel	an old English coin (originally worth 6s. 8d.) used as a touch-piece to bring good health.
antic	a clown, especially one who adopts grotesque postures; grotesque, ridiculous.
antiverminous	tending to counteract vermin.
Apollo	god of the sun, and patron of music and poetry, for whom the Muses sang and danced.
apprehensive	expectant.
approved	esteemed.
Aqua Mirabilis	miraculous water.

Aqua Veneris	water of Venus.
Aretino,	Pietro (1492-1556). Italian writer. The *Postures* were sets of sexually explicit prints based upon the work of Aretino and Guilio Romano.
Argos	in mythology, a monster with a hundred eyes.
Aristotle	(384-322 B.C.). Greek philosopher, scientist, and founder of the Lyceum at Athens where he collected manuscripts, maps and articles for the first systematically arranged library in Europe.
artist	a painter; a craftsman; a medical practitioner; an astrologer.
Augusta	London.
Augustine, St	(354-430). Christian Latin philosopher whose influential works sought to uphold the authority of the Catholic Church.
Bacchus	god of wine.
Bacon, Friar	a character loosely based upon the thirteenth-century scientist and Franciscan monk, Roger Bacon, who was believed to have made a brass head that could speak. In this production of Doggett and Parker's *Fryar Bacon or the Country Justice*, the miller's son, Ralph, was played by the popular actor and showman William Pinkethman.
baggage	a slut.
Balaam	the soothsayer who was called upon by the king of Moab to curse the Israelites. When his ass refused to proceed he beat her, and she spoke to him (Num. XXII-XXIV).
bantling	a child.
Bartholomew Fair	a metropolitan fair held annually at Smithfield for fourteen days from 24 August.
basilisk	a fabulous reptile (hatched by a serpent from a cock's egg), with lethal breath and gaze.
Bateman	unidentified.
Baxter,	Richard (1615-91). Influential Puritan minister, scholar and hymn-writer.
Bayes	see *Rehearsal, the.*
beargarden discourse	coarse language. Proverbial.
beaver	the lower face-guard of a helmet.
Bedlam	Bethlehem Hospital for the 'mad', in Moorfields, erected in 1676.

bedstaff, in the twinkling of a	in a moment. A bedstaff was a stick kept by a bed, probably for protection. It provides a sexual pun. Proverbial.
Beelzebub	prince of the devils.
begorra	an Irish form of 'by God'.
belch	poor beer.
beldam	an old woman, a hag.
bella	belle; a fashionable young woman.
bellman	a night-watchman who called the hours.
bellman's verse	verses recited as condemned criminals were taken to Tyburn.
Bellona	Roman goddess of war.
belly-saint	glutton.
Belphegor	the archdevil, depicted in Wilson's *Belphegor, or the Marriage of the Devil*, produced in 1690.
beray	to defile.
beside the cushion	in error. Proverbial.
bias	a set course.
billet	a one-year-old coal-fish.
Blackacres, Jerry	the foolish son of widow Blackacres in Wycherley's *The Plain Dealer* (1677).
Blackacres, Madam	a litigious character in Wycherley's comedy *The Plain Dealer*.
Black-Guard	the servants and followers of an army.
blowing their nails	biting their nails.
blue-apron	one who wears a blue apron, such as a tradesman or market-woman; a common prostitute.
bluff	surly.
Blunt, Sir Harry	unidentified.
bogged	baulked.
Boglander	an Irish peasant.
bolus	a large pill.
bongrace	a broad-brimmed hat.
booncriton	'bonchrétien': a kind of pear.
boree	a kind of country dance.
boretto-man	a barrator-man; a cheat.
botcher's goose	the smoothing-iron of a mender of old clothes.
bounce	to boast or bully; blustering.
bravado	a bold or swaggering fellow.
brazen head	a brass head.
break	go bankrupt.
breech	the posterior.

Bridewell	a house of correction, between Fleet Ditch and Bride Lane.
brimmer	a hat with a brim (as could be worn by a Quaker).
British worthy	see *Garth, Doctor*.
broomstick-bail	false bail.
bubble	a dupe; to cheat or deceive.
buck	to copulate.
budget	a bundle of books or papers; a bag or wallet.
buggeranto	one who commits buggery.
bull factor	a male courtesan.
bulldog	a sheriff's officer.
bullocks' pettitoes	the entrails of bullocks.
bum	a bailiff or serjeant.
bumming	acting as a bumbailiff, making arrests from behind.
bumsitter	a whore.
bum-firking	mincing (with a sexual pun).
bum-fodder	paper used for toiletry.
Burgess	Daniel (1645-1713). A leading Presbyterian preacher whose meeting-house was the most popular in London.
burgoo	a thick gruel eaten by seamen.
butterboxes	Dutch troops.
Butterfield, Dame	Susana Butterfield. Her 'house-warming' at Mob's Hole on 26 April was advertised in the *Flying Post* on 22 April 1699.
buttocking brimstone	a lusty whore (with puns on 'buttocking', a manouevre in wrestling; and 'brimming', the copulation of pigs).
buttock-ball	a ball attended by whores.
buttock-shrouds	a pun on 'futtock-shrouds', part of a ship's rigging.
cacodemon	an evil spirit; a malignant person.
cadator	a genteel beggar.
calf-skin companion	a book.
Calves' Head	reputedly, a republican association in which a calf's head was served in commemoration of the execution of Charles I.
canary-bird	a jailbird.
cantharides	Spanish fly, used for raising blisters and as an aphrodisiac.
capping	arrest.
carbonado	to score and broil.
carman	the driver of a cart.

Carnis Bubalinae	buffalo flesh.
carnosity	a carbuncle.
cartouche-box	a box for cartridges.
cast	a lift; assistance.
castle-soap	Castile soap, a fine soap made with olive oil and soda.
castor	a hat made from the fur of a beaver or rabbit.
Cave,	Dr John (c.1660-1700). Astrologer, quack and writer who succeeded to Saffold's business in 1691.
Ca-sa-sa-ca-la-man-ca	see *Doctor, the.*
Cerberus	in mythology, the three-headed dog who guarded the gates of Hades.
chair	a sedan-chair.
chalk-accountant	one who 'chalks up' accounts on credit in an alehouse.
chamber-lye	urine.
'Change, the	the Royal Exchange, the centre for stock-jobbing, in Cornhill.
Charles I	King of England, Scotland and Ireland (1625-49). Executed in 1649.
Charles II	King of England, Scotland and Ireland (1660-85). Exiled during the Commonwealth (1649-60), he returned to England at the restoration of the monarchy in 1660.
Charon	in mythology, the old ferryman who conveyed the souls of the dead over the river into Hades.
Chaucer	Geoffrey (1340?-1400). Poet. His 'character of a sempstress' (end of *London Spy* Part III) is Ward's garbled version of the final couplet of 'The Cook's Tale' from *The Canterbury Tales.*
chirurgeon	an old name for a surgeon.
Christmas-box	a money-box in which gratuities were collected at Christmas by apprentices.
chuck-farthing	a game in which coins are thrown at a hole.
Circeii	a promontory in Latium, and home of the enchantress Circe. Her house was surrounded by the visitors that she had transformed into wild beasts.
cit.	a citizen; shopkeepers and tradesmen.
civet-box	a dung-cart.
clap	venereal disease, gonorrhoea.
clicker	a shopkeeper's tout.
close-stool	a chamber-pot enclosed in a stool or box.

clouterly	clumsy, awkward.
clutter	bustle, confusion; clamour.
clyster-pipe	a syringe used to inject the rectum.
coaster	a sailor in the coastal trade.
cock-ale	ale made with a boiled cock and other ingredients.
cock-bawd	a male keeper of a bawdy-house.
cod's head	a fool.
coiner	a maker of counterfeit coins.
Coke and Littleton	Sir Edward Coke (1552-1634), and Sir Thomas Littleton (1422-81). Authors of authoritative works on the law of real property.
colours	military service; outward dress; appearance.
colquintida	the bitter fruit of the colocynth.
comfortable	satisfactory; pleasurable.
commode	a high head-dress worn by women.
Commonwealth's-man	a republican.
composure	composition.
compter	a serjeant-at-law.
Compter, the (Poultry)	a sheriff's prison, in the Poultry.
coney	a dupe; a whore (providing a sexual pun when pronounced 'cunny').
coney-catching	whoring.
congee	a low respectful bow.
coniwable, coniwabble	a constable (with a pun on 'coney').
conjurer	a fortune-teller, astrologer, or juggler; an impostor.
conscience	honesty; real sentiments or thoughts.
conventicle	a meeting-house for Nonconformists or Dissenters.
conversation	behaviour; way of life; sexual intimacy.
convex-lamp	a street-lamp with a convex glass-lens.
cony-fumble	a constable (with puns on 'coney' and 'fumbler').
Copernicus	(1473-1543). Polish astronomer who propounded the theory that the planets move around the sun, in opposition to Ptolemy's system.
coquus	a cook.
cormorant	a rapacious person; a tailor.
cornigerous	bearing horns; cuckolded.
corroborate	to strengthen, to invigorate.
Courtly, Sir	the leading fop in Crowne's comedy *Sir Courtly Nice* (1685).
cous bobby	'caws pobi': cheese-bake.
Cowley	Abraham (1618-67). Celebrated poet.
cozen	to cheat, to defraud.

crabs' eyes	stones from the stomach of a crayfish, used as an antacid.
crack	a whore.
crambo	a word-game in which players search for rhymes.
crape	a black hat worn by the clergy.
crepidarian	a shoemaker.
cringe	an obsequious bow.
Crispin, St	patron saint of shoemakers, commemorated on 25 October.
criss-cross-row	the alphabet.
Croesus	the last king of Lydia (c.560-546 B.C.), reputed to be the wealthiest of men.
crotchet	an unimportant point, a whimsical notion.
crowd(er)	a fiddle(r).
cruppers	the buttocks.
cubicular	of the bedroom.
cuckold	the husband of an unfaithful wife.
cuckolds-all-in-a-row	the trainbands.
cuckold-makers	the lawyers of the Temple.
cucumber-cormorant	an unemployed tailor.
cully	a gullible fellow, a fool.
cunning-man	a fortune-teller, especially one who pretends to recover stolen goods.
cup	to draw blood by cutting the skin and applying a cupping-glass.
cupper	one who administers cupping.
curmudgeon	a churlish or miserly fellow.
Cursus Mathematicus	mathematical discourse.
cut	the striking of one foot against another.
Cutler,	Sir John (1608?-93). Wealthy merchant and benefactor. In 1699 his executors demanded £7,000, plus interest, as repayment for the loans made to the College of Physicians. A settlement of £2,000 was eventually agreed.
cuts, to draw	to draw lots.
D.J. Lecturer	unidentified.
damp	stupor.
dance the hay	to go through serpentine movements like those of the dance; to make good use of time. Proverbial.
Danes' Church	the church built for Danish sailors by Christian V of Denmark, in 1696.

Darien	the proposed site of a Scottish colony on the Isthmus of Panama. Following an expedition in 1698, the scheme was abandoned.
de jure and de facto	'by right' and 'in fact'. Terms commonly used in disputes about the legitimacy of the Revolution.
deadmonger	an undertaker.
Dear Joy	a name for, or the expression of, an Irishman.
death's head	a human skull as an emblem of mortality.
Decoy, the	a series of canals in St James's Park.
Descartes,	René (1596-1650). French philosopher and mathematician. His revolutionary ideas and cosmology were highly influential in the 17th century.
Devil of a Wife, The	a puppet-show by Jevon, produced as *The Devil to Pay* at Drury Lane in 1686.
Diana	Roman virgin goddess associated with fertility and the moon. The patroness of hunting.
diapente	a mixture of five ingredients, such as punch.
diddle-daddle	trifling, nonsense.
digitize	to finger.
Diogenes	(c.412-323 B.C.). Greek Cynic philosopher. According to tradition, he lived in a tub as a sign of his contempt for comforts and conventions.
disreputon	disrepute.
discover	to reveal, to disclose.
Dissenters	Protestants who refused to join the Church of England.
Dives	the rich man in the parable of Lazarus (Luke XVI, 24).
Doctor, the	Titus Oates (1649-1705). The notorious conspirator who, in 1678, invented the Popish Plot to assassinate Charles II. Under interrogation, Oates falsely claimed to have met Don John of Austria, and to have studied at the University of Salamanca. He was imprisoned and tried for perjury in James II's reign. After the Revolution he received pensions from the government, wrote scurrilous pamphlets such as *Imago Regis, or the Picture of the Late King James drawn to Life* (1696-7), and became a preacher at the Baptist chapel in Wapping. He possessed a large chin and a distinctive crowing voice.
Doctors' Commons	the College of Doctors of Civil Law, where ecclesiastical, probate and other cases were heard.

document	an instruction, a warning.
Doggett	Thomas (c.1670-1721). Irish actor.
dog-whipper	a churchwarden.
doit	a very small amount of money.
domine coquus	chief cook.
dominus factotum	master-servant.
Don John	a malignant character in Shakespeare's *Much Ado about Nothing* (1600).
Dorset Gardens Theatre	the theatre in Salisbury Court. Opened in 1671, it was later used as a boxing-booth.
double-clout	a nappy made of cloths.
double-curtal	a kind of bassoon.
double-gamut	two scales.
doxy	a wench or common prostitute.
drabdeberries	cloaks.
dragon	a devil.
Dragon of Wantley	a cruel dragon slayed by More of More Hall in the seventeenth-century ballad *The Dragon of Wantley*.
draught	a sketch.
Drawcansir	a boastful character in *The Rehearsal* (1672), parodying Almanzor in Dryden's *The Conquest of Granada* (1670).
drawer	one who draws beers.
droll	a puppet-show or play.
Dryden	John (1631-1700). Playwright, poet and critic. Converted to Roman Catholicism after James II's accession in 1685, he refused the oath of allegiance to William and Mary in 1689, and was stripped of his honours. He died on 1 May, was embalmed in Physicians' College, and was buried in Westminster Abbey on 13 May 1700.
dug	a breast.
dumb man in the red cap	a clown.
Dutch gloves	pockets.
East India Company	the Old East India Company, founded in 1600, had offices in Leadenhall Street. The rival New East India Company was established in 1698.
edged tool	a sharp fellow. Proverbial.
Edwards, Doctor	possibly, the religious author, Charles Edwards (d.1691 ?).
egad	a minced form of 'by God'.

Elagabalus	Roman emperor (218-222), whose reign was notoriously profligate.
eminent artist, an	Caius Gabriel Cibber (1630-1700). Sculptor.
empiric	a quack doctor.
engineer	one who contrives or plots.
ephemeris	an astronomical almanac.
Epicurus	(341-270 B.C.). Greek philosopher whose hedonism was often portrayed as mere indulgence in pleasures, such as those of eating.
equality, an	that which is fair and right.
Erasmus,	Desiderius (1466-1536). Dutch humanist and Augustinian monk who was a highly influential scholar.
essedarius	the driver of a chariot of war.
Euclid	(lived c.300 B.C.). Greek mathematician and author of the monumental textbook, the *Elements*.
evidence	a witness.
faggot-bat	a bat made from a bundle of sticks.
Fame	Fama, reputation personified.
fancy	imagination, invention.
farthingale	a hooped petticoat.
feeze	to beat, to frighten.
fen	a whore.
Fiery-face, Sir Base-ill	Sir Basil Firebrace (d.1724). Sheriff of London in 1697. Knighted in 1698. As a magistrate, he was a strict regulator of alehouses.
fig	a contemptuous gesture made with thumb and forefinger.
Fingalian	an Irishman.
firk	to move briskly, to dodge.
flambeau	a flaming torch.
flat-cap	a round cap with a low crown; one who wears a flat-cap, a common person; common.
Fleet, the	a prison, mainly for debtors.
flip	a mixture of beer, spirit and sugar, heated with a hot iron.
fluminous	watery.
flux	an excessive discharge of blood, excrement,etc., from the body.
Flying Post	a tri-weekly Whig newspaper.
flying-coach	a big-wheel, a whirligig.
fly-boat	a fast-sailing vessel used in the coastal trade.

footpad	one who robs on foot.
Fopling, Sir	the arch-fop in Etherege's comedy *The Man of Mode* (1676).
foretop	the fore-part of a wig or head-dress.
formality	essential nature.
frape	a rabble.
French Protestants	refugees from persecution in Catholic France.
frenzical	frenzied.
fricatrice	a whore.
frizzle-pate(d)	a curly-headed person; curly-headed.
frontier	a man in the front line.
froward	perverse, wicked, naughty.
frowzy	ill-smelling, musty; unkempt, ragged.
fuddle-cup	a tippler.
Fuller,	Isaac (1606-72). English decorative and portrait painter whose murals adorned several London taverns.
fumbler	a sexually impotent man.
funking	smoking; stinking.
furmety	frumenty: a dish made of hulled wheat boiled in milk and seasoned.
futurely	hereafter.
Galen	(c.129-199). Greek philosopher and physician. His writings covered all aspects of medicine.
galley'd	vexed; condemned to be a galley-slave.
gallipot	a small pot used for medicines or ointments.
gambages	gambadoes: large boots attached to a saddle to protect the feet while riding.
gaming ordinary	a gambling-house.
gardes du corps	bodyguards.
garnish	money extorted by inmates from a new prisoner.
garter	a headband.
Garth, Doctor	Sir Samuel (1661-1719). Physician and poet. Knighted in 1714.
gauger	an Excise officer.
Gazette	the *London Gazette*. The government's official, bi-weekly newspaper.
Geneva Christians	Puritans, Dissenters.
gig	a whipping-top, a toy spun by whipping.
gimcrack	a swift movement; a mechanical contrivance; a bauble or toy; a spruce wench.
glasses	glass windows.

godgel-gut	a glutton.
gold-finder	one who empties cess-pools and scavenges in refuse.
good husbands	thrifty managers.
goose's apron	the belly-skin of a goose.
gossip	a godparent at a christening.
go-cart	a light framework on castors, in which an infant learnt to walk.
Graces	in mythology, the three goddesses who bestowed charm, grace, and beauty.
grannam	an old woman.
grate	a framework of bars in a prison door or gate.
grateful	agreeable, pleasing.
green-bag	a bag made of green material, used by lawyers.
grenado-shell	a grenade-shell.
Gresham College	the museum and meeting-place of the Royal Society, in Bishopsgate Street.
grey mare	a domineering wife.
grizzle (-pated)	a grey-haired old man; grey-haired.
Groom-Porter	an officer of the Royal Household responsible for the provision and regulation of gaming.
grunters' muns	pigs' faces.
gudgeon	a small freshwater fish used as bait; a credulous person.
guzzle	ale.
hab-nab	anyhow.
hack	to fight.
Hackney	common.
halberdier	a civic guard carrying a halbert as a badge of office.
halbert	a combined spear and battle-axe.
half a piece	half a guinea.
handsomely	carefully.
hanging-sleeve	a loose open sleeve.
hautboy	an oboe.
hawk and buzzard, between	between cheat and fool. Proverbial.
hay	a country dance with serpentine movements.
hazard	a game of dice with some arbitrary rules.
helpmate	a wife.
Heraclitus	(lived c.500 B.C.). Greek philosopher whose reputedly melancholy view of the world led to his being known as the weeping philosopher.

Hercules	in mythology, the Greek hero who chose a life of toil and glory.
hey-day	an expression of surprise.
higgler	a pedlar.
Hippocrates	(c.460-380 B.C.). Celebrated founder of Greek scientific medicine, from whose name the Hippocratic oath is derived.
Hippolyte	in mythology, a queen of the Amazons; a character in Shakespeare's *A Midsummer Night's Dream* (1596).
hobbaddyboody	an itinerant countryman.
hobby	a stupid fellow.
hocus-pocus	a juggler.
hog-grubber	a niggardly and sneaking fellow.
hoistings	hustings, platforms providing a kind of balcony.
holland	fine linen.
Homer	(8th cent. B.C.). Greek epic poet, to whom the *Iliad* and *Odyssey* were traditionally attributed.
homogeneal	having the same nature, related.
horn	to cuckold.
Horn Fair	a fair held annually at Charlton on 18 October.
hornbook	an alphabet, etc., for children.
horse-courser	a horse-dealer.
horse-pond	a pond in which petty offenders were ducked.
house of correction	a place of punishment and detention, such as Bridewell.
house-of-office	a latrine.
huffling	by force.
Hugh, St	(? 1246-1255). In popular legend and literature, a child whose body was found in a well at Lincoln after having been tortured by Jews. His grave was said to invoke miracles.
humming	strong.
Hummums	Turkish baths. The hummums in Covent Garden were the most fashionable in London.
Hungary-water	distilled water prepared from rosemary flowers.
hustle-cap	a form of pitch-and-toss with the coins shaken in a cap.
Hymen	in mythology, the personification of marriage.
i'faith	in faith.
i'feck	in faith.

Icarus	in mythology, the son of Daedalus who flew so high, the sun melted the wax with which his wings were fastened. He fell into the sea and was drowned.
ill market	a poor sale.
illustrate	to adorn.
in verbo sacerdotis	in the word of the priest.
in vino veritas	in wine lies the truth. Proverbial.
inabruptible	unbroken, solid.
ingrateful	unpleasant, disagreeable.
intellects	wits, senses, intellectual powers.
Interest	self-interest.
inward man	the soul or mind; the stomach or bowels.
Isis	the River Thames (alluding to the Egyptian nature-goddess associated with the Nile).
issue	a discharge of blood or other matter due to disease or incision.
Jack Adams	a buffoon.
jackanapes	a coxcomb.
Jack-a-dandy	a beau.
jack-o'-lantern	a night-watchman who called the hours.
Jack-pudding	a clown, a merry-andrew, especially one who accompanies a mountebank.
jack-winder	one who oversees the roasting-jack.
Jacobite	a supporter of the exiled James II after his deposition in the Revolution of 1689.
James II	King of England, Scotland and Ireland (1685-88). The Catholic king was deposed by his son-in-law William of Orange at the Revolution of 1689, and exiled in France until his death in 1701.
jangling	wrangling.
Jeffreys, Lord	John, 2nd Baron Jeffreys of Wem (1670?-1702). Son of the notorious Judge Jeffreys.
Jevon's farce	see *Devil of a Wife, The.*
Jews' trump	a Jews' harp.
jilt	a whore, especially one who deceives or capriciously dismisses a lover after giving encouragement; to deceive as a jilt.
jockey	a horse-dealer.
jockey-coat	a kind of great-coat worn by horse-dealers.
John of Gaunt	Duke of Lancaster (1340-99). Soldier and statesman who had children by each of his three wives.
John of Austria, Don	Spanish general and statesman (1629-79).

John-a-nokes, *John-a-stiles*	fictitious names for the parties in a legal action; anyone. Proverbial.
Jonson,	Ben (1572-1637). Dramatist and poet. His work was highly regarded throughout the seventeenth century.
Jove	Roman god of the skies whose weapon was the thunderbolt.
Jubilee, the	the Papal Jubilee of 1700.
juggler	a fortune-teller, astrologer, or conjurer.
Juno	Roman goddess, associated with marriage and the sexual life of women, to whom the peacock was especially sacred.
Keble,	Joseph (1632-1710). Barrister and essayist.
keeping	maintained as a mistress.
kennel	a gutter or ditch in the street.
Kent, the Devil and the Earl of	Proverbial.
kiss of calves'-leather	kiss the bible in taking an oath.
knight of the post	a professional false-witness.
Lancashire evidence	a false witness.
Land Bank	a banking institution which issued notes on the security of landed property. In 1695-6, several attempts were made to found a land bank in order to raise war-revenue from landowners. All of the schemes collapsed.
land-waiter	a Customs officer who keeps account of landed goods.
lawn-sleeves	sleeves of fine linen worn by a bishop; episcopacy.
Law-French	corrupt Norman French used in English law-books.
leash	a group of three.
led horse	a pack-horse.
leman	an unlawful lover, a mistress.
let-go	a bout; baiting; unleashing.
Levite	a contemptuous name for a clergyman.
lick-spigot	one who licks the spigot, a tapster.
Lilliburlero	a popular song championing the Revolution.
Lincoln, the Devil ... looked over	i.e., frowning. Proverbial.
lobcock	a bumpkin.
loblolly	coffee.
Locket's	a fashionable tavern in Charing Cross.
loggerhead	a blockhead.
loobily	clumsy; foolish.

Love for Love	Congreve's comedy, first produced at Lincoln's Inn Fields Theatre, in 1695.
lucky	the mistress of an alehouse.
Machiavelli,	Niccolo (1469-1527). Florentine statesman and political theorist whose writings condoned state treachery and tyranny.
maggie	a Scottish name for a girl.
maggot	a whimsical or perverse notion.
mainprize	suretyship.
malkin	a scarecrow; a beggar; a slut.
mantel-tree	a beam across a fireplace.
manus sanaque in cobile sanaquorum	garbled version of 'mens sana in corpore sano': a healthy mind in a healthy body. Juvenal.
market-place	the face.
Marriott,	John (d.1653). A lawyer whose alleged gluttony was proverbial.
Mars	Roman god of war.
mass, by the	on the whole, an oath.
massy	solid, weighty.
May Fair	St James's Fair, held annually in Brookfield, Piccadilly, from 1-16 May.
mealman	a dealer in ground corn.
measure	a grave or stately dance.
mechanic	a tradesman or manual worker.
meeting-house	a place of worship for Dissenters.
memento mori	a reminder of mortality.
mercurius dulcis	sweet mercury.
Mercury	Roman messenger of the gods, and patron of merchants, travellers and thieves.
merry-andrew	a clown, especially one who assists a mountebank.
Messalina	Valeria, wife of the Roman emperor Claudius. She was renowned for her sexual profligacy.
meteorous	elevated.
microcosmography	a description of a person.
Milky Way	the breast of a woman.
miller and his son, the	see *Bacon, Friar.*
Minerva	Roman goddess of wisdom, often depicted as an owl.
Moabite	a bailiff or serjeant.
mob	a crowd, a tumultuous assembly of the lower orders.
Mob's Hole	a resort in Wanstead parish, Essex.
mobility	the mob, the populace.
Momus	god of criticism amongst the ancients.

money-jobber	a dealer in money or coin.
money-scrivener	one who raises money for clients.
mope-eyed	weak-sighted.
mop-money	money to pay for cleaning.
More of More Hall	the hero of a popular ballad. See *Dragon of Wantley*.
Morpheus	god of dreams, popularly regarded as the god of sleep.
mountebank	an itinerant quack who mounts a platform and promotes his wares with the assistance of a Jack-pudding or merry-andrew.
mountebank's mercury	a Jack-pudding or merry-andrew.
mourning-weeds	black clothes worn after a bereavement.
muckender	an apron; a handkerchief.
muckworm	a covetous wretch; a coffee-drinker.
muddling	confused.
mullet	a figure of a star with five or more points.
mumchance	one who sits silently; a mute.
mumper	a genteel beggar.
mun	shall.
mundungus	strong-smelling tobacco.
Muses	in mythology, the nine daughters of Zeus believed to inspire learning and the arts.
Nantz	brandy.
nappers' nulls	sheep's heads.
native	a particular planet or sign.
neck-verse	usually the beginning of Psalm 51, in Latin. By reading this a person could claim benefit of clergy and thus avoid being hanged.
nemine contradicente	nobody contradicting.
Neptune	Roman god of the sea.
nervous	vigorous.
New Exchange, the	the exchange for fashionable clothes, etc., in the Strand.
nice	refined; delicate; squeamish; precise.
nick and froth ... the double score	ways of serving short measures and overcharging customers in an alehouse.
night-rail	a loose dressing-gown worn by women.
night-walker	a prostitute.
Nine, the	the Muses.
ninny-broth	coffee.
ninny-hammer	a simpleton.

nipperkin	a small measure; half a pint of wine or half a quartern of brandy.
nitty	infested with nits.
Norris, Doctor	Edward (1663-1726). Physician.
nosegay	a bunch of sweet-smelling flowers; an odour.
Noy	unidentified.
numbers	metric lines, verses.
numquam satis	never enough.
Old Gentleman	the Devil.
opsonium	victuals.
orangery	smelling of orange-flower scented snuff.
ordinary	a tavern or eating-house where a meal was provided at a fixed price.
Oronoko	Virginia tobacco.
Orvietan	a medicine believed to expel poison, an antidote.
'ounds	an abbreviation of 'God's wounds' expressing indignation.
outlive	excel in living.
over against	opposite.
Overdo	the name of a censorious J.P. in Jonson's *Bartholomew Fayre* (1614).
overreaching	deceiving, cheating.
Ovid	(43 B.C. - A.D.17). Roman poet. Author of *Metamorphoses*, an epic poem of tales from ancient mythology.
pad	to rob on foot.
Pallas	Athena, the goddess of wisdom, regarded as a virgin and generally portrayed in arms.
panada	bread boiled to a pulp and seasoned.
panpharmacon	a panacea.
Papist	a Roman Catholic.
parcel	a collection, a group.
paring-shovel	a tool for scraping refuse from floors.
parsley-bed	the vagina. Proverbial.
Partridge,	John (1644-1715). Astrologer and almanac-writer. In 1697 he became engaged in a bitter controversy with George Parker, a rival astrologer.
passage	an occurrence, an incident.
passenger	a passer-by; a traveller.
patch	a small piece of black silk or court-plaster worn to adorn the face or hide blemishes.
pearmain	a variety of apple.

peccavi	'I have sinned': an omission of guilt.
peddling	trifling, petty.
pediculous	infested with lice.
peery	fearful.
Pegasus	in mythology, the winged horse who gave rise to the fountain Hippocrene, from which poets drew inspiration.
Pelonga	unidentified.
peripatetic	a travelling philosopher.
Perkins, Sir William	or Parkyns (? 1649-96). Jacobite conspirator whose plot to assassinate William III was discovered, together with a large quantity of arms at his house in Warwickshire, in 1696. Executed for high treason, his head was exhibited at Temple Bar.
pettifogger	a legal practitioner who handles petty cases.
Phaeton	in mythology, he aspired to drive the sun's chariot but, losing control of the horses, might have set fire to the world had not Zeus killed him.
philoginian	a philogynist, an admirer of women.
philomath	a philosopher or lover of learning.
philosophers' stone	a substance, sought by alchemists, which would turn base metals into gold.
Phoebus	a name of Apollo, god of the sun.
phthisical	consumptive.
Phyllis and Chloris	characteristic whores' names.
Physicians' College	the college on the west side of Warwick Lane, Newgate Street.
Pillula Tondobula	minced Latin.
pimpgennet	large, red and pimpled (like a 'Pomme de Jennet': a kind of early apple).
Pindar	(518-438 B.C.) Greek lyric poet, who composed odes in honour of victors at the Games.
pinfold	a pen for sheep or cattle; a stall.
plate-buttoned	silver-buttoned.
plot-evidence	a false witness.
plot-office	a false witness; false evidence.
plough-jobber	an itinerant farm-labourer.
poise on't	on balance, on consideration.
poke-pudding	a pudding made in a bag.
Politicians' porridge	coffee.
pomatum	pomade, an apple-based ointment usually for the skin.
pontificalibuses	vestments.

poop-lantern	a ship's lantern carried at the stern.
popular weasel, the	John Churchill, 1st Duke of Marlborough (1650-1722). Soldier and statesman. He was imprisoned briefly in 1692 when his loyalty to the Revolution was doubted.
porridge	thick soup, stew, pottage.
post	to travel swiftly, to hasten.
Post Boy	a tri-weekly newspaper.
Posture Moll	a girl paid for striptease and flagellation.
posy	a short verse.
Poultry Compter, the	a sheriff's prison, in the Poultry.
powder-monkey	a boy employed on a ship to carry gunpowder.
pox	venereal disease, syphilis.
Practice of Piety	a popular devotional tract (1612), by Lewis Bayly, Bishop of Bangor.
pragmatical	officious, self-important.
prattle-box	a prattler.
prejudice	injury, damage, loss.
presently	immediately, promptly.
Prester John	the name given in the Middle Ages to an alleged Christian priest and king in the extreme Orient, and later identified with the king of Ethiopia or Abyssinia.
pretend	to profess or claim.
Priscian	celebrated Roman grammarian of the 6th century. 'To break Priscian's head' is to violate the rules of grammar. Proverbial.
privities	the genitals.
prize	the seizure of property.
Probatum est	it is proven.
projection	a scheme or plan.
projector	a schemer, a speculator, a promoter.
protection-cursor	a debt collector.
Ptolemy	Alexandrian astronomer and geographer who, in the 2nd century, devised the system in which the sun, planets and stars revolve around the earth.
puff-wig	a puffed or full wig.
pulling a crow	quarrelling. Proverbial.
Pulvis Lubberdatus	dog-Latin: lubber's dust.
punk	a little whore.

Pythagoras	Greek philosopher who, in the 6th century B.C., founded an ascetic scientific-religious society whose members were required to observe silence.
quarterstaff	a stout pole 6-8 ft. long used by peasantry as a weapon.
quean	an importunate woman; a slut.
Queen's Bench, the	a prison, mainly for debtors.
questman	a parish officer elected annually.
Quevedo,	Francisco Gomez de (1580-1645). Spanish poet and satirist whose comic and macabre *Visions* was translated by L'Estrange in 1668.
raffle	a dice game; to gamble by casting dice.
raffling-shop	a gambling-shop where raffle is played.
Rag Fair	the market for old clothes, etc., in Rosemary Lane.
ragged staff	a staff with projecting stumps or knobs.
Ramsey, Father	possibly James Ramsay (? 1624-96). Bishop of Ross.
rapscallion	a rogue or rascal.
rare	unusual; excellent. Also used as an intensive.
raree-show	a show contained or carried in a box, a peep-show; any show or spectacle.
Raw-Head and Bloody-Bones	the name of a bugbear used to frighten children. Proverbial.
red cap	a clown.
redcoat	a soldier.
Rehearsal, The	the Duke of Buckingham's comedy, printed in 1672, satirizing Dryden (portrayed as Bayes), and the heroic tragedies of the period.
reins	the loins.
reverence	to urinate (punning on 'sir-reverence').
Revolution	the Glorious Revolution of 1688-9, when the Catholic James II was deposed by his daughter Mary, and her husband William of Orange.
Robert, Sir	'Oh, good Sir Robert, Knock!' was cried by spectators during the flogging of prostitutes in Bridewell. The punishment stopped at the knock of the governor's hammer.
rocket	a firework.
Roland for an Oliver	an effective retort. Proverbial.
rook	a cheat in gambling.
Rosamond, Fair	Rosamond Clifford (d.1176 ?), mistress of Henry II. In popular legend, the king had a labyrinth made around her house at Woodstock.

round-headed	with closely-cut hair.
Royal Oak	a lottery established by an Act in 1698.
ruby	a red pimple on the face.
rusty	rough, unrefined; old, antiquated; appearing old or neglected.
sable	black.
sack	white wine from Spain.
safeguard	an outer skirt worn to protect dresses while riding.
Saffold,	Thomas (d.1691). Astrologer and quack who advertised his wares by the use of doggerel verses. At his death, his shop in Blackfriars was taken over by Dr Case.
Salamanca saviour	see *Doctor, the.*
salt sinner	a salacious sinner, a lecher.
Sal-Graminis	salt of the pasture.
Saturn	Roman god whose reign was regarded as the golden age.
scaramouch	a buffoon in motley dress, a boastful poltroon.
scoot, Dutch	a scout, a flat-bottomed boat used in the Netherlands.
scrape	an awkward bow.
scraper	a fiddler.
screaking	a shrill noise, such as the sound made by rusty hinges.
scrubbed	stunted.
scrupulous	dubious.
sea-pie	a dish of meat and vegetables.
secundum artem	according to art.
sellenger's round	an old country dance.
septenary	seven-day.
service	employment as a servant.
Seven Provinces	the United Provinces, the Netherlands.
shabroon	a wretch.
Shaftesbury	1st earl of Shaftesbury (1621-83). Statesman. He was an exponent of the Popish Plot, and a leader of the Whig opposition to James, Duke of York's succession to the throne.
shammock	a mean and nasty person.
shanker	a chancre, a venereal ulcer.
sharper	a cheat, a swindler; one who lives by his wits, especially as a fraudulent gamester.
sharps, at	to fight in earnest.
shatter-brained	crack-brained, giddy.

sheep-biter	a sheep-dealer; a poor, sneaking fellow.
Shipton, Mother	a legendary prophetess who lived in Yorkshire at the end of the 15th century.
shock-doggish	shaggy.
shoot (the bridge)	go whoring. Proverbial.
sieve	a sieve used in divination.
sigil	a talisman.
similizer	a drawer of similies.
sir-reverence	human excrement.
skip	a footman.
skipjack	a pert young fellow, a puppy.
slab-dab	a slobbering expert-cook.
sledge	a sledge-hammer.
slip-shoe	a light shoe or slipper.
slip-slop	bad liquor, slops.
smoke	to suspect, to uncover.
smoother	a polished flatterer.
snacks, go	to share the profits. Proverbial.
snappers	castanets.
snapsack	a soldier's wallet or bag.
sneaker	a small bowl.
snip-snap	coin-clipping.
socket-money	money paid or extorted in whoring or marriage.
Socrates	(469-399 B.C.). Greek philosopher whose teachings focussed upon questions of how men should conduct their lives.
Sol	Roman god of the sun.
Solomon	King of Israel (c.969-922 B.C.), renowned for his wisdom.
Sommers,	William (d.1560). Henry VIII's fool. The subject of many apocryphal tales in the seventeenth century.
soph	a sophomore.
sophister	a teacher.
sot	a blockhead; a drunkard.
sotweed	tobacco.
sound as a roach	of an excellent constitution. Proverbial.
sow-gelder	one who gelds or spays sows.
spangled regions	the stars.
spark	a showy and smart young fellow, a beau.
species	the ingredients of a compound drug.
spiritual helmet	a mitre.
splatterdashes	long gaiters worn to protect trousers while riding.

sportsman	a man who engages in 'sports' such as gambling and whoring.
squab	a very fat person; fat; newly born.
Squeamish, Lady	a fastidious character in Wycherley's comedy *The Country Wife* (1675).
Stagirite	Aristotle, who was born at Stagira.
stallion	a cheat or swindler; a whore-master.
star-gazer	an astrologer.
State-tool	a high officer of state.
Stephens, Dr	possibly the Irish physician Richard Steevens (1653-1710).
still sow eats all the draught	Proverbial.
Stocks Market	a market for fish and vegetables.
stones	testicles.
Stourbridge Fair	a rural fair held annually at Barnwell, near Cambridge, from 24 August to 29 September.
streak	to stretch, to extend.
stroller	a strolling player, an itinerant actor.
strumpet	a prostitute.
subtle	penetrating; skilful; crafty, cunning.
suck-fosset	one who sucks the faucet, a tapster.
sumpter-horse	a beast of burden, a pack-horse.
supporters	legs.
sweet-bag	a sachet of scented substances.
sweet-lipped	sweet-talking.
swing-swang	swinging to and fro.
swore by his bush	swore by his trade. Ivy bushes were traditionally hung outside taverns to show that wine was for sale.
swyve	to copulate.
tale of a tub	an apocryphal tale.
tallyman	one who supplies goods on credit.
tarpaulin	a common sailor; seafaring.
tatterdemalion	a ragamuffin.
Teague	an Irishman.
teem	to bear offspring.
Templar	a lawyer or student at the Inns of Court.
tender	young, frail.
term	a designated period within which law courts sat.
terra firma	an estate in land.
Terra Incognita	unknown land.
theorbo	a large kind of lute with a double neck.

thoroughbass	accompaniment, harmony.
thrum-cap	a cap made of coarse woollen or hempen yarn; a common person.
thumps	respiratory disorders.
Thynne,	Thomas, of Longleat (1648-82). Wealthy squire and M.P. Following his marriage to a young heiress in 1681, he was murdered, at the instigation of a suitor, while riding in his coach in Pall Mall.
tierce, carte or seconde	parries in sword-play.
tipstaff	a sheriff's officer who carries a metal-tipped staff as a badge of office.
tit	a small horse.
Tom turd-man	a man who empties cess-pools and scavenges in refuse.
Tom-fool	a buffoon, especially one who acts the fool in a drama.
tongue-padder	a smooth-talker.
toper	a hard drinker, a drunkard.
topknot	a bow of ribbon worn on the top of the head by women.
topping	first-rate; very fine, excellent.
Tories	supporters of the Crown who were opposed to Whig attempts to exclude the Catholic Duke of York (James II) from the throne. After the Revolution of 1689, some Tories sympathised with the Jacobites.
trainband	a trained company of citizens forming a militia.
trap, to understand	to know one's interest (with a pun on 'trapes', a slattern).
trencher	a wooden platter.
trencher-scraper	a caterer.
trepan	to trap, beguile or cheat.
tringam-trangam	a conundrum, a ridiculous idea.
Tritons	in mythology, sea-deities or monsters, generally represented as mermen.
trugmoldy	an old prostitute.
trull	a low prostitute; a tinker's travelling wife or wench.
Turkish sobriety	coffee.
turnover	a turn-down collar.
twatling-strings	the anal sphincter.
Twelve Tribes	the divisions of the people of Israel, claiming descent from the twelve sons of Jacob.
ub bob bou	ub(b)ubboo: a characteristic Irish expression or cry.

Ulysses	in Homer's *Iliad*, the Greek hero who, in contention with Ajax, won the arms of Achilles during the Trojan War.
umbrage	shade.
umbrella	a loose cloak.
unborn-doctor	a quack (alluding to the popular belief that the seventh son of a seventh son would be a doctor).
univerbal	characteristically verbose.
unluckiness	mischief.
unlucky	mischievous, malicious; unfortunate; inauspicious.
vapulation	flagellation.
varlet	a servant; a rogue.
vaulting-school	a bawdy-house.
venery	sexual indulgence.
Venus	Roman goddess of love and beauty who won the contest for the golden apple. While married to Vulcan, she was caught in the arms of her lover, Mars.
Virgil	(70-19 B.C.). Generally regarded as one of the greatest of Roman poets. His works were translated by Dryden in 1697.
virtuoso	a dilettante or assumed connoisseur.
Vulcan	Roman god of fire, and the patron of metal-workers.
wagtail	a breezy wench.
waits	an official band of street singers and musicians who roamed the streets by night at Christmas and New Year performing carols, etc.
Walsingham	an old, popular song, beginning: 'As I went to Walsingham, to the shrine with speed, / Met I with a jolly palmer in a pilgrim's weed.'
warden	a kind of pear.
water-dog	a ferryman.
water-rats of Europe	Dutchmen.
weasel, the popular	see *popular weasel, the.*
Westminster, go to	go whoring. Proverbial.
Wheel of Fortune	an illegal lottery established in 1699.
Whetstone's Park	a lane between Holborn and Lincoln's Inn Fields, formerly notorious for prostitution.
whiffling	insignificant.
Whigs	supporters of the political group that tried to exclude the Catholic Duke of York (later James II) from the throne. After the Revolution of 1689, their leaders

held offices under William and Mary, and championed the war against France.

Whitechapel portions   worthless dowries.

white-pot   a dish made of milk, eggs and other ingredients.

whoop-and-hide   a form of hide-and-seek.

whow ball   a milkmaid or her distinctive cry.

William, King   King of England, Scotland and Ireland (1689-1702), and stadtholder of the Netherlands (1672-1702). A staunch Protestant, he invaded England in 1688 to overthrow his Catholic father-in-law, James II. After accepting the 'Declaration of Rights', William and Mary were crowned in 1689.

Winchester quart   a standard measure.

wise-woman   a fortune-teller.

Witch of Endor   the woman addressed by Saul (1 Sam. XXVIII).

without   outside; unless.

Wits' Coffee-house   Will's Coffee-house at the corner of Bow Street and Russell Street. The fashionable resort for writers.

wit-monger   a bookseller.

wooden horse   an instrument of military punishment.

wounds   an abbreviation of 'God's wounds' expressing indignation.

woundy   very great, extremely.

zounds   an abbreviation of 'God's wounds' expressing indignation.